Biology HL

FOR THE IB DIPLOMA

Ashby Merson-Davies

PEAK

Published by:
Peak Study Resources Ltd
1 & 3 Kings Meadow
Oxford OX2 0DP
UK

www.peakib.com

Biology HL: Study & Revision Guide for the IB Diploma

ISBN 978-1-913433-15-4

© Ashby Merson-Davies 2016–2020

Ashby Merson-Davies has asserted his right under the Copyright, Design and Patents Act 1988 to be identified as the author of this work.

Peak Study & Revision Guides for the IB Diploma have been developed independently of the International Baccalaureate Organization (IBO). 'International Baccalaureate' and 'IB' are registered trademarks of the IBO.

Books may be ordered directly through the publisher's website www.peakib.com. For enquiries regarding titles, availability or local stockists, please email books@peakib.com or use the form at www.peakib.com/contact.

Printed and bound in the UK by:
CPI Group (UK) Ltd, Croydon CR0 4YY
www.cpibooks.co.uk

International Baccalaureate Higher Level Biology

Using this Revision Guide

Welcome to the Peak Study Resources Higher Level Biology Revision Guide for International Baccalaureate Diploma Programme exams up to November 2023.

The format is clear, colourful and simple to follow. Key points, facts and principles are listed for easy learning, and diagrams are designed to make them easy to learn and reproduce in an exam. Remember that a clear diagram provides an instant essay plan therefore helping you to gain the extra mark for clarity and organisation.

Although the guide covers every aspect of the Higher Level course the layout does not follow the sequence of the syllabus. Instead it has been reorganised to follow a more developmental sequence as Chapters, starting with Mathematical Requirements, Molecular Biology, Cell Biology, Cell Metabolism, Animal Physiology and Plant Physiology. These are followed by Ecology, Genetics and finally Evolution and Biodiversity.

'Pale blue boxes' contain information that helps with understanding by providing additional information. However you do not need to learn this.

Other *'coloured boxes'*, such as these green and yellow ones, contain information that you do need to know.

 This means you need to be able to *'draw'* the diagram or diagrams.

 This means you need to be able to *'identify'* the diagram when it is given in an exam question.

 *'Annotate'* means adding some further information to the labels.

This is **your** revision book, so every few pages are sets of *'Grey Box Questions'*. These contain simple questions and you should be able to complete these. The answers are at the end of the chapter.

24. What type of cell division do prokaryotic cells use?

In addition to these there are a few larger *'Revision'* boxes.

Krebs Cycle

At the end of each chapter there are a number of Self-test Quizzes, containing *'multiple choice questions'*. A suggested way to approach revision would be to work your way through a chapter and test yourself with the Grey Box Questions. Then at a later date check how much you have really learnt by trying the Self-test Quizzes.
Remember that when you answer multiple choice questions NEVER choose the first one that sounds right. Examiners sometimes put in a trick answer as A or B. Always read ALL four answers and try to think of the reason why the other three are wrong. The answers are in **Appendix 1** on pages 304-7.

In Chapter 8, Genetics, there is a 'worked example' for each section followed by a problem for you to practise. The answer is at the end of the chapter. Then at the end of the chapter there are a further 18 problems with the worked answers in **Appendix 2** on pages 308–315.

The 'External Exam Assessments' are given in **Appendix 3** on page 316.

The extended response exam questions start with a 'Command Term' and so it is essential that you understand what these mean as you will be expected to apply them in your answers. There are three levels of depth of treatment and are all given in **Appendix 4** on page 317.

Appendix 5 on pages 318–322 has model answers for 'Extended Response' answers using some of these command terms.

Appendix 6 on page 323 gives you some advice on what you should, and what you should **not** take into your exams.

Interesting websites worth looking at are http://www.sciencedaily.com and also http://www.sci-news.com/biology.

I am grateful to Pam Watson, Senior Biology Technician, and Georgina Kemp, Assistant Biology Technician at Sevenoaks School, for their invaluable help with experiments and microscope slide photographs, and also to Tony Stuart for his idea for the diagram of the endosymbiotic theory. Thanks also to many people for generously allowing me to use their images.

I would greatly value any feedback on this Revision Guide so that later editions can continue to help students throughout the world. Please feel free to email me at feedback@peakib.com.

Ashby Merson-Davies

Contents

Chapter One

Mathematical Requirements and Statistics

Many aspects of modern Biology require mathematical manipulation of data. This chapter looks at some basic maths along with graphs and statistics. Further information on this is available in the *Student Guide for Internal Assessment in Biology*.

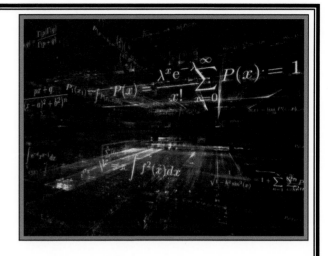

Size units in Biology

Scientists now use the International System of units or SI units. Ones commonly used in Biology are:

Length
- **metre** or **m**
- **millimetre** or **mm** = 10^{-3} of a metre
- **micrometre** or **μm** = 10^{-6} of a metre or 10^{-3} of a millimetre
- **nanometre** or **nm** = 10^{-9} of a metre or 10^{-6} of a millimetre or 10^{-3} of a micrometre

Time
- **hour** or **h**
- **minute** or **min**
- **second** or **s**

Area
- **Square metre** or m^2 etc

Volume
- **Cubic metre** or m^3 etc

Concentration
- **mol dm^{-3}**

per
This is shown by a minus sign, e.g.
per second or s^{-1}
per square metre or m^{-2}
per cubic millimetre or mm^{-3}

Centimetre or **cm** (10^{-2} of a metre) is often used for convenience, especially when measuring volumes – cubic centimetre cm^3.

Relative sizes

Molecules	Membrane thickness	Viruses	Bacteria	Organelles	Cells
1nm	10nm	100nm	1μm	upto 10μm	upto 100μm

Scale bars

A scale bar is a short line usually drawn on an electron micrograph that will allow you to calculate the magnification of the photograph.

Using a scale bar to calculate magnification. (See photo on right.)
1. Measure the scale bar on the photograph in mm with your ruler.
   15mm
2. Convert these mm into the same units as the scale bar using the information above.
   15mm = 15000μm
3. Divide this number by the number on the scale bar.
   15000 ÷ 5 = 3000

Therefore magnification = 3000x.

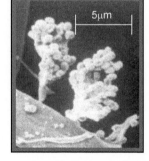

1.1 Scale bar on an image

Calculating magnification

An alternative is that the image states the magnification. From this you can calculate the actual size.

Example:
The 'cell' on the right has been magnified 750x.
Calculate its actual length.

1. Measure the length of the cell.
   41mm
2. Divide this by the magnification.
   41 ÷ 750 = 0.055mm
3. Convert to a sensible unit.
   0.055mm × 1000 = 55μm

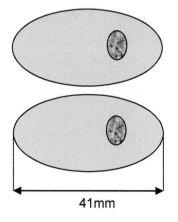

41mm

1. 22mm = _____ μm	2. How many nanometres in a millimetre?	3. How many micrometres in a millimetre?	4. List the three steps in determining magnification from a scale bar. i. ii. iii.

5. How would you write in SI unit symbols cubic millimetres per minute?

Averages

The term average is often used when talking about samples. There are three ways of measuring the average – **mean, median, and mode**. Which one is used depends on what you want to do with the data.

Calculating the mean

The mean is the sum of a set of values divided by the number of values. The mathematical symbols used have been standardised. Each measurement or **value** from a sample is given the symbol x. The sum of all measurements is written as $\sum x$. ($\sum$ is the Greek letter sigma).

The number of values in the sample is n.
The mean of the sample is x-bar, $\bar{x}$

The mean = <u>sum of all samples</u>
                   sample size

$$\bar{x} = \frac{\sum x}{n}$$

> Most of the time you are calculating the **mean** and so use this word rather than average.

Calculating the median

This is the middle number for the results when arranged in rank order. (Remember median and middle).

Calculating the mode

This is the measurement that occurs the most number of times. (Remember mode and most).

Take the following set of results obtained from measuring the width of 10 beech leaves.

Raw data

The same data, but sorted into ascending rank order.

Sample	Leaf width / cm ±0.5cm
1	1.6
2	1.4
3	1.7
4	1.4
5	1.4
6	2.0
7	1.2
8	1.6
9	1.8
10	1.5

	Leaf width / cm ±0.5cm
	1.2
	1.4
	1.4
	1.4
	1.5
	1.6
	1.6
	1.7
	1.8
	2.0
mean	1.56
median	1.55
mode	1.4

> Since there is an even number of samples the median is the mean between the fifth and sixth values when arranged in rank order.

Calculating a percentage

Suppose there are 15 students in your class and 11 of these are girls. Calculate the percentage of girls in the class.

<u>number of girls</u>
total number of students × 100

$\frac{11}{15}$ × 100 = 73%

> My calculator gives me the number 73.33333333. This should be rounded to a sensible number.

Calculating a percentage change

Suppose three more students joined your class after the start of term.
Calculate the percentage change in the number of students.

$$\frac{\text{change in number of students}}{\text{original number of students}} \times 100 \qquad \frac{3}{15} \times 100 = 20\% \text{ increase}$$

> The formula is always
> $\frac{\text{change}}{\text{original}} \times 100$
> Always state if the change is an increase or decrease.

However a little later 2 students left.
Calculate the percentage change in the number of students.

$$\frac{\text{change in number of students}}{\text{original number of students}} \times 100 \qquad \frac{2}{15} \times 100 = 13\% \text{ decrease}$$

Calculating a ratio

Key points
➢ Always bring one of the values to 1.
➢ This should be the first one stated in the ratio.

In a class of 28 students there are 11 girls and 17 boys.

What is the ratio of girls to boys?
$\frac{11 \text{ girls}}{11} = 1$ $\frac{17 \text{ boys}}{11} = 1.5$
The girl : boy ratio is 1 : 1.5

What is the ratio of boys to girls?
$\frac{17 \text{ boys}}{17} = 1$ $\frac{11 \text{ girls}}{17} = 0.6$
The boy : girl ratio is 1 : 0.6

Variables

There are four categories
➢ Independent – This is the one that is manipulated over a range of values.
➢ Dependent – This is the one that is measured.
➢ Controlled or Fixed – These are all the ones that are controlled at a fixed value.
➢ Uncontrolled – These are the ones that cannot be controlled.

Standard deviation

Key points
➢ Standard deviation is used to summarise the spread of values around the mean.
➢ A small value for standard deviation indicates that the data is close to the mean.
➢ A large value indicates that the data is spread out.
➢ If the standard deviation is greater than 33% of the mean then that is large.
➢ In a normal distribution:
  • 68% of the data falls within + or – one standard deviation of the mean,
  • 95% falls within + or – two standard deviations.
➢ Standard deviation has the same units as the values.

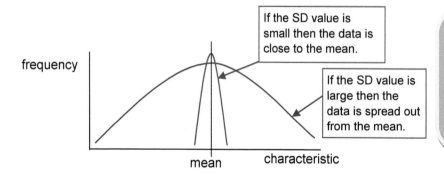

If the SD value is small then the data is close to the mean.

If the SD value is large then the data is spread out from the mean.

> **Example**
>
> Let us say the mean is 30 seconds and the standard deviation is 5 seconds.
>
> 68% of the values will fall within the times of 25 to 35 seconds, and 95% of the values will fall within the times of 20 to 40 seconds.

Calculating standard deviation

The symbol for standard deviation is **s** or sometimes σ.

- ❖ You should learn how to calculate standard deviation using your calculator.
- ❖ Remember that standard deviation has the same units as the data values.

When using your calculator to find standard deviation for a sample it may give you two possible standard deviations. Always choose the larger one as this uses n-1 rather than n. Likewise with other calculators if there is a key σ_{n-1} or s_{n-1} then use that in preference to σ_n or s_n.

> Take great care that any calculator you take into your IB exams is a permitted model – see Appendix 6 on page 321.

Graphs

Graphical representation of data allows for an easy interpretation of a set of data and also comparisons between sets of data. Bar charts, histograms and line graphs are the most common types but in Papers 2 and 3 expect to see some more unusual ones.

Bar charts

Key points
- ➢ Each set of data is represented by a bar which can go vertically or horizontally.
- ➢ There must be a space between each bar or groups of bars.

Example 1

A student set up clear glass dishes containing sugar water on different coloured backgrounds and counted the number of bees visiting each colour over a 2-hour period at midday.

Number of bees on each colour		
Red	Yellow	Blue
3	25	14

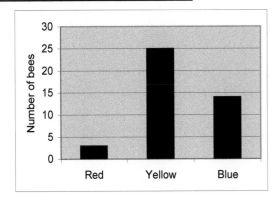
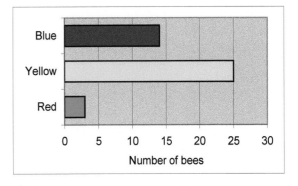

Example 2

A student noticed that several species of plant growing in a shaded woodland had leaves a different shade of green from members of the same species growing in a meadow. He made acetone extracts of the chloroplast pigments and measured the % light transmission using a colourimeter.

Plant species	% light transmission ±3%	
	Sun	Shade
A	45	61
B	36	40
C	22	59

Table 1. Colourimeter % transmission of acetone extracts from sun and shade leaves of three plant species.

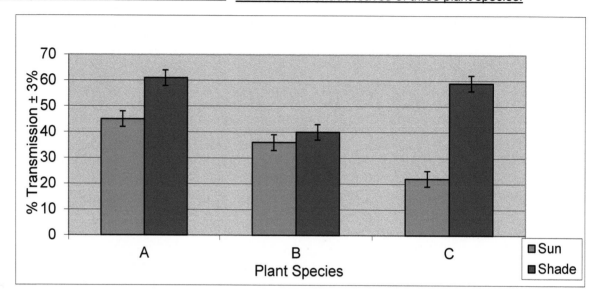

Graph 1. Colourimeter % transmission of acetone extracts from sun and shade leaves of three plant species

6. State the formula for calculating a percentage change.

7. In order for the standard deviation to be called large, what percentage of the mean must it be greater than?

8. If the standard deviation is large what does that tell you about the data?

9. What percentage of values falls within ±1 standard deviation of the mean?

10. What percentage of values falls within ±2 standard deviations of the mean?

11. State the formula for calculating the mean of a set of values.

12. What is the mode of a set of values?

13. What is the median of a set of values?

Histograms

Key points

➤ Also have a bar format.
➤ There is no space between each bar.
➤ The independent variable is continuous.

Example

A student collected the lengths of 24 leaves from each of two laurel bushes, one growing in a sunny environment and one in shade, and organised the data into groups as shown in the table below.

Leaf length / mm ±0.5mm	Number of leaves	
	sun	shade
90 – 94	2	1
95 – 99	3	1
100 – 104	3	2
105 – 109	5	4
110 – 114	4	7
115 – 119	3	7
120 – 124	3	5
125 – 129	1	3

Note that each set of values continues from the one before, i.e. 95 follows from 94 and 100 follows from 99, and each group is the same size.

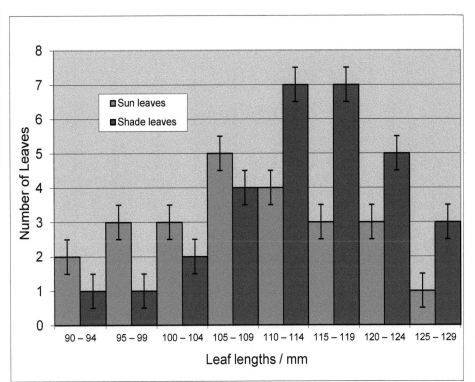

Line graphs

Key points

➤ Plotting dependent variables against independent variables.
➤ Plotting one variable against another to show a correlation.
➤ The relationship can be linear or non-linear.

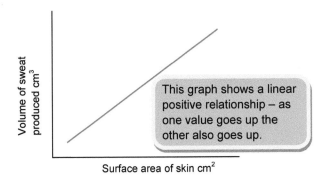

This graph shows a linear positive relationship – as one value goes up the other also goes up.

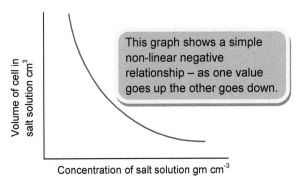

This graph shows a simple non-linear negative relationship – as one value goes up the other goes down.

Scattergraphs and correlation

Key points

➤ A scattergraph is a plot of two sets of variable data.
➤ The line may show a positive correlation, negative correlation or no correlation.

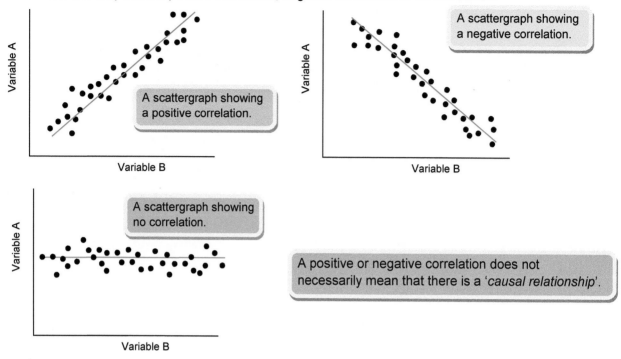

A scattergraph showing a positive correlation.

A scattergraph showing a negative correlation.

A scattergraph showing no correlation.

A positive or negative correlation does not necessarily mean that there is a *causal relationship*.

- **Example 1**: In many countries obesity has increased and so has the incidence of type II diabetes, i.e. a positive correlation implying obesity causes diabetes. Experimental data would need to be collected to provide evidence that this is the case, and in fact this has proved to be correct.

- **Example 2**: Shale gas production in the USA has increased dramatically in the last few years and the population of honey bees has decreased dramatically – there is a negative correlation. However it would be unreasonable to state that the fall in honey bee populations has been caused by shale gas production.

Error bars

Key points

➤ Error bars show the variability or uncertainty in a set of data.
➤ This may take several forms such as simply the range of values, or standard deviation, or standard error of the mean.

Here is a basic table of some data.

	Data
	16
	18
	19
	15
	15
	17
	18
Mean	16.9
Standard deviation	1.6

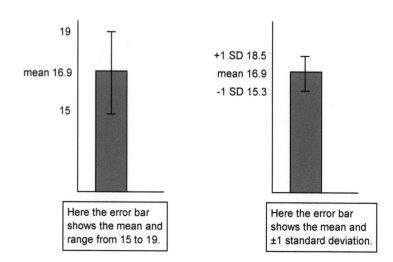

Here the error bar shows the mean and range from 15 to 19.

Here the error bar shows the mean and ±1 standard deviation.

➤ Error bars can be used when comparing sets of data.

For example data set A is without using a drug, the control. Data set B is using the drug.

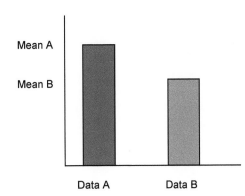

Mean A

Mean B

Data A   Data B

It appears that using the drug has an effect. However if we add error bars, say standard deviation, we can see that the upper values for data B overlap a lot with the lower values for data A. This indicates that the drug may not in fact be having an effect.

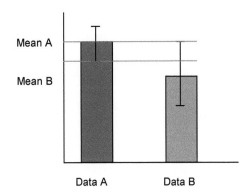

Mean A

Mean B

Data A   Data B

Hypotheses and significance testing

Hypotheses
A hypothesis is a prediction of the outcome of an investigation. There are two forms that the hypothesis can take and these are in opposition to each other. The statistical test you choose aims to prove one hypothesis right and the other one wrong.
The two forms of the hypothesis are the **null hypothesis**, H_0, and the **alternative hypothesis**, H_1.

The null hypothesis states that there is no link between the sets of data (observed and expected values), whereas the alternative hypothesis states that there is.

The null hypothesis is used if you are not able to predict a result.

Significance
➤ In biology 5% is taken as the boundary, meaning that the probability of the difference happening by chance is 5 times in 100.
➤ If the difference happens more than 5 times in 100, then it is due to chance.
➤ If the difference happens less than 5 times in 100, then it is probably due to a causal factor.
➤ Some statistics tests use tables of critical values and we compare the calculated result from a statistics test with the critical value.
➤ If the **calculated** value is **greater than** the **critical** value then the difference is **significant**, i.e. something has caused the difference.

Statistics – The chi-squared test

Key points
➤ This test compares the relationship between an observed set of data and an expected set of data.
➤ Each measurement must be independent from the others.
➤ The expected values must be greater than 5.

There are a great many statistical tests which can be used on collected data. One used in genetics and ecology is the chi-squared test.

Chi-squared in genetics
Key points
➤ Two values are needed, the observed value and the expected value.
➤ The expected value is calculated using the Mendelian ratio expected for that cross.
➤ The formula to use is:

$$\chi^2 = \sum \frac{(O-E)^2}{E}$$

Where
$\sum$ = sum of
O = the observed result
E = the expected result

➤ Degrees of freedom value is number of classes -1.

You do not need to know what degrees of freedom means but you do need to know how to calculate it.

Example

A breeding investigation was carried out with fruit flies. Long wing is dominant to short wing and red eye is dominant to white eye. A number of flies that were all heterozygous for both characteristics were crossed and the following numbers obtained.

Long wing, red eye   257
Long wing, white eye   81
Short wing, red eye   86
Short wing, white eye   24
Total   448

Since this was a standard dihybrid cross the expected results were a 9 : 3 : 3 : 1 ratio. The observed ratio is 10.7 : 3.4 : 3.6 : 1. The chi-squared test can be used to determine if this difference in the ratio is significant or not.

> The expected ratio is 9:3:3:1 – see page 261. To calculate the actual ratio divide the total, 448, by 16 (9+3+3+1). This gives the smallest number, the 1. Then multiply this by 3 and by 9 to give the other three numbers.

Classes (Phenotypes)	Observed O	Expected E	O – E	$(O-E)^2$	$\dfrac{(O-E)^2}{E}$
Long wing, red eye	257	252	5	25	0.1
Long wing, white eye	81	84	-3	9	0.1
Short wing, red eye	86	84	2	4	0.04
Short wing, white eye	24	28	-4	16	0.57
Totals*	448	448	0		$\Sigma = 0.81$

* The totals row is not really necessary, but it helps prevent calculation errors. The totals of the Observed and Expected columns must be the same, and the total of the O – E column must = zero.

Degrees of freedom	Significance Level Probability				
	20% 0.2	10% 0.1	**5% 0.05**	2% 0.02	1% 0.01
1	1.64	2.71	**3.84**	5.41	6.64
2	3.22	4.61	**5.99**	7.82	9.21
3	4.64	6.25	**7.82**	9.84	11.34
4	5.99	7.78	**9.49**	11.67	13.28
5	7.29	9.24	**11.07**	13.39	15.09

← decreasing   significance   increasing →

> Degrees of freedom = Number of classes – 1

<u>Table of chi-squared values</u>

Here there are 4 classes so degrees of freedom = 4-1 = 3.

Null hypothesis – there is no difference between the observed and expected ratios.

The 5% critical value on the table for 3 degrees of freedom is 7.82. Remembering that if the calculated value is greater than the critical value then the difference is significant. Since the calculated figure of 0.81 is well below this then the observed difference from the 9:3:3:1 ratio is not significant. We have proved our null hypothesis to be correct.

> You can check your calculations very quickly by going to:
>
> http://graphpad.com/quickcalcs/chisquared1.cfm
>
> (The column headed 'Category' is the Class).

Chi-squared in ecology

Key points

➢ In ecology it often is not possible to predict what the results should be as this would simply be guessing.

➢ Therefore we use the *null hypothesis* and the statistics is used to prove or disprove it.

➢ The data is collected using quadrats positioned randomly in the sample area.

➢ In order to test for an association between two species, in each quadrat the number of both species is recorded.

➢ The data is recorded as a 2 × 2 contingency table.

The null hypothesis
This states that there is no difference between the observed and expected values.

Number of quadrats	Number of quadrats		Row totals
	Species A present	**Species A absent**	
Species B present	present / present	present / absent	
Species B absent	absent / present	absent / absent	
Column totals			**Grand total**

Adding the row totals **or** the column totals should give the same grand total.

A 2 × 2 contingency table   NB. The table must be set out in this way.

The formulae

To calculate the expected frequencies:

E = row total × column total / grand total

To calculate degrees of freedom:

(number of rows – 1) × (number of columns – 1)

Again you need to know how to calculate degrees of freedom.

To calculate chi-squared:

$$\chi^2 = \sum \frac{(O - E)^2}{E}$$

Where
$\sum$ = sum of
O = the observed result
E = the expected result

Example

The diamond leaf willow (*Salix pulcha*) and the Arctic willow (*Salix arctica*) are both found on rocky outcrops in marshy ground in the Arctic tundra. A survey was carried out to see if there was an association between these two species.

Number of quadrats	Number of quadrats		Row totals
	***S. pulcha* present**	***S. pulcha* absent**	
***S. arctica* present**	52	38	90
***S. arctica* absent**	45	20	65
Column totals	97	58	**Grand total** 155

We now calculate the expected values, E.

Number of quadrats	Number of quadrats		Row totals
	***S. pulcha* present**	***S. pulcha* absent**	
***S. arctica* present**	90 × 97 = 56.3 / 155	90 × 58 = 33.7 / 155	90
***S. arctica* absent**	65 × 97 = 40.7 / 155	65 × 58 = 24.3 / 155	65
Column totals	97	58	**Grand total** 155

E = row total × column total / grand total

Check that your expected row and column totals match the observed totals.

This data can now be entered into a standard chi-squared table

	O	E	O – E	$(O - E)^2$	$\dfrac{(O - E)^2}{E}$
Both present	52	56.3	-4.3	18.49	0.328
S. pulcha **only**	45	40.7	4.3	18.49	0.454
S. arctica **only**	38	33.7	4.3	18.49	0.549
Both absent	20	24.3	-4.3	18.49	0.761
Totals	155	155	0		$\sum = 2.09$

	Significance Level Probability				
Degrees of freedom	20% 0.2	10% 0.1	**5% 0.05**	2% 0.02	1% 0.01
1	1.64	2.71	**3.84**	5.41	6.64
2	3.22	4.61	**5.99**	7.82	9.21
3	4.64	6.25	**7.82**	9.84	11.34
4	5.99	7.78	**9.49**	11.67	13.28
5	7.29	9.24	**11.07**	13.39	15.09

◄——— decreasing   significance   increasing ———►

Degrees of freedom = $(2 - 1) \times (2 - 1) = 1$

Table of chi-squared values

The null hypothesis, H_0, states that there is no association between the two *Salix* species.

The 5% critical value on the table for 1 degree of freedom is 3.84 Remembering that if the calculated value is **greater** than the critical value then the difference is significant. The calculated figure of 2.09 is smaller than this so the observed difference is not significant. We would accept the null hypothesis – there is no association between the two species of *Salix*.

You can check your calculations very quickly by going to:

http://www.physics.csbsju.edu/stats/contingency_NROW_NCOLUMN_form.html

Enter 2 and 2 for the rows and columns, click submit, enter your 4 observed values and click calculate now. Make sure you match the number to the box as putting the values in different positions may give the wrong calculation. This gives you the expected numbers, the chi-squared value and the probability.

Nomograms

Key points
- A nomogram is a group of three or more scales.
- Each scale shows a different set of values.
- Data is collected for two of the values and these are used to read off a value on the third scale.
- The scales can be positioned vertically or horizontally

Example

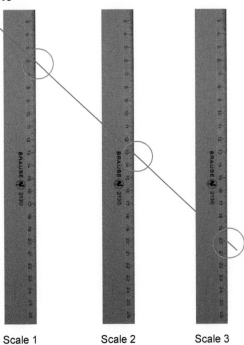

Scale 1 Scale 2 Scale 3

Given value for scale 1 = 6.0 units,
Given value for scale 3 = 20.0 units,
Draw a straight line between these two values,
Read off scale 2 value = 13.1 units.

Glossary

CAUSAL RELATIONSHIP	A relationship between one event, X, and another, Y, in which X precedes and causes Y.
CORRELATION	A relationship between two variables where a change in one causes a corresponding or proportional change in the other values.
ERROR BAR	Used on a graph to show some measure of upper and lower values about the mean. Commonly this is standard deviation.
HYPOTHESIS	A testable explanation of an observed event.
QUADRAT	A measured square area which encloses a sampling area.
NORMAL DISTRIBUTION	A bell shaped curve on a graph which is symmetrical each side of the mean.
NULL HYPOTHESIS	Used in statistics, this states that there is no difference between the observed and predicted values.
SIGNIFICANCE	In a statistics test the significance is whether one variable has an effect on another variable or if the result is simply due to chance, In Biology the most common level of significance is 5%, i.e. if the investigation was carried out 100 times then it is acceptable to have 5 of them where the effect was due to chance.
STANDARD DEVIATION	A statistical measure of the spread of data about the mean of a set of values with a normal distribution. 68% of the values fall within ±1 standard deviation of the mean, 95% of the values fall within ±2 standard deviations of the mean.

Answers to Grey Box Questions

1. 22000μm
2. 10^6
3. 10^3
4. a. Measure the scale bar on the photograph in mm.
   b. Convert these mm into the same units as the scale bar.
   c. Divide this number by the number on the scale bar.
5. $mm^3 min^{-1}$
6. $\underline{\text{difference in values}} \times 100$
      original value
7. 33%
8. It is spread out on either side of the mean.
9. 68%
10. 95%
11. total of all the values ÷ number of values
12. the most frequent value
13. the middle value

Self-test Quiz

1. Which line in the table is correct?

	Molecules	Membrane thickness	Viruses	Bacteria	Organelles	Cells
a.	1μm	10nm	1μm	Upto 10μm	10nm	Upto 100μm
b.	10nm	1μm	100nm	100nm	Upto 10μm	Upto 100μm
c.	1nm	10nm	Upto 10μm	1μm	Upto 100μm	100nm
d.	1nm	10nm	100nm	1μm	Upto 10μm	Upto 100μm

2. Determine the magnification of these scale bars.

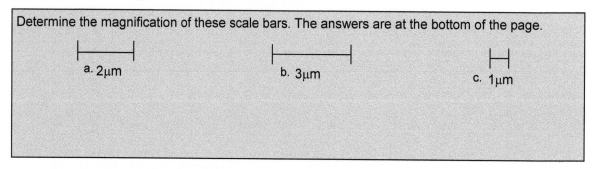

Determine the magnification of these scale bars. The answers are at the bottom of the page.

a. 2μm   b. 3μm   c. 1μm

3. Calculate the actual size of these drawings.

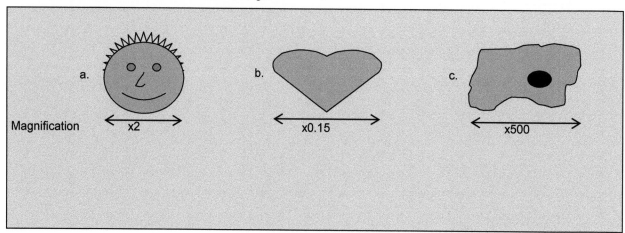

Magnification   a. x2   b. x0.15   c. x500

4. Use the data in the table to calculate the mean, median and mode.

	height of student / m
	1.5
	1.6
	1.6
	1.7
	1.9
	2.0
mean	
median	
mode	

5. The number of bacterial colonies on a petri dish on day 1 was 12 and on day 2 was 35. Determine the percentage change in the number of colonies.

6. In a new forest plantation there are 376 planted forest trees and 85 self-seeded trees. Determine the ratio of self-seeded to forest trees.

7. Use your calculator to calculate the mean and standard deviation of the following data.

Set 1 mm	Set 2 mm	Set 3 mm	Set 4 mm	Set 5 mm	Mean	Standard deviation
13	12	15	14	11		

8. Which type of correlation does the graph below show?

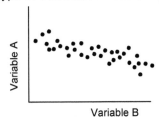

Variable B

9. A student calculated the mean and standard deviation for a set of measurements of light transmission through an extract of anthocyanin, a red plant pigment. She found the mean value was 47% with a standard deviation of 13%. Was she right in stating that the standard deviation was very small?

10. Standard deviation can be applied to a population with a normal distribution. In this case:
    a. 68% of the population falls within ± 1 standard deviation of the mean,
    b. 95% of the population falls within ± 1 standard deviation of the mean,
    c. 68% of the population fits under the curve,
    d. 68% of the population falls within ± 2 standard deviation of the mean.

11. Population A has a standard deviation of 2.7 units and population B has a standard deviation of 3.2 units. It can be deduced that:
    a. Population A is smaller than population B.
    b. The mean value of population B is greater than the mean value of population A.
    c. Population B shows greater variation than population A.
    d. The sampling procedure used for population A was different from that used for population B.

Table of chi-squared values

Degrees of freedom	Significance Level Probability				
	20% 0.2	10% 0.1	5% 0.05	2% 0.02	1% 0.01
1	1.64	2.71	3.84	5.41	6.64
2	3.22	4.61	5.99	7.82	9.21
3	4.64	6.25	7.82	9.84	11.34
4	5.99	7.78	9.49	11.67	13.28
5	7.29	9.24	11.07	13.39	15.09

12. Bean plants were grown in temperature controlled rooms at two different temperatures and after 10 days the mean height of a sample of 50 from each room was measured. State the null hypothesis and use the chi-squared test to determine if there is a significant difference in the two means. (The table of chi-squared values is at the top of the page.)

Mean height of bean plant, mm	Observed O	Expected E	O – E	$(O-E)^2$	$\dfrac{(O-E)^2}{E}$
10°C	17				
20°C	31				
Totals					

13. A breeding investigation was carried out with fruit flies. The expected ratio was 1:2:1 and the observed numbers were 22:28:6. A chi-squared test was carried out and the result was 9.14. What would be your conclusion, giving reasoning for your answer?

14a. On the island of Madeira water channels called levadas have been cut into the rock to provide water for irrigation. Over time the cut rock surfaces have become covered by a growth of mosses and liverworts. A student wanted to find out if there was an association between the mosses and liverworts and so she collected the following data:
   - Rock surfaces with both moss and liverwort – 120
   - Rock surfaces with only moss – 46
   - Rock surfaces with only liverwort – 29
   - Rock surfaces with neither moss nor liverwort – 5

Draw a contingency table for this data.

14b. Calculate the expected values based on the null hypothesis.

14c. Calculate the number of degrees of freedom.

14d. Calculate the chi-squared value and state whether the null hypothesis has been rejected or accepted.

	Observed O	Expected E	O – E	$(O-E)^2$	$\dfrac{(O-E)^2}{E}$
Both moss and liverwort	120				
Moss only	46				
Liverwort only	29				
Neither	5				
Totals	200	200	0		

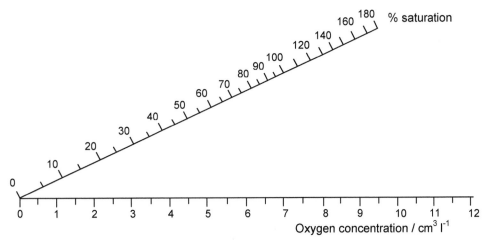

Use the nomogram above to answer the following.

15a. If the temperature of the water is 15°C what is the % saturation when the oxygen concentration is 4cm^3 l^{-1}?

15b. Determine the temperature change that causes a change in % saturation from 25 to 35 while the oxygen concentration remains at 2cm^3 l^{-1}.

16. To measure growth rate an apple grower collected 1000 apples from trees in one of his fields. Assuming the sample had a normal distribution how many apples would be within two standard deviations of the mean?
    a. 680
    b. 950
    c. 500
    d. 475

17. The apple grower also wanted to compare the productivity of the same apple variety growing in two different fields. The table shows the data he collected:

	Mean number of apples per tree	Number of trees sampled	Standard deviation
Field A	350	1000	7.1
Field B	300	800	2.5

Which of the following statements is correct?
    a. The results from field A are more accurate because a larger number of trees was sampled.
    b. The results from field A are more reliable because the standard deviation is higher.
    c. Only the results from field B have a normal distribution.
    d. The trees in field B each have a number of apples closer to the mean than the trees in field A.

18. The number of peas in a sample of 10 pods was counted and the data shown in the table.

1	2	3	4	5	6	7	8	9	10	Mean
5	6	6	7	7	7	7	8	8	9	7

What is the best estimate of the standard deviation?
    a. 5
    b. 9
    c. 7
    d. 1

19. The Carrot Root fly lays its eggs in the soil around the carrot plant. Soil samples were collected from 10 plants and the number of eggs counted. The data is shown in the table:

1	2	3	4	5	6	7	8	9	10	Mean	Standard deviation
44	52	71	45	69	72	83	68	75	81	66	14.1

What statistical percentage of the soil samples has between 52 and 80 eggs?
   a. 14.1%
   b. 33%
   c. 68%
   d. 95%

20. What do error bars on graphs indicate?
   a. The variability of the data.
   b. The method used to collect the data.
   c. The statistical analysis used on the data.
   d. The result which is closest to the mean value.

Chapter Two
Molecular Biology Part 1
Carbon, water, carbohydrates, lipids

Molecular Biology looks at four major groups
of biological molecules – carbohydrates, lipids,
proteins and nucleic acids.
All organic molecules are based on the carbon atom.

Molecules
Key points
➢ Living organisms are made up from only a small proportion of all the elements.
➢ The four most common elements are carbon, hydrogen, oxygen and nitrogen.
➢ Other important elements include calcium, sodium, potassium, phosphorus, sulphur, and iron.
➢ Elements are bonded together to form compounds.
➢ Organic compounds are those that contain carbon, but excluding carbonates, hydrogen carbonates and oxides of carbon, e.g. carbon dioxide.
➢ All other compounds are inorganic, e.g. water.
➢ Living organisms are made up of both inorganic and organic compounds.
➢ The four major groups of organic carbon compounds are:
• carbohydrates,
• lipids,
• proteins,
• nucleic acids.
➢ Living processes are the result of chemical interactions.
➢ Molecular biology can explain these interactions.
➢ Urea - is an organic compound that is produced by living organisms,
- can by synthesised artificially.

Hydrophilic and hydrophobic
Chemical substances can be hydrophilic or hydrophobic.
▪ A hydrophilic substance has an affinity for and interacts with water through hydrogen bonding.
▪ A hydrophobic substance will not interact with water.

> Examples of hydrophilic substances:
> ▪ sugars,
> ▪ salts,
> ▪ vitamin C.

> Examples of hydrophobic substances:
> ▪ Fats,
> ▪ vitamins A, D and E.

Amphipathic
An amphipathic molecule has part of it hydrophilic and part hydrophobic.

> Example of an amphipathic substance:
> ▪ phospholipid.

> Hydro = water
> philic = like
> phobic = hate

Carbon
Key points

➢ The dark grey ball is the carbon atom.
➢ The pale grey balls are other atoms that can be bonded on.
➢ Carbon atoms can form four covalent bonds shown in black.
➢ These bonds may be single as in methane CH_4, or double as in carbon dioxide CO_2, or even a mixture as in fatty acids – see page 24.
➢ This allows carbon to form a large diversity of stable compounds.

Water
Key facts
➢ Water is a dipolar molecule – it has negative and positive ends (poles).
➢ The oxygen atom has a slight negative charge.
➢ The hydrogen atoms each have a slight positive charge.
➢ The positive and negative charges on different molecules attract each other.
➢ This attraction forms hydrogen bonds ·········
➢ This is called **cohesion**.
➢ The polarity of water allows it to dissolve other polar molecules such as sugars and amino acids with polar side groups – see page 36.

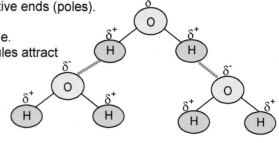

➢ Other substances form ions in water and dissolve, e.g. sodium chloride (salt) forms sodium ions Na^+ and chloride ions Cl^-.
➢ Water is also attracted to other molecules.
➢ This is called **adhesion**.
➢ Water has a high specific heat, i.e. it can store a large amount of heat.
➢ Water has a high latent heat of vaporisation, i.e. it takes a lot of energy to turn liquid water to water vapour.
➢ Water has a high density.

Comparing the thermal properties of water and methane

	Water	Methane
Chemical formula	H_2O	CH_4
Hydrogen bonding	Yes	No
Latent heat of vaporisation	2,257J g^{-1}	760J g^{-1}
Boiling point	100^0C	-161^0C

> When a liquid boils the molecules evaporate. The difference in boiling point and latent heat of vaporisation clearly shows the significance of the hydrogen bonding.
> A much greater input of energy is required before the water molecules evaporate compared to methane which, because it is non-polar, does not have hydrogen bonding.

Water as a heat transporter

Significant property

❖ High specific heat.
  ➢ Plasma forms 55% of the blood.
  ➢ Plasma is 92% water.
  ➢ Heat can be transported from a hotter part of the body to a cooler part.

> Example:
> A lizard sunbathing in the morning can transport heat absorbed through the skin to its internal organs.

Water as a habitat

Significant property

❖ High specific heat.
  ➢ A large amount of heat energy is required to warm water.
  ➢ It loses this heat energy slowly.
  ➢ This makes water a very stable habitat.

Water as a coolant

Significant properties

❖ High specific heat.
❖ High latent heat of vaporisation.
  ➢ When water is in a liquid form the molecules are held together by hydrogen bonding.
  ➢ When water evaporates these hydrogen bonds are broken.
  ➢ Breaking the bonds requires energy.
  ➢ Heat energy is transported to the skin surface in the blood.
  ➢ This heat energy is used to break the hydrogen bonds in the sweat on the skin surface and this cools the blood.

2.1 Beads of sweat show on this woman's back

Water as a transporter in blood

Significant property

❖ Polar solvent.
  ➢ Polar substances such as sugars and amino acids readily dissolve.
  ➢ Non-polar molecules such as fats and cholesterol (mostly non-polar) are transported as lipoproteins – see page 25.

Water as a transporter in plants

Significant properties

❖ Polar solvent:
  ➢ Polar substances such as sucrose, amino acids and mineral salts readily dissolve in the water of the phloem sap and the water in the xylem vessels – see page 216.
❖ Adhesion:
  ➢ Water molecules are attracted to the surface of the xylem vessel wall.
  ➢ Water molecules move from the xylem vessels to the mesophyll cell surface through cell walls.
  ➢ Cellulose cell walls have molecule sized channels.
  ➢ This small channel size creates very high adhesive forces.
❖ Cohesion:
  ➢ As water molecules evaporate from the surface of a leaf cell further water molecules are pulled from behind creating the transpiration stream in the xylem.

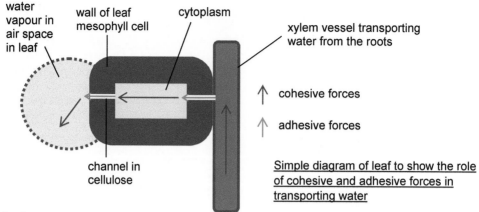

Simple diagram of leaf to show the role of cohesive and adhesive forces in transporting water

Carbohydrates

These include:

- sugars – monosaccharides and disaccharides,
- starch,
- glycogen, ⎤ polysaccharides
- cellulose. ⎦

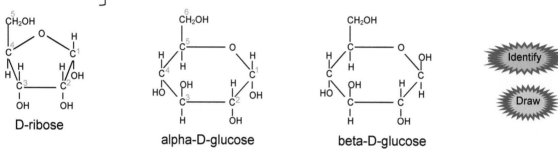

D-ribose

alpha-D-glucose

beta-D-glucose

Identify

Draw

The difference between alpha and beta glucose

Imagine the ring as lying horizontally.

Note the position of the hydroxyl group –OH on carbon 1.

In alpha glucose it is below the ring and in beta glucose it is above the ring.

In alpha glucose the hydroxyl groups are down, down, up, down – DDUD.

In beta glucose the hydroxyl groups are up, down, up, down – UDUD.

Monosaccharides and disaccharides

Key points

➤ Monosaccharides have a single ring of carbon atoms.

➤ Glucose and ribose are monosaccharides.

➤ Ribose is a pentose because it has 5 carbon atoms.

➤ Glucose is a hexose because it has 6 carbon atoms.

➤ Two monosaccharide monomers (hexoses) are joined by condensation to form a disaccharide – see page 28.

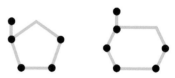

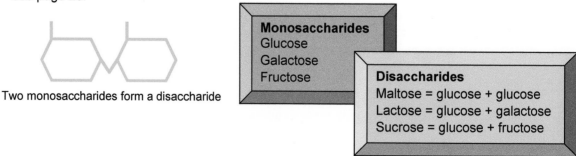

Two monosaccharides form a disaccharide

Monosaccharides
Glucose
Galactose
Fructose

Disaccharides
Maltose = glucose + glucose
Lactose = glucose + galactose
Sucrose = glucose + fructose

Polysaccharides

Definition

➢ More than two monosaccharides joined to form a chain.

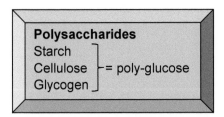

Polysaccharides
Starch
Cellulose ⎤ = poly-glucose
Glycogen ⎦

1-4 and 1-6 linkage mean that carbon 1 of one monosaccharide is linked to either carbon 4 or carbon 6 of the other monosaccharide.

	Structure	Function
Cellulose	Made of polyglucose residues – see page 27, Uses beta-D-glucose, Joined by a 1-4 linkage, Unbranched, Straight chains, Chains cross-linked by hydrogen bonding, Very strong.	Cell wall of plant cells, Supports plant, Porous and allows water to flow through it – see Water as a transporter in plants on page 21.
Starch	Polyglucose residues, Uses alpha-D-glucose, Joined by a 1-4 linkage, Two forms – amylose and amylopectin, Amylose is unbranched, Amylopectin is slightly branched using 1-6 linkages, Both forms are coiled, Insoluble.	Energy storage molecule in plants, Both forms found together in starch grains.
Glycogen	Made of polyglucose residues, Uses alpha-D-glucose, Joined by a 1-4 linkage, Profusely branched using 1-6 linkages, Insoluble.	Energy storage molecule in animals, Stored in liver and skeletal muscle cells, Forms tiny granules in cytoplasm.

Cellulose

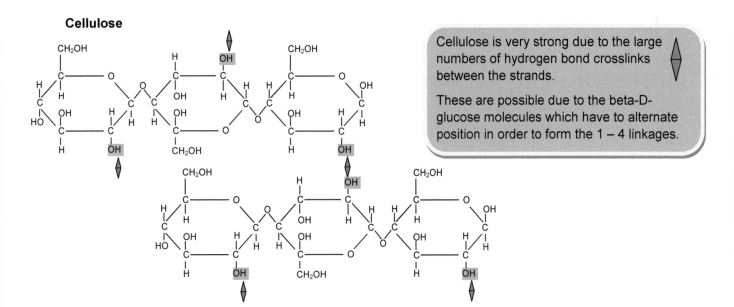

Cellulose is very strong due to the large numbers of hydrogen bond crosslinks between the strands.

These are possible due to the beta-D-glucose molecules which have to alternate position in order to form the 1 – 4 linkages.

Starch

Starch obtained from potatoes is used as an adhesive;
The presence of amylose reduces the adhesive property;
Potatoes have been genetically modified to reduce the amylose content.

Branching occurs using a 1 – 6 condensation linkage.

Amylose is unbranched;
Amylopectin is slightly branched using 1-6 linkages.

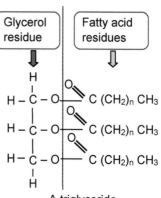

Lipids

These include:

- triglycerides,
- phospholipids,
- steroids.

Triglycerides

Key points

Composed of:

- glycerol,
- three fatty acids,
- the fatty acids may be saturated, monounsaturated or polyunsaturated,
- triglycerides are formed by condensation – see page 27.

Glycerol residue	Fatty acid residues

A triglyceride

Fatty acid structure

Key facts

$$CH_3 — (CH_2)_n — COOH \qquad HOOC— (CH_2)_n —CH_3$$

Three different ways of writing the structure of a fatty acid.

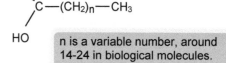

n is a variable number, around 14-24 in biological molecules.

➤ Saturated fatty acids have no double bonds between the carbon atoms of the $-CH_2$ region.

➤ Unsaturated fatty acids have one or more double bonds between the carbon atoms.

➤ Mono-unsaturated fatty acids have only one double bond.

➤ Polyunsaturated fatty acids have two or more double bonds.

Draw

Identify

A saturated C7 fatty acid

➤ **Cis** means the hydrogen atoms are on the same side on each side of a double bond.

➤ **Trans** means the hydrogen atoms are on opposite sides on each side of a double bond.

Hint – to transverse means to go across.

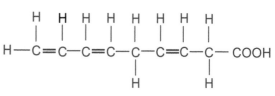

A polyunsaturated C9 cis fatty acid

IBHL Biology 2016 © Ashby Merson-Davies

Phospholipids

Key point
- This is a modified triglyceride.
- The third fatty acid has been replaced by a phosphate group.
- Phospholipids are a major component of membranes – see page 83.

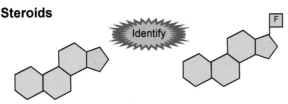

This region is hydrophilic

This region is hydrophobic

Phospholipid

Steroids

Identify

The simplest steroid

The characteristic structure of steroids is three six sided rings and one five sided ring.
There can be a functional group F attached to the five sided ring to form the different types of steroid. (This is like the R group of amino acids).

Carbohydrates and lipids as energy stores

Carbohydrates
⇒ 17kJ of energy released per gram;
⇒ Easily built up for storage;
⇒ Easily broken down to release energy quickly;
⇒ Glycogen in animals: starch in plants;
⇒ Both of these converted to glucose when energy required.

Lipids
⇒ 38kJ of energy released per gram – over twice as much;
⇒ hence more efficient as energy store;
⇒ storage efficiency increased because lipids are hydrophobic and less mass is taken up storing water;
⇒ Metabolic pathways to build up and break down more complex and therefore slower;
⇒ Converted to fatty acids and glycerol when energy required;
⇒ Both of these converted to acetyl CoA – see page 129.

Scientific evidence for health risks of trans fats and saturated fatty acids

Key facts
- High levels of LDL (see blue box) in the blood stream increase the risk of coronary heart disease due to atherosclerosis – see page 153.
- Some studies have shown that trans fats and saturated fats in the diet increase the levels of LDL and lower the levels of HDL.
- In November 2014 research published by Ohio State University showed that a diet high in saturated fat but low in carbohydrate did not raise LDL as the fats were used for energy production. On the other hand a high carbohydrate / low saturated fat diet increased levels of LDL.

LDL and HDL
Fats are insoluble and cholesterol is only very slightly soluble. They are carried in the blood as tiny lipoprotein particles. There are two main types of lipoprotein – HDL (high density lipoprotein) and LDL (low density lipoprotein). Fats are less dense than water so LDL particles contain a high proportion of fat and cholesterol.
LDLs are referred to as 'bad' cholesterol and HDLs as 'good' cholesterol.

Evaluation of evidence for health claims about lipids

For
- Several studies have shown that rTFAs (see second blue box) could be beneficial by lowering LDL.
- Studies in rodents showed that CLA was highly effective in reducing the development of arterial plaques.
- Two Kenyan tribes have a diet rich in saturated fatty acids yet coronary heart disease is very rare.

Trans fatty acids
Trans fatty acids, TFAs, are uncommon in nature but two particular types, VA and CLA, are found in beef and dairy products. These are rTFAs (r for ruminant).
Most TFAs are manufactured from liquid cis fats such as vegetable oils to make them solid for food production. These are iTFAs (i for industrial).

- ➢ All studies have shown that iTFAs increase plasma LDL increasing the risk of coronary heart disease.
- ➢ A study by the US Department of Agriculture showed that VA raised LDL but also raised HDL.

Conclusions
- ➢ Although there is a positive correlation between coronary heart disease and certain dietary fatty acids there is insufficient evidence for a causal link.
- ➢ The presence or absence of other dietary components such as fibre could modify the effect.
- ➢ In view of the variability of evidence and lack of agreement amongst researchers, along with lack of sufficiently controlled studies on humans it is recommended that trans fats are excluded from the diet.

Methods used to obtain evidence

Research using humans
- ▪ The sample needs to be very large to allow for genetic variability.
- ▪ The sample should be selected for similarities in age, gender, state of health and life style.
- ▪ Allowance must be made for peoples' honesty and accuracy in reporting their dietary intake.
- ▪ Does the statistical analysis show a wide variation making it less reliable?
- ▪ Are any statistical differences significant?

Research using animals
- ▪ Animals can be selected to be genetically uniform.
- ▪ Diets, environment, exercise can be carefully controlled.
- ▪ Trials using animals should only be done if no other methods are available.
- ▪ The importance of the results must be significant enough to justify animal experimentation.
- ▪ Any procedures used must avoid causing suffering.
- ▪ Anaesthetics should be used to prevent suffering.
- ▪ Animals should not be collected from the wild.

Condensation and hydrolysis

Key points
- ➢ Many macromolecules or polymers can be built up from monomer building blocks and similarly broken back down into the constituent monomers.
- ➢ Building up is by **condensation** – water is released.
- ➢ Breaking down is by **hydrolysis**.
- ➢ In some cases an 'O' and an 'OH' are used to make the water; in other cases two 'OH' groups are used. In the latter case the extra oxygen joins the two monomer residues.

Basic principles

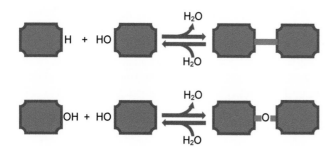

Monomers and residues
A monomer is the individual building unit, e.g. a glucose or an amino acid.

Residue is a term used when part of a monomer has been lost during formation by condensation of a dimer/polymer. For example when two glucose monomers form a maltose dimer one glucose loses an H becoming $C_6H_{11}O_6$, and the other an OH becoming $C_6H_{11}O_5$.

IBHL Biology 2016 © Ashby Merson-Davies

Condensation and hydrolysis in carbohydrates

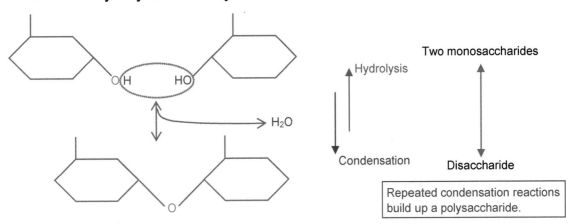

Condensation and hydrolysis in lipids

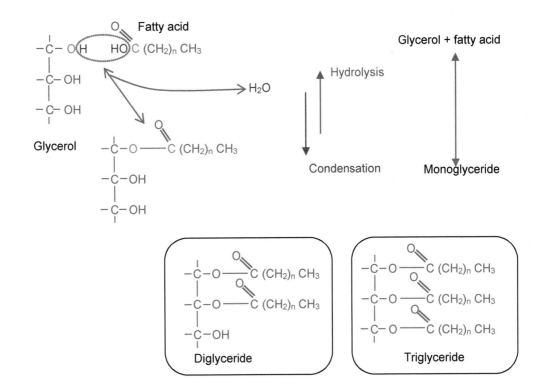

Condensation and hydrolysis in amino acids

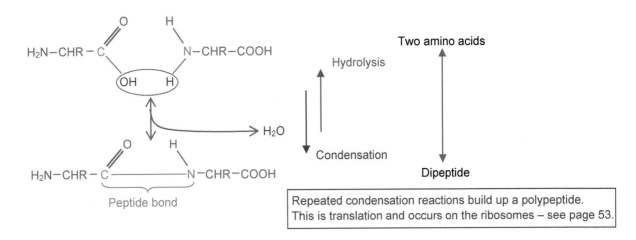

Body mass index (BMI)

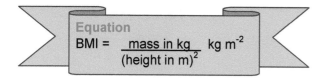

Equation

$$BMI = \frac{\text{mass in kg}}{(\text{height in m})^2} \quad kg\,m^{-2}$$

BMI kg m^{-2}	Status
Below 18.5	Underweight
18.5 – 24.9	Normal
25.0 – 29.9	Overweight
Over 30.0	Severely overweight / obese

You are expected to know the equation and how to use a nomogram – revise page 13.

When a person has been diagnosed as obese by a doctor they are called **clinically obese**.

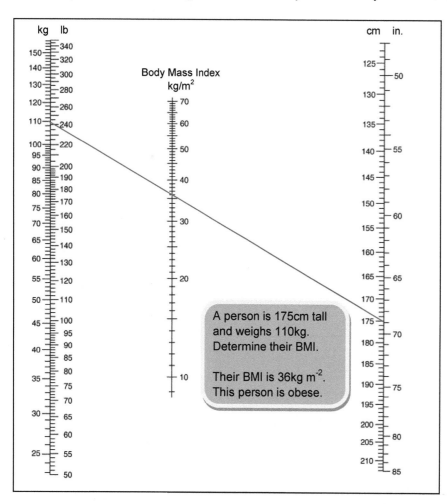

A person is 175cm tall and weighs 110kg. Determine their BMI.

Their BMI is 36kg m^{-2}. This person is obese.

2.2 These two photographs illustrate the increasing problem of obesity.

Are you the right weight?

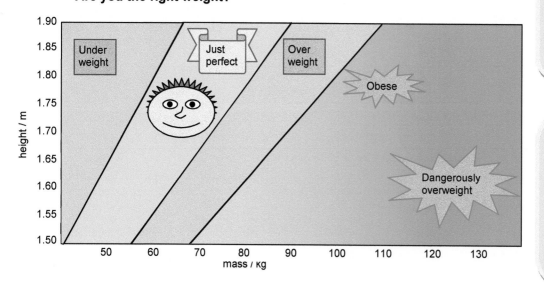

There is increasing evidence that epigenetic modification – see page 49 – during fetal growth can result in the development of childhood obesity.

A report in *The Lancet Diabetes and Endocrinology* in December 2014 found a positive correlation between age, obesity and reduced life expectancy. Being obese at an age of 20-39 could reduce life expectancy by up to 9 years in men and 7.5 years in women.

Molecular visualisation software

Molecular visualisation software is used to produces models of molecules that can be manipulated in various ways, including rotating them to show their 3D structure.

This is a model of a triglyceride taken from http://biomodel.uah.es/en/model3/tag.htm.
(You do not need to know any names or details from this example).

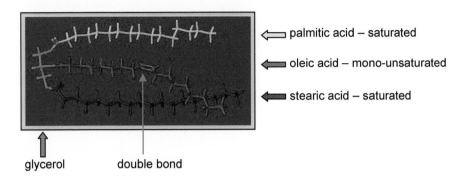

palmitic acid – saturated

oleic acid – mono-unsaturated

stearic acid – saturated

glycerol   double bond

The double bond causes the oleic acid to bend as shown below by rotating the model.

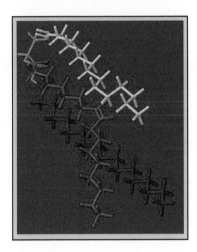

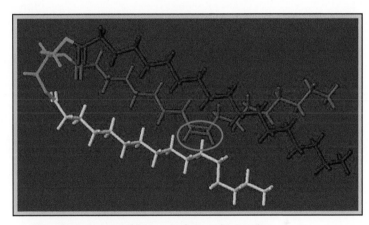

The chain is bent if it is a cis fatty acid, i.e. the hydrogens are on the same side of the carbon chain. This can clearly be seen in the red oval.

This bent fatty acid means the chains cannot pack so tightly in the phospholipid bilayer which makes the membrane more fluid which is especially important for on the rER and Golgi apparatus, and for endocytosis and exocytosis – see page 87.

1. What does hydrophobic mean?

2. What does amphipathic mean?

3. State an example of an amphipathic molecule.

6. Is hydrogen carbonate an organic or inorganic molecule?

9. How many covalent bonds can carbon form?

4. List the four most common elements used by organisms.

7. List the four major groups of organic compounds.

10. What property of water makes it good at transferring heat?

5. Which one is branched – amylose or amylopectin?

8. Distinguish between adhesion and cohesion.

11. What property of water makes it good as a coolant?

13. Identify this molecule.

14. Draw lines to link the sugar to its pattern of hydroxyl groups.
alpha-D-glucose   up down up down

beta-D-glucose   down down up down

12. What property do sugars have which allow them to dissolve in water?

15. State the missing sugar.
Maltose = glucose +

Lactose = glucose +

Sucrose = glucose +

16. Which molecule, alpha-D-glucose or beta-D-glucose is used to make cellulose?

17. Which molecule, alpha-D-glucose or beta-D-glucose is used to make starch?

18. List the components of a triglyceride.

19. Name the type of reaction used to build a triglyceride.

20. Name the type of reaction used to join monosaccharides together.

21. Which sugar, amylose or amylopectin, reduces the adhesive property of a starch paste?

22. What feature of cellulose makes it such a strong structure?

23. Draw the trans form of a fatty acid chain.

24. Draw a saturated fatty acid containing 4 carbon atoms.

25. State an example of a carbohydrate monomer.

27. What is the characteristic feature of an unsaturated fatty acid chain?

28. Draw a beta-D-glucose molecule.

26. List the components of a phospholipid.

Glossary

ADHESION	Attraction between water molecules and different molecules.
COHESION	Hydrogen bonding between water molecules.
COMPOUND	A substance made from two or more elements chemically combined.
COVALENT BOND	A strong chemical bond between molecules, e.g. between the sugar and phosphate and the sugar and base in a nucleotide.
ELEMENT	A substance which cannot be broken down into a simpler substance, e.g. phosphorus P, calcium Ca.
HYDROGEN BOND	A weak chemical bond between the weak positive charge on a hydrogen atom and the weak negative charge on either an oxygen or a nitrogen atom.
HYDROPHILIC	Having an affinity for water.
HYDROPHOBIC	A reluctance to mix with water.
ION	A charged particle, e.g. sodium ion Na^+, chloride ion Cl^-, phosphate ion PO_4^{3-}.
LATENT HEAT OF VAPORISATION	The amount of heat energy required to convert a liquid into a vapour.
LYSIS	Splitting.
POLAR MOLECULE	A molecule in which the electric charge is not distributed evenly in the covalent bonds.
POLAR SOLVENT	A substance that will dissolve polar molecules.
SPECIFIC HEAT	The amount of heat that must be absorbed by 1g of a substance to raise its temperature by 1^0C.

Answers to Grey Box Questions

1. Water hating.
2. Having both hydrophilic and hydrophobic regions.
3. Phospholipid.
4. Carbon, hydrogen, oxygen, nitrogen.
5. Amylopectin.
6. Inorganic.
7. Carbohydrates, lipids, proteins, nucleic acids.
8. Adhesion – an attraction between different types of molecule; cohesion – an attraction between the same type of molecule.
9. 4.
10. High specific heat.
11. Cohesion.
12. They are polar.
13. Ribose.

14.
> Draw lines to link the sugar to its pattern of hydroxyl groups.
> alpha-D-glucose   up down up down
> beta-D-glucose   down down up down

15. Maltose – glucose.
    Lactose – galactose.
    Sucrose – fructose.
16. Beta-D-glucose.
17. Alpha-D-glucose.
18. Glycerol + **three** fatty acids.
19. Condensation.
20. Condensation.
21. Amylose.
22. Numerous hydrogen bond cross-links.

23.

24.

25. Glucose / galactose / fructose.
26. Glycerol; **two** fatty acid chains; one phosphate group.
27. It has one or more double bonds.
28.

1. Which line in the table is correct?

	Monosaccharide	Disaccharide	Polysaccharide
a.	galactose	maltose	glycogen
b.	glucose	starch	galactose
c.	fructose	galactose	starch
d.	glucose	fructose	cellulose

2. The four most frequently occurring elements in organisms are:
   a. hydrogen, nitrogen, oxygen, sulphur,
   b. carbon, hydrogen, oxygen, nitrogen,
   c. carbon, nitrogen, oxygen, calcium,
   d. carbon, nitrogen, hydrogen, sodium.

3. Hydrogen bonding is:
   a. only found in water,
   b. an attraction between weak negative and positive charges,
   c. a bond between hydrogen atoms,
   d. formed during a condensation reaction.

4. Cohesion between water molecules means that:
   a. water is a good solvent,
   b. substances can diffuse in water,
   c. osmosis can occur within a cell,
   d. a transpiration stream can occur in plants.

5. Carbohydrates, lipids, proteins and nucleic acids **all** contain the elements:
   a. nitrogen and oxygen,
   b. carbon, hydrogen and nitrogen,
   c. hydrogen, carbon and oxygen,
   e. nitrogen, carbon and oxygen.

6. The term organic can be described as:
   a. the element carbon,
   b. a compound containing water,
   c. a compound containing carbon,
   d. a compound that dissolves in water.

7. Which one of the following represents the general structure of an amino acid?

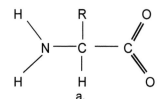

a.

NH$_2$CHRCOOH
b.

NH$_3$CHRCOOH
c.

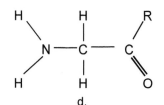

d.

8. Which of the following represents the basic structure of the sugar ribose?

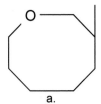

a.

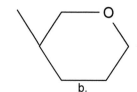

b.

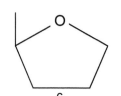

c.

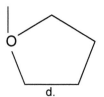

d.

9. How many covalent bonds can carbon form?
   a. 2,
   b. 4,
   c. 6,
   d. 8.

10. Adhesion only occurs:
    a. between different molecules,
    b. between carbon-containing molecules,
    c. between organic molecules,
    d. between water molecules.

11. Which line in the table shows the correct sugar used for the polysaccharide?

	Starch	Cellulose	Glycogen
a.	alpha-D-glucose	alpha-D-glucose	beta-D-glucose
b.	alpha-D-glucose	beta-D-glucose	alpha-D-glucose
c.	beta-D-glucose	alpha-D-glucose	alpha-D-glucose
d.	beta-D-glucose	alpha-D-glucose	beta-D-glucose

12. Which type of bond makes cellulose very strong?
    a. covalent,
    b. disulphide bridge,
    c. ionic,
    d. hydrogen.

13. Polymerisation occurs in carbohydrates due to:
    a. repeated condensation reactions,
    b. hydrogen bonding,
    c. bonding to proteins to form glycoproteins,
    d. repeated hydrolysis reactions.

14. Identify this molecular structure:
    a. steroid,
    b. fatty acid,
    c. amino acid,
    d. polysaccharide.

15. Which of the following is **not** a lipid?
    a. cholesterol,
    b. triglyceride,
    c. phospholipid,
    d. glycerol.

16. The number of carbon atoms in glycerol is:
    a. dependent upon the size of the fatty acids,
    b. n,
    c. 3,
    d. 6.

17. Which of the following shows the cis structure in a fatty acid?

         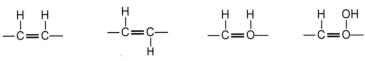

    a.   b.   c.   d.

18. Which of the following bonds does **not** occur in a saturated fatty acid?

C=O	C—O	C=C	C—H
a.	b.	c.	d.

19. Approximately how many kJ of energy per gram are released from lipids?
    a, 17,
    b. 38,
    c. 24,
    d. 54.

20. A person is 1.2m tall and has a body mass of 30kg. Their BMI is:
    a. 25 kg m^2,
    b. 0.04 kg m^2,
    c. 21 kg m^2,
    d. 40 kg m^2.

IBHL Biology 2016 © Ashby Merson-Davies

Molecular Biology Part 2
Amino acids, proteins, and nucleic acids

Proteins are the major structural molecules of animals. Proteins also form most enzymes which are the molecules that control and regulate metabolism. Nucleic acids contain the genetic code that is used to build an organism.

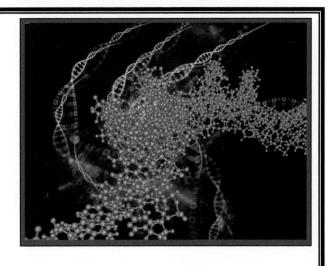

Amino acids

Key points
- These are the building blocks of proteins.
- The key characteristic is that they contain nitrogen in the amino group $-NH_2$.

Amino acid structure

$$NH_2CHRCOOH$$

Three different ways of writing the structure of an amino acid.

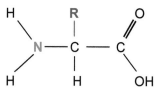

Key points
- A specific amino acid is determined by its **R** group.
- The simplest R group is H giving the amino acid glycine – NH_2 CH_2 COOH.
- R groups can be neutral, have a positive charge ($-NH_3^+$) or a negative charge ($-COO^-$).
- These charged R groups are essential in holding the 3 dimensional structure together.
- The charged R groups are affected by changes in pH – see page 39.
- The R group can be polar or non-polar – see page 37.

Are there only 20 amino acids?
Key points
- There are 20 standard amino acids – see the codon table on page 51.
- Two additional genetically coded amino acids have been discovered more recently.
- They are pyrrolysine and selenocysteine – see blue box below.

- Organisms can modify a '*standard*' amino acid in a polypeptide to make a different one.
- This occurs as a post-translational modification – see yellow box below.
- The purpose is to alter the function of the protein.

> There are 64 codons and they have all been assigned a function, either one of the 20 standard amino acids or a stop codon. How can these additional two amino acids be coded for?
> Pyrrolysine is found in methanogenic archaea (see pp. 156 & 199) and one known species of bacterium. These organisms use the UAG codon which in other organisms is a stop codon.
> Selenocysteine is widespread in both prokaryotes and eukaryotes. It uses the codon UGA which is also a stop codon, but where selenocysteine needs to be incorporated into the polypeptide the codon is 'recoded' using a special RNA molecule.

> There are many ways amino acids are modified after the polypeptide has been formed. One example is the modification of glutamine to pyroglutamate which commonly occurs in antibodies to make them more resistant to aminopeptidases. These enzymes are used to break down unwanted cellular proteins, especially during antigen processing and presentation – see page 159.

Proteins

Key points
- Composed of linear sequence of amino acid residues – see page 26.
- Linked together by condensation – see page 27.
- Polypeptide formation occurs on the ribosomes during translation – see page 53.
- Most polypeptides are formed from the common 20 amino acids (but see above).
- These can be linked in any combination or number giving a huge range of polypeptides
- The sequence is coded for by the gene.
- The sequence determines the 3 dimensional conformation (shape) of the polypeptide due to interaction between the different R groups.
- A single chain of amino acids is a polypeptide but is often called a protein – see yellow box on next page.
- Every individual has a unique proteome – see green box on next page.

Proteome

This is the set of expressed proteins in a particular cell or organism under a given set of environmental conditions.

The proteome is therefore unique to an individual and will change depending on what proteins the cell/organism requires. For example your proteome will be different when you have a cold compared to before you caught the virus.

The proteome shows what is actually happening compared to the genome which shows what could potentially happen.

Proteomics

This is the production of proteins by cells cultured in fermenters.

This offers many opportunities for the food, pharmaceutical, and other industries.

Difference between a polypeptide and a protein

A polypeptide is just a single linear sequence of amino acid residues.

A protein could also be the same or two or more polypeptide chains linked together.

Examples - myoglobin is a polypeptide;
- haemoglobin is a protein consisting of four polypeptide chains.

Levels of protein structure

Level	Characteristics	Bonding involved
Primary	Number and linear sequence of amino acids	Covalent – peptide bonds
Secondary	Alpha helix Beta-pleated sheet	Hydrogen bonding between amino acids some distance apart in the linear sequence
Tertiary	Folding into a three-dimensional shape. Beta-pleated sheet, Alpha helix. This folding creates pockets which form the active site in enzymes or binding sites for other molecules, or the binding site in active transport proteins.	Covalent – disulphide bridges between cysteine amino acids. Weak links including – • Hydrogen bonds, • Ionic bonds – see page 39. • Mutual attraction between non-polar groups.
Quaternary	Two or more polypeptide chains linked together. This can also create pockets as with tertiary structure.	Covalent – disulfide bridges Weak links including – • Hydrogen bonds, • Ionic bonds, • Mutual attraction between non-polar groups.

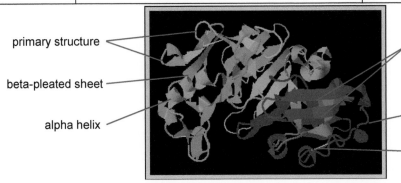

primary structure

beta-pleated sheet

alpha helix

beta-pleated sheets

primary structure

disulphide bridge (two more are visible in the green region)

2.3 The 3D quaternary structure of the protease enzyme pepsin showing primary, secondary and tertiary structure

Sometimes tertiary and quaternary level proteins have a non-protein group (the prosthetic group) attached. This is called a **conjugated protein**. In myoglobin and haemoglobin for example the prosthetic group is haem. The glycoproteins in membranes (see page 82) are also conjugated proteins, the non-protein group being the carbohydrate.

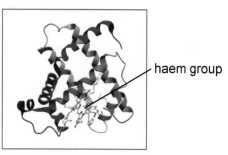

2.4 The 3D tertiary structure of muscle myoglobin

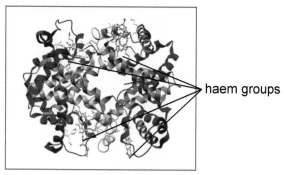

2.5 The 3D tertiary structure of haemoglobin

Fibrous and globular proteins

Key points
- Proteins are found in two forms – fibrous and globular.
- The shape of the protein is closely linked to its function.
- Fibrous proteins are mainly secondary structure.
- Globular proteins are tertiary or quaternary structure, and may also be conjugated.

2.6 A blood clot showing red cells and platelets (white) trapped in a mesh of fibrin fibres.

Protein functions

> The examples in black are the ones in the syllabus. Other interesting ones are in blue.

Function	Example	Structure	Description
Defence	Immunoglobulins	Globular	These are antibodies produced by plasma cells (see page 159) and are used to destroy antigens.
Enzyme	Rubisco	Globular	This is one of hundreds of enzymes that catalyse the metabolic processes within organisms. Rubisco (full name ribulose bisphosphate carboxylase) is involved in the light independent reaction of photosynthesis – see page 124.
Hormone	Insulin	Globular	This is one of many hormones. It is produced by the beta cells of the pancreas to reduce plasma glucose – see page 169.
Structural	Collagen.	Fibrous	A fibrous protein found in artery walls and tendons.
Trapping	Spider silk	Fibrous	This incredibly strong protein is used for capturing prey.
Light receptor	Rhodopsin	Globular, conjugated	This is found in the photoreceptor cells of the retina in the eye.
Transport	Haemoglobin	Globular, conjugated	This red coloured protein transports oxygen within the blood.
DNA packing	Histones	Globular	The DNA molecule is wrapped around clusters of 8 histone proteins – see page 43.
Contractile	Actin	Globular	This forms microfilaments in cells. Bundles form actin filaments in muscle – see page 182.
Osmoregulation	Albumin	Globular	This is one of many plasma proteins that has an important role in controlling the water potential of the blood and in buffering the blood pH.

Denaturing of proteins by temperature and pH

Key points

➢ Many proteins are large molecules folded into a three-dimensional shape.
➢ This shape is held in place by a variety of bonds and these are strongest at the optimum pH and temperature.
➢ If these bonds are broken then the shape of the protein is changed and it loses its function.
➢ The protein has become denatured.
➢ Denaturing is especially significant with enzymes – see page 111.

1. Effect of temperature

Key points

➢ At every temperature above absolute zero (0^0 Kelvin) atoms vibrate.
➢ As the temperature increases so does the amount of vibration.
➢ Eventually the movement of the atoms is so great that the weak bonds break and the protein structure begins to break down.

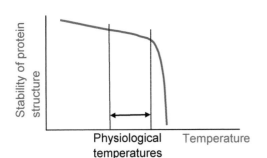

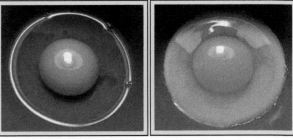

2.7 Albumen is the protein in egg white. It is normally a clear jelly but when heated it becomes a white solid.

2. Effect of pH

Key points

(Refer back to amino acid structure on page 36).
➢ Amino acids with opposite charges on their side groups can form an ionic bond.

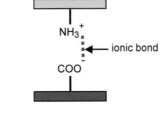

2.8 Albumin solution before and after adding acid.
The albumin in the second photograph is more cloudy.

➢ If the pH increases then there are fewer protons.
➢ Thus a proton dissociates from the NH_3^+ group leaving an NH_2 which breaks the ionic bond.

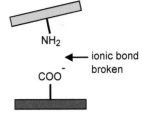

➢ If the pH decreases then there are more protons.
➢ A proton can associate with the COO^- group forming COOH which breaks the ionic bond.

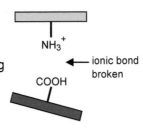

▪ Note the symmetry of the curve.

1. Draw the structure of an amino acid.

2. What is an amino group?

3. What is the key element that will allow you to recognise an amino acid?

4. Which component of an amino acid determines the type of amino acid?

5. How many amino acids are commonly used to make a polypeptide?

6. Give the names of two additional amino acids.

7. What does post-translational modification mean?

8. State what a proteome is.

9. What determines the sequence of amino acid residues in a polypeptide?

10. Which part of the amino acid residue determines the 3D structure of a polypeptide?

11. State the type of reaction used to build a polypeptide.

12. Where does polypeptide synthesis take place?

13. State two types of covalent bond in a polypeptide chain.

14. State three types of weak bond in a polypeptide chain.

15. State two structural forms that make up the secondary structure.

17. Are these bonds close together or far apart in the linear sequence?

16. Name the bond that holds these structures together.

18. Name the covalent bond specific to the tertiary structure.

19. What is the primary structure of a protein?

20. What is the quaternary structure of a protein?

21. What additional component is required for a conjugated protein?

24. State five examples of the functions of proteins with a named example for each.

22. Give one example of this additional component.

23. State two examples of conjugated proteins.

IBHL Biology 2016 © Ashby Merson-Davies

The Hershey-Chase experiment
What is the genetic material – DNA or protein?

➤ Bacteriophages are viruses that infect and are reproduced in bacteria; (Bacteriophages is often abbreviated to phages).
➤ The T2 phage infects the bacterium E.coli.
➤ The T2 phage consists of:
  • a protein coat,
  • DNA inside.

Key points
➤ DNA contains phosphorus; protein does not.
➤ Protein contains sulphur; DNA does not.
➤ ^{32}P and ^{35}S are radioactive isotopes of phosphorus and sulphur.

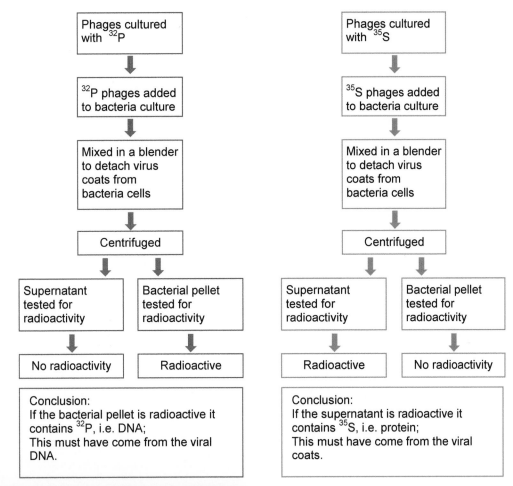

| Phages cultured with ^{32}P | Phages cultured with ^{35}S |

^{32}P phages added to bacteria culture

^{35}S phages added to bacteria culture

Mixed in a blender to detach virus coats from bacteria cells

Mixed in a blender to detach virus coats from bacteria cells

Centrifuged

Centrifuged

Supernatant tested for radioactivity — No radioactivity

Bacterial pellet tested for radioactivity — Radioactive

Supernatant tested for radioactivity — Radioactive

Bacterial pellet tested for radioactivity — No radioactivity

Conclusion:
If the bacterial pellet is radioactive it contains ^{32}P, i.e. DNA;
This must have come from the viral DNA.

Conclusion:
If the supernatant is radioactive it contains ^{35}S, i.e. protein;
This must have come from the viral coats.

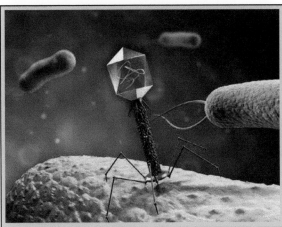

2.9 A digital illustration of a bacteriophage infecting a bacterial cell

Nucleic acids

➤ There are two types – DNA (deoxyribonucleic acid) and RNA (ribonucleic acid).

➤ There are three types of RNA - mRNA (messenger) – see page 48,
  - tRNA (transfer) – see page 50,
  - rRNA (ribosomal) – see page 51.

➤ DNA and RNA are polymers of nucleotides.

➤ DNA is a double helix of two antiparallel strands of nucleotides linked by hydrogen bonding between complementary base pairs.

Differences between DNA and RNA

	DNA	RNA
Number of strands	**Double** stranded	**Single** stranded, but can fold back on itself to form double stranded regions.
Pentose sugar	**Deoxy**ribose	Ribose
Bases	Adenine, cytosine, guanine, **thymine**	Adenine, cytosine, guanine, **uracil**

Nucleotide structure

Key points

➤ Three components
  - pentose sugar, deoxyribose or ribose,
  - phosphate
  - base

➤ There are five bases
  - adenine A
  - cytosine C

adenine ⎫
guanine ⎬ are purines
  - guanine G

cytosine ⎫
thymine ⎬ are pyrimidines
uracil ⎭
  - thymine T
  - uracil U

sugar – in RNA it is ribose and in DNA it is deoxyribose

phosphate ⟶

Draw

base

Strong covalent bonds link the sugar to the base and the phosphate

A single nucleotide

DNA structure

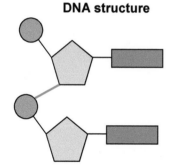

Two nucleotides are linked together by a covalent bond shown in red.

This is attached to carbon 3 of the upper sugar, and the phosphate which is attached to carbon 5 of the lower sugar – see page 23.

This shows just one side, or strand, of the DNA double helix.

Weak hydrogen bonds link the bases to hold the two stands together.

5'

3'

| Adenine | Thymine |

| Cytosine | Guanine |

3'

5'

The two sugar-phosphate strands run in opposite directions – they are antiparallel.

The DNA double strand

Complementary base pairing
Key points

➤ The bases always pair in a specific way.

➤ This is essential to ensure the two daughter molecules produced during replication are identical – see page 45.

• adenine pairs with thymine   A – T
• cytosine pairs with guanine   C – G.

Use a simple idea to link the bases, eg Apple Tart

Strand orientation

Each strand has a 5' or 5 prime end, and a 3' or 3 prime end.

These indicate the free ends where another nucleotide could be attached.

Nucleic acids always work in a 5' to 3' direction.

Francis Crick and James Watson deduced the structure of DNA in 1953 by collecting data from other scientists and making models.

These other scientists were:

Rosalind Franklin and Maurice Wilkins who produced very clear X-ray diffraction photographs of DNA. From these Crick and Watson determined that DNA was formed of two strands wound into a double helix and linked together by pairs of bases.

Erwin Chargaff who discovered that the numbers of adenine and thymine molecules in any given length of DNA were always equal, as was the number of cytosine and guanine molecules. This allowed Crick and Watson to deduce that adenine must be paired with thymine and cytosine must be paired with guanine.

Nucleosomes

Key points

➢ Nucleosomes are clumps of proteins around which is coiled the DNA.
➢ They have two functions:
  • supercoiling the DNA,
  • regulating transcription – see page 49.

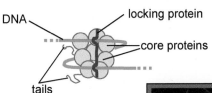

See molecular visualisation images of a nucleosome on page 57.

2.10 DNA wound around a group of histone beads

DNA replication in prokaryotes

Key vocabulary

The simple double helical structure of DNA along with complementary base pairing suggested a mechanism for replication.

- 5 prime to 3 prime direction
- Complementary base pairing
- Helicase
- DNA gyrase
- DNA polymerase I
- DNA polymerase III
- DNA primase
- DNA ligase
- Nucleoside triphosphates
- Deoxynucleoside triphosphates
- Okazaki fragments
- Leading strand
- Lagging strand
- Replication fork
- Single-stranded binding proteins (SSBs)

This key vocabulary is used in DNA replication, transcription and translation.

Enzyme	Function
Helicase	• Unwinds the DNA at the replication fork; • Breaks the hydrogen bonds between the bases; • Requires ATP.
DNA gyrase	• Removes the supercoiling created by the action of helicase.
DNA polymerase III	• Adds deoxynucleoside triphosphates to the 3' end.
DNA primase	• Adds nucleoside triphosphates on the lagging strand to form an RNA primer.
DNA polymerase I	• Removes the RNA primer; • Replaces it using deoxynucleoside triphosphates.
DNA ligase	• Joins the Okazaki fragments together.

Deoxynucleoside triphosphates, dNTPs, and nucleoside triphosphates, NTPs, are the building blocks for DNA and RNA respectively. As the enzyme joins them to the 3' end of the strand the two extra phosphate groups are removed leaving just the nucleotide.

The NTP to add an adenine nucleotide to an RNA strand is ATP. Remember that ATP is also the energy currency molecule.

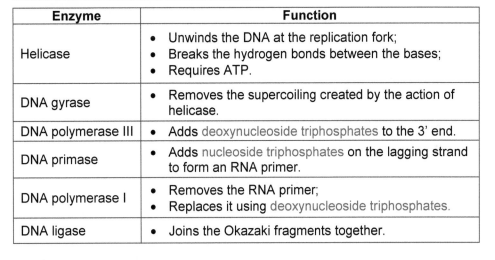

2.11 The DNA double helix

Key points

➤ Replication is 5' → 3' because the polymerase enzymes can only add to the 3' end of the strand.
➤ Replication is continuous on the leading strand and discontinuous on the lagging strand.
➤ DNA primase can bind to a single strand.
➤ DNA polymerases can only bind to a double strand, hence the need for an RNA primer.
➤ In order to start the leading strand an Okazaki fragment will need to be made.

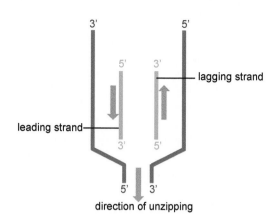

Leading strand: the new strand of DNA that is synthesised continuously in the same direction as the unzipping.

Lagging strand: the new strand of DNA that is synthesised in the opposite direction to the unzipping. It is made by joining the Okazaki fragments together.

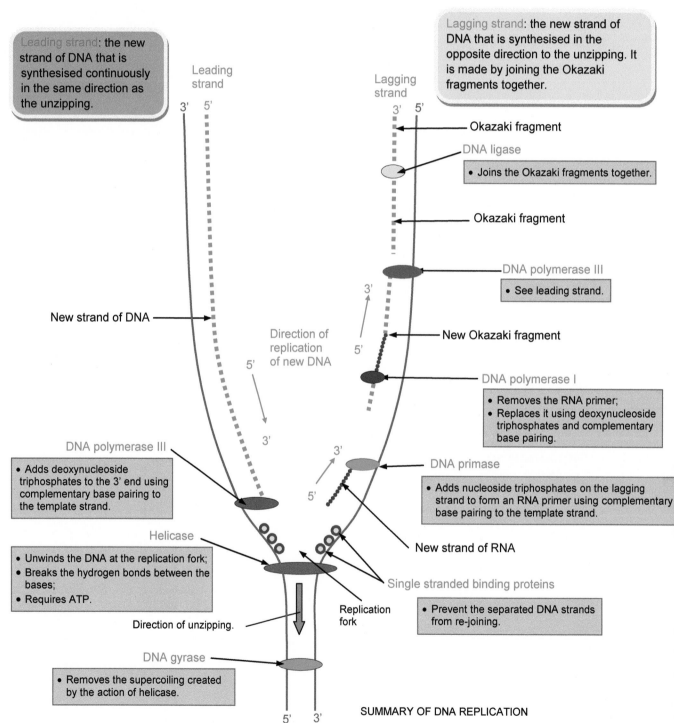

Leading strand

Lagging strand

Okazaki fragment

DNA ligase
• Joins the Okazaki fragments together.

Okazaki fragment

DNA polymerase III
• See leading strand.

New strand of DNA

Direction of replication of new DNA

New Okazaki fragment

DNA polymerase I
• Removes the RNA primer;
• Replaces it using deoxynucleoside triphosphates and complementary base pairing.

DNA polymerase III
• Adds deoxynucleoside triphosphates to the 3' end using complementary base pairing to the template strand.

DNA primase
• Adds nucleoside triphosphates on the lagging strand to form an RNA primer using complementary base pairing to the template strand.

Helicase
• Unwinds the DNA at the replication fork;
• Breaks the hydrogen bonds between the bases;
• Requires ATP.

New strand of RNA

Single stranded binding proteins
• Prevent the separated DNA strands from re-joining.

Replication fork

Direction of unzipping.

DNA gyrase
• Removes the supercoiling created by the action of helicase.

SUMMARY OF DNA REPLICATION

Meselson and Stahl
Proving semi-conservative replication of DNA
Key point
➢ These two scientists set out to discover which of the two hypotheses about DNA replication was
true – conservative or semi-conservative.

Bacteria are cultured in a medium containing normal nitrogen ^{14}N; The DNA is collected and centrifuged in a special fluid; It forms a precise band in the centrifuge tube.	The bacteria are now cultured for several hours in a medium containing heavy nitrogen ^{15}N; The DNA is again centrifuged this time the band is much lower.	The bacteria from the ^{15}N culture are transferred to a medium containing normal nitrogen ^{14}N; After each division of the bacteria (roughly 20 minutes) some bacteria were collected; The DNA from all the samples was centrifuged and this time the band was midway.

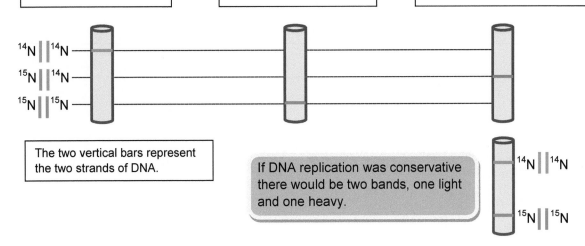

The two vertical bars represent the two strands of DNA.

If DNA replication was conservative there would be two bands, one light and one heavy.

Dideoxyribonucleotides
Key points
➢ DNA is composed of deoxynucleotides.
➢ These are joined using a condensation reaction.
➢ Therefore an OH group is required.
➢ Ribose has an OH at C^2 and C^3.
➢ Removing the oxygen from the C^2-OH giving a deoxyribose prevents a 5' – 2' linkage from forming.
➢ Therefore only the normal 5' – 3' linkage can be formed.
➢ Removing the oxygen from the C^3-OH as well giving a dideoxyribose prevents the 5' – 3' linkage from forming.
➢ This blocks DNA replication as the strand cannot be elongated.

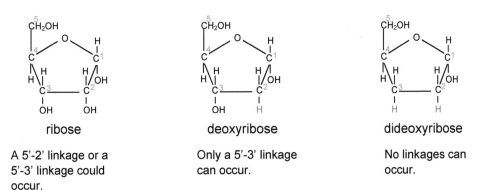

ribose	deoxyribose	dideoxyribose
A 5'-2' linkage or a 5'-3' linkage could occur.	Only a 5'-3' linkage can occur.	No linkages can occur.

Uses of dideoxyribonucleotides

Key points

➤ Long lengths of a DNA strand are not suitable for base sequencing as they are difficult to handle.
➤ As the strand is being replicated using the polymerase chain reaction (see page 56) the process can be stopped by adding a dideoxynucleoside triphosphate, ddNTP.

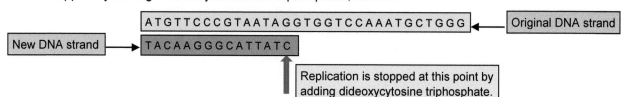

| ATGTTCCCGTAATAGGTGGTCCAAATGCTGGG | ◄── Original DNA strand |

New DNA strand ──► | TACAAGGGCATTATC |

Replication is stopped at this point by adding dideoxycytosine triphosphate.

➤ The strand to be sequenced is mixed with dNTPs, enzymes and small quantities of ddNTPs that have been labelled with a dye.
➤ Each type of ddNTP has a different colour.
➤ The ddNTPs will be incorporated randomly resulting in a mixture of fragments of different lengths.
➤ After separation by electrophoresis the different coloured bands can be scanned by a laser.

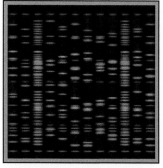

2.12 The banding patterns shown by fragments of DNA after separation by electrophoresis

Types of nuclear DNA

DNA can be divided into three types:

• Protein coding DNA,
• Non-protein coding DNA,
• Non-coding DNA.

1. Protein coding DNA

➤ These DNA sequences are called genes.
➤ These code for the functional polypeptides/proteins used by the cell or body, e.g.
  • structural proteins, e.g. collagen;
  • transport proteins, e.g. haemoglobin;
  • enzymes, e.g. rubisco;
  • hormones, e.g. insulin.

2. Non-protein coding DNA

➤ These code for a range of different molecules –
  ▪ tRNA and rRNA;
  ▪ RNA molecules and other types of molecule used to control gene expression.

3. Non-coding DNA

➤ Introns – see page 50.
➤ Telomeres
➤ Promoter region – see transcription page 49.

---

25. List the components of a DNA nucleotide.

26. What type of bond joins the components of a nucleotide?

27. Explain fully what is meant by complementary base pairing.

28. Draw and label a nucleotide.

---

29. List the two functions of nucleosomes.	30. State the names of the two replicating strands during DNA replication.	31. The two DNA strands are antiparallel. What does this mean?

32. List the enzymes involved in DNA replication.	33. Describe the role of the single-stranded binding proteins.	
	34. In which direction does DNA replication occur?	35. Name the short fragments of DNA synthesised during replication.

36. Name the building blocks used to synthesise DNA.	37. Name the building blocks used to synthesise RNA.	38. Name the region on the DNA molecule where helicase is acting.

39. State the functions of helicase.	40. State the functions of DNA primase.
41. State the functions of DNA polymerase I.	42. State the functions of DNA polymerase III.
43. State the function of DNA ligase.	44. State the function of DNA gyrase.

45. Describe briefly Meselson and Stahl's investigation.	46. Name the molecule used to block DNA replication.
	47. List four products of protein coding DNA.

48. List two products of non-protein coding DNA.	49. List three functions of non-coding DNA.

Transcription

Key point
➢ This is the formation of a molecule of RNA from a DNA template in the nucleus.

Key vocabulary
- 5 prime to 3 prime direction
- Complementary base pairing
- RNA polymerase
- Promoter region
- Terminator region

- Sense strand
- Antisense strand
- Nucleosomes
- Regulatory protein
- Nucleoside triphosphates NTPs

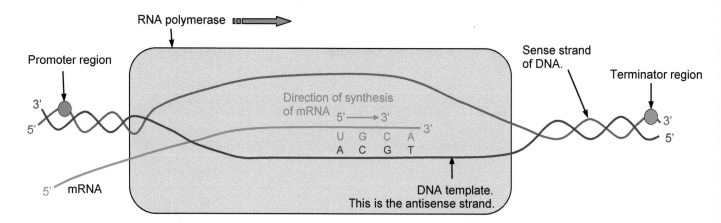

Key points
➢ **DNA template** – only one side of the DNA double helix is a **gene**. This is called the **sense strand.** The other side is the complementary sequence of bases. It is called the **antisense strand** and is transcribed into RNA by RNA polymerase. The sense strand has the same sequence of bases as the mRNA but with T not U.

> Remember – the antisense strand is transcribed.

➢ **Promoter region** – a specific sequence of DNA bases at the start of a gene to which RNA polymerase binds. This is an example of a non-coding region of DNA.
➢ **RNA polymerase** – this enzyme adds the 5' end of nucleoside triphosphates (NTPs) to the free 3' of the RNA molecule.
  - Complementary base pairing to the DNA template determines the RNA nucleotide sequence.
  - It can only bind to the DNA in the presence of special proteins called regulatory proteins (see next page) made by genes elsewhere in the genome.
➢ The NTP paired with adenine on the DNA has the base uracil.
➢ As the RNA polymerase moves forward it:
  - unwinds and separates the DNA strands at the front,
  - rewinds and rejoins them at the back. (In the diagram above the RNA polymerase is moving from left to right.)
➢ As the RNA is synthesised it separates from the DNA.
➢ **Terminator region** – a specific sequence of DNA bases marking the end of the transcription process. (Another example of a non-coding region of DNA.)
  - RNA polymerase breaks free.
  - The mRNA strand is released.
➢ **Nucleosomes** – see page 43.
➢ **Regulatory proteins** – see page 49.
➢ **DNA methylation** – see page 49.
➢ **Post-transcriptional modification** of RNA takes place – see page 49.

IBHL Biology 2016 © Ashby Merson-Davies

Regulation of transcription
Key points
- ➢ It is essential that transcription is regulated to prevent:
  - • the production of unwanted proteins/enzymes,
  - • energy and amino acids being used up unnecessarily.
- ➢ Three methods are used:
  - • nucleosomes,
  - • regulatory proteins called transcription factors produced by regulator genes,
  - • methylation of DNA.

Nucleosomes [Recall nucleosome structure on page 43 and the molecular visualisation pictures on page 58].
Key points
- ➢ They restrict access to DNA preventing transcription.
- ➢ Lysine residues (lysine is an amino acid) in the histone tails bind the DNA tightly.
- ➢ Adding acetyl groups (acetylation) to the lysine weakens the binding.
- ➢ The nucleosome can 'slide' along the DNA exposing regions that were previously bound to the nucleosome and allow transcription.
- ➢ Regions of DNA containing regulator genes have fewer nucleosomes.
- ➢ The region of DNA with the promoter sequence has few nucleosomes.

Regulatory proteins
Key points
- ➢ Regulatory proteins (called transcription factors) bind to the promoter region and allow the RNA polymerase to bind.
- ➢ Other genes, sometimes on different chromosomes, produce proteins that block the binding of RNA polymerase to the promoter region and prevent transcription.

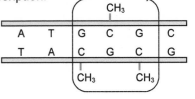

Methylation of DNA
Key points
- ➢ Methylation is the addition of a methyl group, CH3.
- ➢ It is commonly added to the cytosine base next to a guanine base.
- ➢ These C-G pairs occur in clusters called CpG islands.
- ➢ The CpG islands are often close to the promoter region at the 5' end of the gene.
- ➢ This blocks transcription of the gene.
- ➢ It is a way of controlling gene activity.
- ➢ Methylation can be brought about by environmental factors.
- ➢ Environmental factors could include stress, diet, pollutants.
- ➢ This suggests epigenetic control – see blue box.

> **Epigenetics**
> This is a form of genetics that is heritable but does not involve changes to the genome. These changes remain associated with the cell, but since the DNA sequence has not been changed some non-genetic factors must be influencing the expression of the genes.

Environment and gene expression
Key points
- ➢ Factors include temperature, water levels, day length, stress.
  - • Flowering in many plants species is controlled by day length – see page 222.
  - • The gender of many species of turtles and all crocodilians is determined by the temperature the eggs are incubated at.
  - • In western spadefoot toad tadpoles (*Pelobates cultripes)* decreasing water level of their habitat stimulates the production of the hormones thyroxine and corticosterone which increase rate of metamorphosis into adults.

Post-transcriptional modification of RNA

1. Multiple splicing
Key points

2.13 *Pelobates cultripes.*

- ➢ Much eukaryotic DNA is transcribed into primary mRNA.
- ➢ Primary mRNA contains sequences (introns) that are not translated into part of the protein.
- ➢ Introns are removed. (Introns are an example of non-coding DNA – see pages 46 and 48).
- ➢ Exons make up the mature mRNA.
- ➢ This takes place in the nucleus.
- ➢ The exons can be spliced together to form different polypeptides.
- ➢ Thus one gene can form more than one polypeptide.

> These names come from –
> Introns are intervening RNA;
> Exons are expressed.

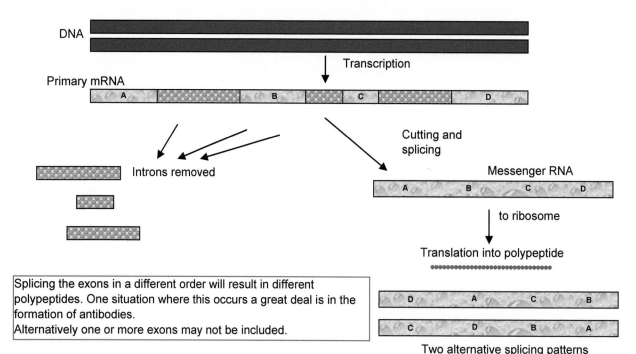

DNA

Transcription

Primary mRNA

Cutting and splicing

Introns removed

Messenger RNA

to ribosome

Translation into polypeptide

Splicing the exons in a different order will result in different polypeptides. One situation where this occurs a great deal is in the formation of antibodies.
Alternatively one or more exons may not be included.

Two alternative splicing patterns

2. Selenocysteine (Refer back to page 36)

Key points

> Assume the stop codon UGA is at the end of section D.
> If that is then spliced in at the beginning, then in the examples of re-splicing only section D in the first one, and sections C and D in the second one would be transcribed.
> Since the stop codon can be recoded using a special RNA, selenocysteine can be inserted at UGA and transcription continued.

tRNA

Key points

> There are 61 codons (excluding the three stop codons).*
> Therefore there are 61 anticodons.
> Therefore there are 61 different types of tRNA.
> All tRNA molecules have the same basic shape.
> The amino acid is joined at the CCA terminal of the 3' end.
> Adding the amino acid requires energy from ATP and a specific enzyme called a tRNA activating enzyme.
> Each amino acid has its own enzyme.
> The enzyme recognises:
> ▪ the specific anticodon,
> ▪ the specific amino acid due to its R group
> ▪ the CCA 3' terminal.

* This is the usually accepted view but refer back to page 37.

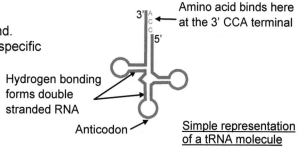

Amino acid binds here at the 3' CCA terminal

Hydrogen bonding forms double stranded RNA

Anticodon

Simple representation of a tRNA molecule

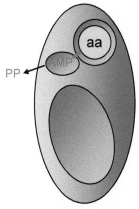

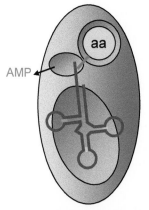

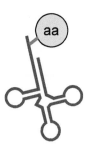

1. ATP and amino acid bind to enzyme

2. ATP is hydrolysed to AMP which binds to amino acid.
PP released.

3. Specific tRNA binds. AMP released. Energy used to bond amino acid to CCA terminal.

4. Charged tRNA released.

Ribosome structure

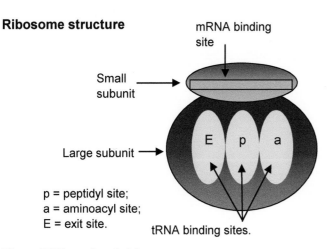

mRNA binding site

Small subunit

Large subunit

p = peptidyl site;
a = aminoacyl site;
E = exit site.

tRNA binding sites.

- Ribosomes are composed of ribosomal RNA (rRNA) and protein.
- There are two subunits.
- The small one binds to mRNA.
- The large one has three binding sites for tRNA.
- They are manufactured in the nucleolus within the nucleus.

The mRNA codon table

Key points

➤ The amino acids are in groups.
➤ In general it is the first two bases that are critical, e.g. GG = glycine.
➤ Only two amino acids have a single codon – methionine and tryptophan.
➤ The codon for methionine, AUG, is the start codon in prokaryotes.

> You need to know how to use the codon table.

		Second letter								
		U		**C**		**A**		**G**		
First letter	**U**	UUU UUC	Phenyl-alanine	UCU UCC	Serine	UAU UAC	Tyrosine	UGU UGC	Cysteine	U C
		UUA UUG	Leucine	UCA UCG		UAA UAG	*Stop codon* *Stop codon*	UGA UGG	*Stop codon* Tryptophan	A G
	C	CUU CUC	Leucine	CCU CCC	Proline	CAU CAC	Histidine	CGU CGC	Arginine	U C
		CUA CUG		CCA CCG		CAA CAG	Glutamine	CGA CGG		A G
	A	AUU AUC	Iso-leucine	ACU ACC	Threonine	AAU AAC	Asparagine	AGU AGC	Serine	U C
		AUA AUG	Methionine	ACA ACG		AAA AAG	Lysine	AGA AGG	Arginine	A G
	G	GUU GUC	Valine	GCU GCC	Alanine	GAU GAC	Aspartic acid	GGU GGC	Glycine	U C
		GUA GUG		GCA GCG		GAA GAG	Glutamic acid	GGA GGG		A G

(Third letter on right-hand side)

It is useful to remember these two shaded ones, start AUG and stop UAG – A is the start of the alphabet and then simply change AU to UA for the stop.

> Look back at the blue box on page 36 for an interesting point about the UGA stop codon, and also UGA in mitochondria.

Is the genetic code universal?

➤ Most genomes use the same code.
➤ This allows genetic modification of organisms e.g. bacteria synthesising human insulin, or goats synthesising spider silk in their milk.
➤ Some minor variations have accumulated since the common origin of life on Earth.
➤ A significant example is human mitochondrial DNA.

Codon	Result with nuclear DNA	Result with mitochondrial DNA
AGA	arginine	stop
AGG	arginine	stop
UGA	stop	tryptophan
AUA	isoleucine	methionine

> You do not need to know all these but learn one to illustrate an exam answer, perhaps the first one as AGA sounds like arginine.

50. Name the enzyme involved in transcription.

51. In which direction does transcription occur?

52. Name the two DNA strands.

53. Which strand is transcribed?

54. Name the regions on the DNA where transcription starts and ends.

55. Name the building blocks used to synthesise the RNA strand.

56. Which base on the RNA strand pairs with adenine on the DNA strand?

57. What is the role of the promoter region?

58. What is the role of the regulatory proteins?

59. Describe the role of nucleosomes in the regulation of transcription.

60. Describe the role of methylation in gene regulation.

61. What is removed from primary RNA to form mature RNA?

62. How can this process result in different mature RNA molecules?

63. Name the amino acid that can be used for the stop codon UGA.

64. State the 5' – 3' sequence of bases on the tRNA where the amino acid attaches.

65. What is the role of the tRNA activating enzyme?

66. What additional molecule is required by the tRNA activating enzyme?

67. To which subunit of a ribosome does mRNA bind?

68. Name the three tRNA binding sites on the ribosome.

69. How many bases form a codon?

70. Use the codon table on page 52 to determine the amino acid for the DNA sequence ACA.

71a. The genetic code is not quite universal. Describe one situation where it is essential it is universal.

71b. The genetic code is not quite universal. State one situation where it is not universal using a specific example.

Translation in prokaryotes

Key point
➢   This is the formation of a polypeptide from a messenger RNA molecule.

Key vocabulary
➢   5 prime to 3 prime direction
➢   Complementary base pairing
➢   4 steps:
  - Initiation
  - Elongation
  - Translocation
  - Termination

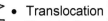
These two steps are cyclical.

➢   Ribosome
  - small subunit
  - large subunit

➢   mRNA
➢   tRNA / charged tRNA*
➢   p, a, and exit sites
➢   ATP
➢   Start codon
➢   Stop codon
➢   Peptide bond
➢   Polypeptide
➢   Releasing factors

*A charged tRNA is a tRNA with its amino acid attached.

1.   Initiation

Translation can occur immediately after transcription in prokaryotes due to the absence of a nuclear envelope and no post-transcriptional modification.

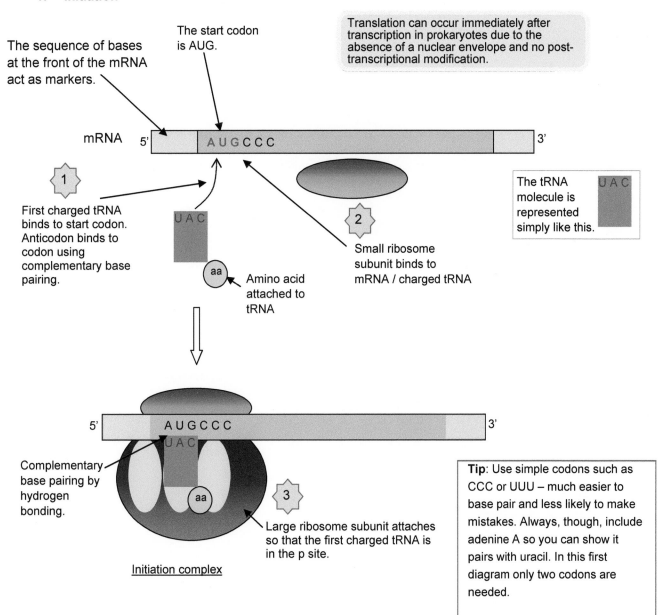

The sequence of bases at the front of the mRNA act as markers.

The start codon is AUG.

mRNA   5'   A U G C C C   3'

1   First charged tRNA binds to start codon. Anticodon binds to codon using complementary base pairing.

U A C

aa   Amino acid attached to tRNA

2   Small ribosome subunit binds to mRNA / charged tRNA

The tRNA molecule is represented simply like this.   U A C

5'   A U G C C C   3'
U A C

Complementary base pairing by hydrogen bonding.

aa

3   Large ribosome subunit attaches so that the first charged tRNA is in the p site.

Initiation complex

Tip: Use simple codons such as CCC or UUU – much easier to base pair and less likely to make mistakes. Always, though, include adenine A so you can show it pairs with uracil. In this first diagram only two codons are needed.

2. Elongation

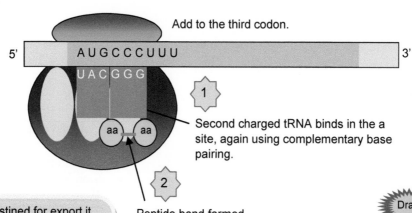

Add to the third codon.

1 Second charged tRNA binds in the a site, again using complementary base pairing.

2 Peptide bond formed between the two amino acids.

If the polypeptide is destined for export it needs to be synthesised on the rER. The first part of the polypeptide is a signal that causes the ribosome to bind to the rER. As the polypeptide is synthesised it is passed through a protein channel into the rER.

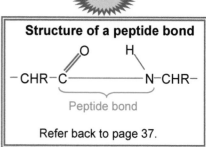

Draw

Structure of a peptide bond

$$-CHR-\overset{\overset{\displaystyle O}{\|}}{C}\underbrace{\qquad\qquad}_{\text{Peptide bond}}\overset{\overset{\displaystyle H}{|}}{N}-CHR-$$

Refer back to page 37.

3. Translocation

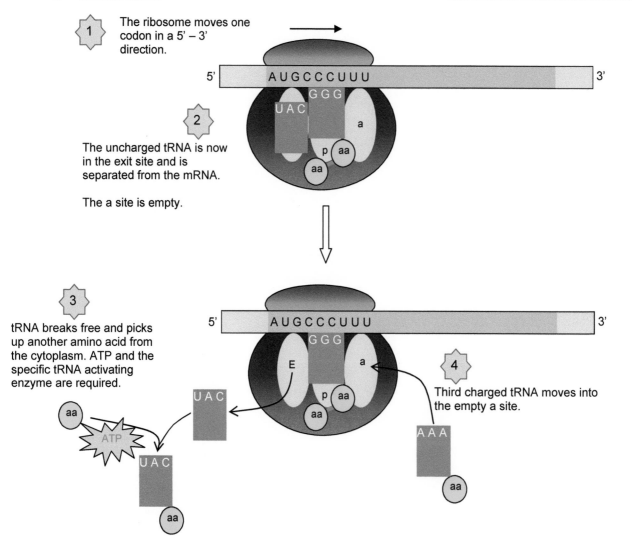

1 The ribosome moves one codon in a 5' – 3' direction.

2 The uncharged tRNA is now in the exit site and is separated from the mRNA.

The a site is empty.

3 tRNA breaks free and picks up another amino acid from the cytoplasm. ATP and the specific tRNA activating enzyme are required.

4 Third charged tRNA moves into the empty a site.

4. Termination

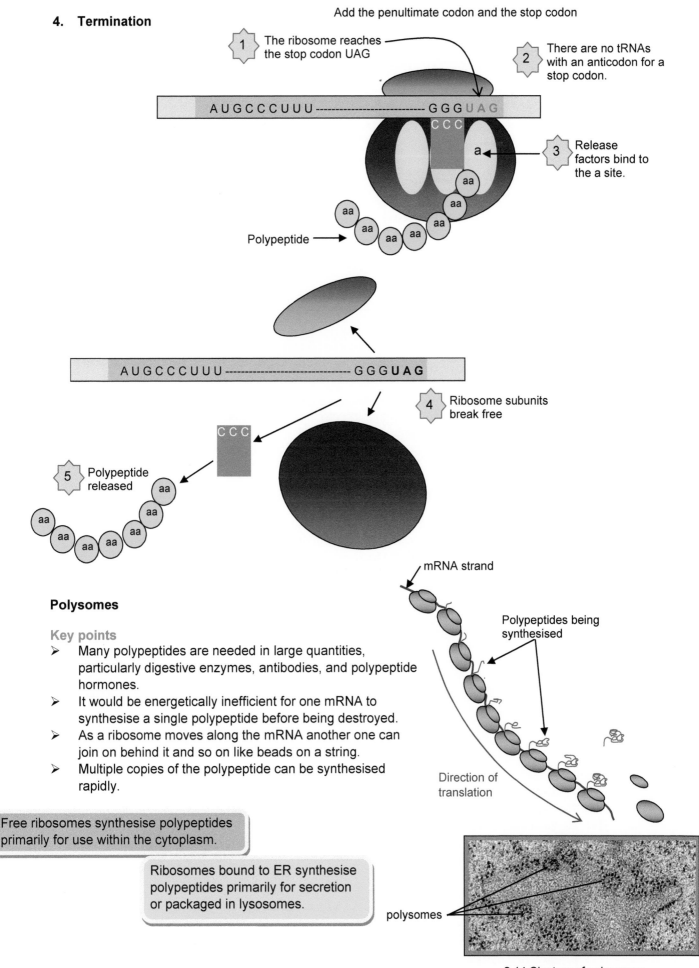

Add the penultimate codon and the stop codon

1 The ribosome reaches the stop codon UAG

2 There are no tRNAs with an anticodon for a stop codon.

3 Release factors bind to the a site.

AUGCCCUUU ----------------------------- GGGUAG
CCC
a
aa

Polypeptide

AUGCCCUUU ------------------------------- GGGUAG

4 Ribosome subunits break free

CCC

5 Polypeptide released

Polysomes

Key points

➢ Many polypeptides are needed in large quantities, particularly digestive enzymes, antibodies, and polypeptide hormones.

➢ It would be energetically inefficient for one mRNA to synthesise a single polypeptide before being destroyed.

➢ As a ribosome moves along the mRNA another one can join on behind it and so on like beads on a string.

➢ Multiple copies of the polypeptide can be synthesised rapidly.

Free ribosomes synthesise polypeptides primarily for use within the cytoplasm.

Ribosomes bound to ER synthesise polypeptides primarily for secretion or packaged in lysosomes.

mRNA strand

Polypeptides being synthesised

Direction of translation

polysomes

2.14 Clusters of polysomes

The polymerase chain reaction – PCR

Key facts
➢ The polymerase chain reaction (PCR) copies and amplifies minute quantities of nucleic acid.
➢ It is used in many situations such as forensic analysis and archaeological investigations.
➢ The polymerase used is Taq DNA polymerase because it is heat stable.

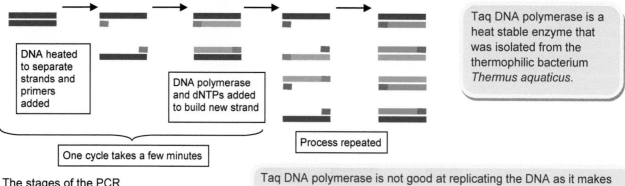

DNA heated to separate strands and primers added

DNA polymerase and dNTPs added to build new strand

Process repeated

Taq DNA polymerase is a heat stable enzyme that was isolated from the thermophilic bacterium *Themus aquaticus*.

One cycle takes a few minutes

The stages of the PCR

Taq DNA polymerase is not good at replicating the DNA as it makes many mistakes because it does not have a proofreading function. It has now largely been replaced by another heat stable enzyme (again from a thermophilic bacterium) called Pfu DNA polymerase.

DNA profiling

Principles
➢ Tandem repeats are short sequences of DNA repeated many times – see below.
➢ They vary between individuals so much that the probability of two individuals being the same is zero.
➢ PCR may be used to increase the amount of DNA.
➢ Great care to prevent contamination is required as the PCR will also amplify contaminant DNA.
➢ The DNA is cut up with restriction enzymes (see section Gene Transfer on page 57).
➢ Gel electrophoresis separates the DNA fragments.
➢ The banding patterns are compared.

Uses
➢ Paternity – sometimes a woman is unsure who the father might be, or the man disputes being the father or wants to know if he is the father.
  ▪ DNA profiling from a mouth swab is used.
➢ Forensic investigations – often tiny samples of DNA can be found such as a drop of blood or saliva, a hair follicle, scrapings under a finger nail, and the DNA can be amplified using the PCR before profiling.

Other uses
➢ Family relationships for immigrants.
➢ Determining if rare birds and other animals being sold as captive bred have actually been captive bred or been stolen from the wild.

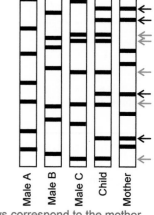

Male A | Male B | Male C | Child | Mother

An example of how DNA profiling has been used to determine paternity.

The black arrows correspond to the mother. The red arrows show that the father of the child is male C.

Tandem repeats

Key points
➢ A tandem repeat is a short sequence of bases repeated, e.g. GGTGGTGGTGGT.
➢ The repeats are tandem, i.e. clustered together.
➢ Individual repeats can be removed or added through recombination or replication errors.
➢ This results in alleles with different numbers of repeats.
➢ On each side of the repeats are segments of non-repetitive bases which allows the sections to be extracted with restriction enzymes.

In these four individuals the tandem repeats range from 2 to 6.

Restriction enzyme cuts here to release tandem repeat.

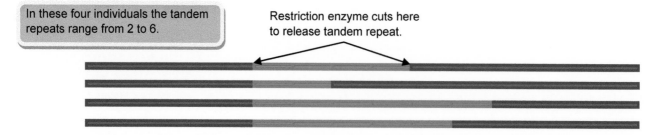

Molecular visualisation of a nucleosome

Go to

http://bioinformatics.org/firstglance/fgij//fg.htm?mol=1AOI

and you can manipulate the molecule for yourself.

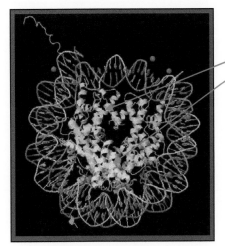

Viewed from above

Each of the eight histone proteins is shown in a different colour.

DNA

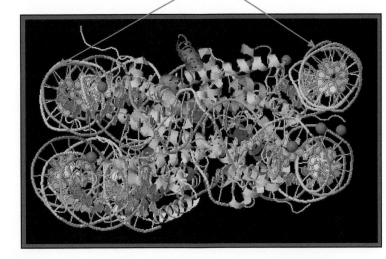

Side view

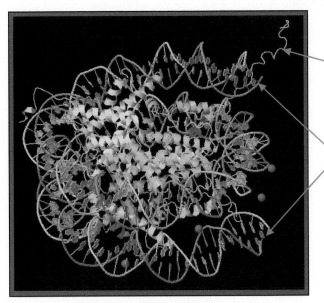

Viewed from a different angle

A protein tail. The tails of the other proteins are not shown.
Chemical modification of these tails is involved in regulating gene expression.

These places are where the DNA strand would continue to the next nucleosome.

72. Name the enzyme involved in translation.

73. In which direction does translation occur?

74. What is the name of a tRNA molecule with its amino acid attached?

75. List the sequence of events during the initiation stage.

76. List the sequence of events during the elongation stage.

77. List the sequence of events during the translocation stage.

78. List the sequence of events during the termination stage.

79. Which two stages in translocation are cyclical?

80. Where are polypeptides in secretory vesicles synthesised?

81. What is a polysome?

82. What is the role of polysomes?

83. What does the polymerase chain reaction do?

84. Name the enzyme used in the PCR.

85. Why is this enzyme significant?

86. Name the building units used by the enzyme.

87. State two uses for the PCR.

Glossary

Activation Energy	The energy a substrate molecule must achieve before it can change chemically.
Gel electrophoresis	Using an electrical current in a gel to separate charged molecules in a mixture based on their charge and size.
Supernatant	The fluid remaining on top after centrifuging a liquid containing suspended particles.

Answers to Grey Box Questions   **Any words underlined are required.**

1. $NH_2CHRCOOH$ or $NH_2CH\overset{R}{}COOH$.   2. NH_2.   3. Nitrogen.
4. The R group.   5. 20.   6. Selenocysteine; pyrrolysine.
7. The primary RNA molecule is changed to mature RNA by the removal of introns. The exons can be spliced together in different ways to make different mature MRA molecules from the same gene.
8. The set of expressed proteins in a particular cell or organism (under a given set of environmental conditions).
9. The sequence of bases/codons in the DNA/gene.
10. The R group.   11. Condensation.   12. Ribosomes.
13. Peptide bond; disulphide bridge.   14. Hydrogen; ionic; mutual attraction between hydrophobic groups.
15. Alpha helix; beta-pleated sheet.   16. Hydrogen.   17. Far apart.
18. Disulphide bridge.   19. Linear sequence of amino acid residues.
20. Two or more polypeptide chains held together.   21. Prosthetic group.
22. Haem group.   23. Myoglobin; haemoglobin.
24. Defence – immunoglobulins; enzyme – rubisco; support – collagen; hormone – insulin; light receptor – rhodopsin; trapping – spider silk, or any others from the table on page 38.
25. deoxyribose, phosphate, base.   26. Covalent.
27. Bases are paired in a specific pattern – adenine with thymine and cytosine with guanine.
28.

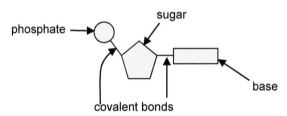

29. Supercoiling DNA; regulating transcription.   30. Leading and lagging.
31. The deoxyribose – phosphate strands run in opposite directions, one in 5'-3' and the other 3'-5'.
32. helicase; (DNA) gyrase; DNA primase; DNA polymerase I; DNA polymerase III; (DNA) ligase.
33. They prevent the DNA strands that have been separated by helicase from re-joining.
34. 5' to 3'.   35. Okazaki fragments.   36. Deoxynucleoside triphosphates.
37. Nucleoside triphosphates.   38. Replication fork.
39. Unwind the double helix; separate the DNA strands.
40. Builds an RNA primer; on the lagging strand; using nucleoside triphosphates; and complementary base pairing to the template strand.
41. Replaces the RNA nucleotides; with corresponding DNA nucleotides; using deoxynucleoside triphosphates.
42. Builds the new DNA strand; using nucleoside triphosphates; and complementary base pairing to the template strand.
43. Joins the Okazaki fragments.
44. Prevents the DNA becoming supercoiled as a result of the action of helicase.
45. Cultured bacteria with 14N and heavy nitrogen 15N, then back to 14N;
    Centrifuged and measured position of bands of DNA;
    Found intermediate band proving semiconservative replication.
46. Dideoxynucleoside triphosphate.
47. Structural proteins, enzymes, hormones; transport proteins; immunoglobulins/antibodies.
48. rRNA, tRNA.   49. Introns, promoters, telomeres.   50. RNA polymerase.
51. 5' to 3'.   52. Sense and antisense.   53. Antisense.
54. Promoter, terminator.   55. Nucleoside triphosphates.   56. Uracil.
57. To bind the RNA polymerase.   58. To assist in the binding of RNA polymerase.
59. To control transcription by regulating the exposure of DNA.

60. Methylation of cysteine bases blocks transcription. Environmental factors affect methylation, e.g. diet, stress, temperature.

61. Introns. 62. The exons can be spliced into different patterns.

63. Selenocysteine. 64. CCA.

65. To join a tRNA molecule to its specific amino acid.

66. ATP. 67. Small. 68. Aminoacyl, peptidyl, exit. 69. Three 70. Cysteine.

71a. When eukaryotic DNA is transferred to a prokaryote in order to synthesise a required protein, e.g. human insulin.

71b. The human nuclear codon UGA is a stop codon but in the mitochondrion it codes for the amino acid tryptophan. (Or use any of the other three examples on page 51.)

72. tRNA activating enzyme.

73. 5'to 3'. 74. Charged tRNA.

75. Charged tRNA binds to start codon; mRNA binds to small ribosome subunit; large subunit binds to small subunit.

76. Second charged tRNA binds to aminoacyl site; peptide bond formed.

77. Ribosome moves along one codon in a 5'-3' direction; first amino acid detaches from its tRNA; tRNA leaves exit site; activating enzymes uses ATP to re-charge the tRNA.

78. Stop codon enters aminoacyl site; releasing factors bind; ribosome subunits separate; polypeptide released.

79. Elongation and translocation. 80. Rough endoplasmic reticulum / rER.

81. A number of ribosomes attached to a single mRNA molecule.

82. To allow rapid synthesis of many polypeptides from the same mRNA molecule.

83. Multiplies minute quantities of DNA. 84. Taq DNA polymerase.

85. It is able to catalyse polymerisation at the high temperatures required for the process.

86. Deoxynucleoside triphosphates.

87. Amplify small amounts of DNA for forensic or archaeological investigations.

IBHL Biology 2016 © Ashby Merson-Davies

Self-Test Quiz

1. Identify this molecule:
    a. steroid,
    b. saturated fatty acid,
    c. amino acid,
    d. unsaturated fatty acid,

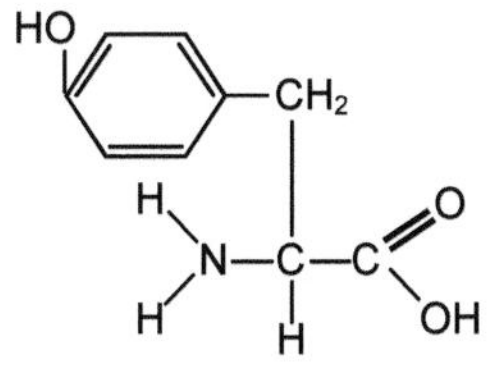

2. Which of the following diagrams represents a peptide bond?

    a. 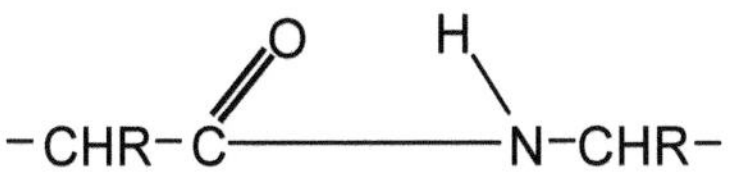 $-CHR-C \overset{O}{=} N-CHR-$ with H on N

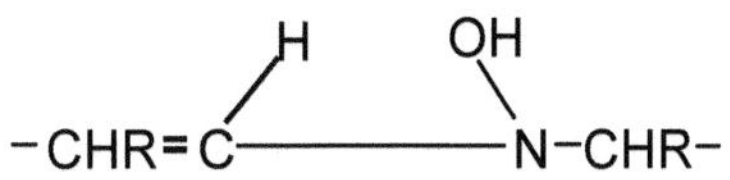

    b. $-CHR=C N-CHR-$ with H and OH

    c. $-CHR-C \overset{R}{=} N-CHR-$ with H on N

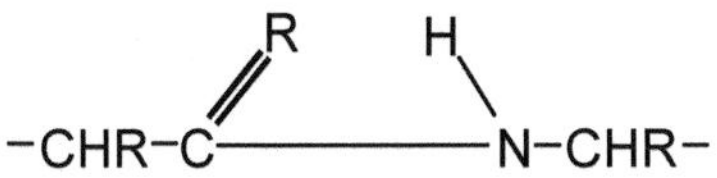

    d. 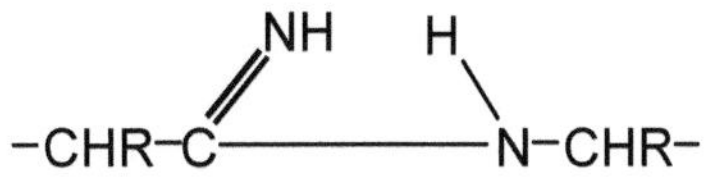 $-CHR-C \overset{NH}{=} N-CHR-$ with H on N

3. A polypeptide can be made up from which of the following number of different amino acids?
    a. 10,
    b. 22,
    c. 61,
    d. 64.

4. A proteome can be described as:
    a. a set of proteins,
    b. the proteins produced by a species,
    c. all the proteins produced by a gene,
    d. the set of proteins produced by a genome.

5. An alpha helix can be found:
    a. only in the secondary structure of a protein,
    b. only in secondary and tertiary structures of a protein,
    c. only in secondary, tertiary and quaternary structures of a protein,
    d. only in conjugated proteins.

6. In protein structure a disulphide bridge is a type of bond used in:
    a. the primary structure,
    b. the secondary structure,
    c. the tertiary structure,
    d. both secondary and tertiary structure,

7. A conjugated protein is one that:
    a. contains a prosthetic group,
    b. has more than one polypeptide chain,
    c. has both secondary and tertiary structure,
    d. is folded into a 3D shape.

8. Denaturing of a protein occurs:
    a. when bonds holding the structure together are broken,
    b. only when molecular movement causes hydrogen bonds to break,
    c. only when changes in pH cause ionic bonds to break,
    d. only when the disulphide bridges of the tertiary structure break.

9. The minimum level of protein structure for an enzyme is:
    a. primary,
    b. secondary,
    c. tertiary,
    d. quaternary.

10. The function of the active site of an enzyme is to:
    a.   bind the products so substrates can form,
    b.   bind the substrates in the correct orientation for catalysis to occur,
    c.   prevent substrates from moving in the cytoplasm,
    d.   unfold protein substrates so catalysis can occur.

11. Which of the following graphs represents the effect of substrate concentration on an enzyme controlled reaction with a fixed amount of enzyme?

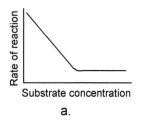
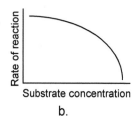
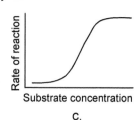
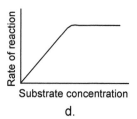

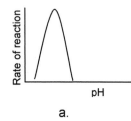
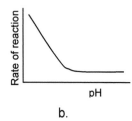
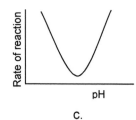
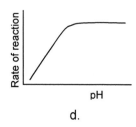

| a. | b. | c. | d. |

12. Which of the following graphs represents the effect of pH on an enzyme controlled reaction?

| a. | b. | c. | d. |

13. For a chemical reaction to take place an input of energy is normally required. This is called the activation energy. The function of enzymes is to:
    a.   provide the activation energy,
    b.   prevent the activation energy from increasing,
    c.   decrease the activation energy,
    d.   increase the activation energy.

14. Denaturation can be defined as:
    a.   breakdown of a protein into its amino acids,
    b.   loss of the functional properties of a protein,
    c.   failure of an enzyme to catalyse a reaction,
    d.   break down of the primary structure of a protein.

15. Competitive inhibition of enzymes occurs when:
    a.   an inhibitor binds to the active site,
    b.   a substrate binds to the active site,
    c.   both inhibitor and substrate bind together in the active site,
    d.   an inhibitor binds to a part of the enzyme separate from the active site.

16. Which of the following statements about activation energy is correct?
    a.   In an exothermic reaction the energy level of the products is higher than that of the substrate.
    b.   Activation energy is the heat released from an exothermic reaction.
    c.   Enzymes can only catalyse a reaction if the activation energy is lower than the energy level of the substrate.
    d.   A high activation energy prevents most biological reactions from occurring at physiological temperatures.

IBHL Biology 2016 © Ashby Merson-Davies

17. Which of the following statements is true?
    a.   Competitive inhibitors and non-competitive inhibitors both bind to the active site.
    b.   Non-competitive inhibitors are able to control metabolic pathways.
    c.   Non-competitive inhibition cannot be reversed.
    d.   Competitive inhibitors are used to control metabolic pathways.

18. Which dotted line on the graph represents competitive inhibition?

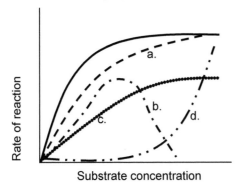

Rate of reaction

Substrate concentration

19. Which of the following statements describes an immobilised enzyme?
    a.   The enzyme does not take part in the reaction.
    b.   The enzyme is denatured before being added to the substrate.
    c.   The enzyme is attached to an inert molecule to hold it in place.
    d.   Only enzymes involved in hydrolysis reactions can be immobilised.

20. A molecule of DNA:
    a.   is made up from two strands of nucleotides linked by covalent bonds,
    b.   contains five different types of base,
    c.   has the bases linked to sugar molecules via phosphate,
    d.   differs from RNA because it contains the base thymine.

21. Which of the following represents a nucleotide?

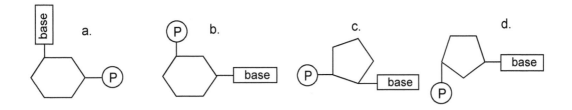

22. In a strand of DNA the nucleotides are joined by a:
    a.   2' – 3' linkage,
    b.   5' – 1' linkage,
    c.   3' – 6' linkage,
    d.   3' – 5' linkage.

23. Which of the following statements about DNA gyrase is correct?
    a.   It removes the supercoiling caused by the action of helicase.
    b.   It prevents the DNA strands that have been separated from re-joining.
    c.   It twists the DNA strands to assist helicase.
    d.   It uncoils the DNA strands to allow helicase to separate them.

24. In the table below which line represents the correct function for the listed enzymes? (NTPs = nucleoside triphosphates; dNTPs = deoxynucleoside triphosphates)

	DNA polymerase I	DNA primase	DNA ligase	DNA polymerase III
a.	Joins dNTPs to the leading strand only.	Adds an RNA sequence at the end of Okazaki fragments.	Joins two Okazaki fragments together.	Uses dNTPs on both leading and lagging strands.
b	Replaces RNA nucleotides on the lagging strand using dNTPs.	Adds an RNA sequence on the lagging strand.	Joins two Okazaki fragments together.	Uses dNTPs on both leading and lagging strands.
c.	Joins dNTPs on both leading and lagging strands.	Joins two Okazaki fragments together.	Adds an RNA sequence at the end of Okazaki fragments.	Replaces NTPs on the lagging strand with dNTPs.
d	Joins dNTPs on both leading and lagging strands.	Joins NTPs to the leading strand only.	Adds an RNA sequence on the lagging strand.	Joins two Okazaki fragments together.

25. Which of the following statements about single-stranding binding proteins is correct?
    a. They assist with the binding of DNA polymerase III to the lagging strand.
    b. They prevent the separated DNA strands from re-joining.
    c. They mark the place on the DNA strand where DNA primase has to bind.
    d. As helicase unwinds the helix they break the hydrogen bonds between the bases.

26. Which of the following statements about dideoxyribonucleotides is correct?
    a. They are the building blocks used to build DNA.
    b. They can be used to make new types of DNA.
    c. They are used during DNA replication to build the lagging strand.
    d. They are used in the laboratory to block DNA replication.

27. Protein coding DNA is used to make:
    a. structural proteins and enzymes,
    b. rRNA and proteins,
    c. rRNA and tRNA,
    d. introns and exons.

28. In the process of transcription which of the following enzymes unwinds the DNA helix?
    a. helicase,
    b. DNA polymerase,
    c. primase,
    d. RNA polymerase.

29. In which direction does the enzyme involved in transcription read the DNA strand?
    a. 5' to 3',
    b. 3' to 5',
    c. 5' to 5',
    d. 3' to 3'.

30. Which of the following statements about transcription is correct?
    a. The sense DNA strand is used as a template.
    b. Both rRNA and tRNA molecules are required.
    c. It takes place in the cytoplasm.
    d. The antisense DNA strand is used as a template.

31. Complementary base pairing occurs during the process of transcription. Which base in the RNA strand pairs with adenine in the DNA strand?
    a. thymine,
    b. uracil,
    c. guanine,
    d. cytosine.

32. Which of the following statements about post-transcriptional modification of RNA is correct?
    a. It takes place in the nucleus.
    b. It takes place in the cytoplasm.
    c. Exons are cut out and the remaining introns spliced together.
    d. It is used to repair the mRNA strand transcribed from a mutated gene.

33. Which of the following DNA strands corresponds to the mRNA sequence AACGUAUUC?
    a. AACGTATTC,
    b. CTTATGCAA,
    c. UUGCAUAAG,
    d. TTGCATAAG.

34. Use the codon table on page 51 to determine which is the correct the amino acid from the DNA sequence CCG GAA CGA AGC GAC.
    a. proline – glutamic acid – arginine – serine – aspartic acid,
    b. proline – leucine – arginine – alanine – aspartic acid,
    c. glycine – leucine – arginine – serine – leucine,
    d. glycine – leucine – alanine – serine – leucine.

35. Which of the following statements about tRNA is true?
    a. It has a sequence of three bases called a codon.
    b. It is composed of two strands.
    c. It has a sequence of three bases called an anticodon.
    d. It has a sequence of three bases at the 5' end where the amino acid binds.

36. Which of the following statements about ribosomes is correct?
    a. The mRNA binding site is on the small subunit.
    b. The mRNA binding site is on the large subunit.
    c. The large subunit has two binding sites for tRNA molecules.
    d. The subunits are synthesised on the rER.

37. Which of the following shows the correct sequence for the initiation phase of translocation?

	First step	Second step	Third step
a.	Charged tRNA binds to start codon	Large ribosome subunit binds to small subunit	Small ribosome subunit binds to mRNA/charged tRNA
b.	Charged tRNA binds to start codon	Small ribosome subunit binds to mRNA/charged tRNA	Large ribosome subunit binds to small subunit
c.	Small ribosome subunit binds to mRNA	Large ribosome subunit binds to small subunit	Charged tRNA binds to start codon
d.	Large ribosome subunit binds to small subunit	Charged tRNA binds to start codon	Small ribosome subunit binds to mRNA/charged tRNA

38. During which phase of translocation does the peptide bond form?
    a. Initiation,
    b. Elongation,
    c. Translocation,
    d. Termination.

39. Which of the following statements about the process of translocation is correct?
    a. The first charged tRNA molecule binds to the aminoacyl (a) site.
    b. Elongation takes place in a 5' to 3' direction.
    c. Translocation occurs when the second charged tRNA molecule binds to the large subunit.
    d. The second charged tRNA molecule binds to the aminoacyl (a) site.

40. A polysome is:
    a. a linear sequence of amino acids,
    b. a linear sequence of nucleotides,
    c. a group of ribosomes on an mRNA molecule,
    d. a group of ribosomes on a tRNA molecule.

41. Which of the following enzymes is used in the polymerase chain reaction?
    a. DNA polymerase,
    b. RNA polymerase,
    c. DNA primase,
    d. DNA ligase.

42. A restriction endonuclease is one that:
    a. joins two fragments of DNA together,
    b. prevents the replication of DNA,
    c. cuts DNA at specific places,
    d. cuts tandem repeats in DNA.

43. The insulin gene cannot be cut from the pancreatic beta cell DNA because:
    a. a sufficient numbers of beta cells cannot be obtained,
    b. it is not known where the insulin gene is within the cell's genome,
    c. a gene cut from the cell's DNA will not have the correct sticky ends,
    d. the insulin gene cut from the cell DNA would produce primary RNA containing introns.

IBHL Biology 2016 © Ashby Merson-Davies

Chapter Three
Cell Biology

Cells are the building blocks of life. The cell nucleus contains the genetic code in the form of DNA, and membranes have a key role, not only in surrounding the cytoplasm, but compartmentalising the cell. Cells can divide by mitosis and meiosis.

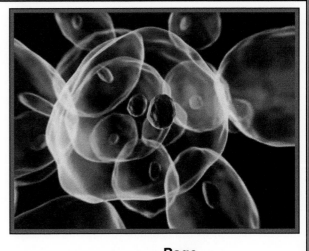

Cell theory

The cell theory states that:
- Cells are the smallest units of life.
- Living organisms are composed of one or more cells.
- Cells come from pre-existing cells.

Questioning the cell theory

Points for discussion
- A cell is a functional unit of cytoplasm surrounded by a membrane and containing genetic material.
- Most multicellular organisms do contain many cells that conform to this cell structure – liver, pancreas, nerve, leucocytes; palisade, epidermal, cortex.
- Many cells do not conform to this:
  - Striated muscle tissue does not have separate cells as the nuclei are spread around in a single mass of cytoplasm – multinucleate cytoplasm.
  - Aseptate fungal hyphae are the same.
  - Some giant algae, such as *Codium*, also have multinucleate cytoplasm.

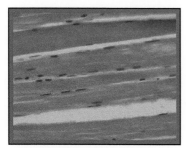

3.1 Striated muscle showing multinucleate cytoplasm

3.2 Fungal hyphae

3.3 *Codium fragile* (Dead Man's Fingers), Massachusetts coast

- Further examples:
  - Many plant cells have holes in their walls called plasmodesmata. The plasma membranes and cytoplasm of adjacent cells are continuous through these holes. This makes some plant tissues similar to muscle tissue and fungi in that a single mass of cytoplasm has several nuclei.
  - Mature red blood cells in humans do not have a nucleus.
  - The water transport cells in plants (xylem) are dead and have lost their end walls – see pages 216–7.
  - The food transport cells in plants (phloem) have lost their nucleus and the cytoplasm is very changed.

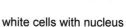

plasmodesma

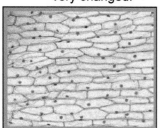

3.4 Epidermis cells from an onion

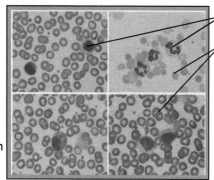

white cells with nucleus

red cells with no nucleus

3.5 Human blood cells

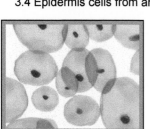

3.6 Human cheek cells

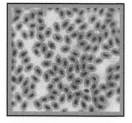

3.7 Red blood cells from a bird. Note the nuclei

IBHL Biology 2016 © Ashby Merson-Davies

Spontaneous generation – Pasteur's experiments (around 1850s)

Key points
- Pasteur boiled up a nutrient broth in a flask and left the flask open – Experiment 1.
  - After a few days it had gone bad due to bacterial growth.
- He repeated the experiment but sealed the flask after heating – Experiment 2.
  - The broth remained sterile.
- He repeated the experiment again using an open swan-necked flask – Experiment 3.
  - The broth remained sterile.
- He then broke off the swan neck – Experiment 4.
  - The broth went bad.

Deductions
- The sterile boiled broth cannot spontaneously produce life.
- The bacteria that caused the broth to go bad could enter an open flask only if they could fall in directly.
- The bacteria could not enter through the open swan neck.

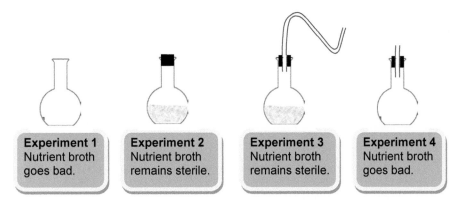

| Experiment 1 | Experiment 2 | Experiment 3 | Experiment 4 |
| Nutrient broth goes bad. | Nutrient broth remains sterile. | Nutrient broth remains sterile. | Nutrient broth goes bad. |

Surface area to volume ratio

Principle
- As an organism increases in size its surface area to volume ratio decreases.

This can easily be seen by comparing the following cubes.

Dimensions	1×1×1
Surface area	6cm^2
Volume	1cm^3
SA :V ratio	6 : 1

Dimensions	2×2×2
Surface area	24cm^2
Volume	8cm^3
SA :V ratio	3 : 1

Dimensions	3×3×3
Surface area	54cm^2
Volume	27cm^3
SA :V ratio	2 : 1

Key points
- The metabolism of a cell is linked to its mass : volume ratio.
- The surface area provides the exchange surface for heat and substances.
- The more cytoplasm the more heat and waste products generated, and the greater the demand for oxygen and nutrients.
- The models above show that the relative surface area decreases as the cube gets bigger.
- Thus organisms and cells develop strategies to cope with this problem. Examples are:
  - Plant cells develop a large central vacuole,
  - Intestinal cells and proximal convoluted tubule cells have microvilli,
  - Leaf palisade cells are column shaped.

1. What does the cell theory state?	2. Describe one tissue or organism that does not follow the cell theory.
3. Describe simply Pasteur's experiment.	4. What was the essential point shown by Pasteur's experiment?

Functions of life

- **Metabolism** – all the chemical pathways that take place in the cell to build up molecules (anabolism) or break down molecules (catabolism).
- **Response** – reactions given to stimuli to help survival.
- **Homeostasis** – maintaining a constant internal environment.
- **Growth** – increasing the cell size or number of cells.
- **Reproduction** – producing offspring, either asexual or sexual.
- **Nutrition** – taking in nutrients for growth and energy.
- **Excretion** – removal of the waste products of metabolism.

Chlorella – a unicellular alga

- metabolism – respires, photosynthesises, synthesises protein, synthesises nucleic acids.
- growth – after dividing they grow by increasing the volume of cytoplasm.
- reproduction – divide into two, this is called binary fission, it is asexual reproduction.
- excretion – removes excess carbon dioxide by diffusion over the cell surface.

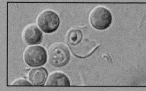

3.8a Chlorella

Paramecium – a unicellular organism

- metabolism – respires, synthesises protein, synthesises nucleic acids.
- response – can follow a chemical gradient to find food, this is called chemotaxis.
- homeostasis – species living in fresh water can pump out excess water flowing in due to osmosis by using a special structure called a contractile vacuole.
- growth – after dividing they grow by increasing the volume of cytoplasm.
- reproduction – divide into two, this is called binary fission, it is asexual reproduction.
- nutrition – feeds by taking in particles of organic matter in the water.
- excretion – removes carbon dioxide by diffusion over the cell surface.

contractile vacuole

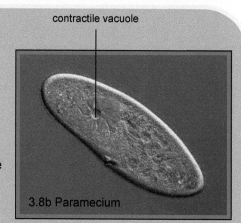

3.8b Paramecium

Cell differentiation

- ➤ This means to become different and therefore specialise in a particular function.
- ➤ Cells in a multicellular organism are produced by mitosis.
- ➤ Hence each cell has all the chromosomes and a complete genome.
- ➤ Most of these genes will be switched off as they will code for functions that the cell does not do, e.g. liver cells will have the genes for eye cells, stomach cells, brain cells etc. switched off.
- ➤ The genes that are switched on are those associated with 'house-keeping' such as respiration to keep the cell alive, plus those associated with its specialist function.
- ➤ Differentiation of groups of cells produces specialised tissues.

Emergent properties
Key points

- ➤ Only multicellular organisms show emergent properties.
- ➤ Emergent properties arise from the interaction of differentiated cells.
- ➤ Differentiated cells can group together to form tissues, tissues group to form organs, and organs group to form organ systems.
- ➤ These interactions result in the whole organism being better than the sum of its parts.

Example 1 – the lungs (see page 147)
- Type 1 pneumocytes are very thin and specialised for gas exchange.
- Type 2 pneumocytes produce a surfactant which stops the alveolar walls sticking together.
- Without the two cell types working together the lungs could not function efficiently.

Example 2 – temperature homeostasis
- Blood transports heat around the body;
- Sweat glands produce sweat;
- Heat from the blood is used to evaporate the sweat cooling the body;
- The animal can survive in hotter environments that would kill other organisms.

Stem cells

Stem cells
Stem cells are undifferentiated cells found in multicellular organisms that can differentiate into specialised cells and can divide by mitosis to produce more stem cells. In mammals there are two main types of stem cell: embryonic stem cells, which are isolated from the blastocyst, (see page 194), and adult stem cells which are found in a variety of tissues such as bone marrow. Stem cells can also be taken from the umbilical cord blood just after birth.
Autologous harvesting means removing stem cells from the person in whom they are going to be used.

Stem cell potency
Potency specifies the level of ability to differentiate. The more cell types a cell can divide into the greater its potency. There are 5 categories – see Stem Cell Glossary on page 102.

Key points
- ➤ Stem cells are undifferentiated cells.
- ➤ There are several different categories.
- ➤ They retain the capacity to divide and to have the ability to differentiate along different pathways such as during embryonic development.
- ➤ Some tissues retain stem cells in order to continue producing new cells or to replace damaged cells.
- ➤ Some types of stem cell have the potential for therapeutic use – see boxes on next page.

Stargardt's disease – background
This is an inherited disease which results in a gradual loss, starting in early childhood, of the central area of vision. It can lead to complete blindness. It is caused by a recessive allele (see page 253) which destroys cells in the retinal pigment epithelium (RPE). These cells lie just underneath the layer of photoreceptor cells and maintain the functions of the photoreceptors. If the RPE cells cannot function the photoreceptor cells will degenerate and vision is lost.

Stargardt's disease

Key points

➤ Stem cell therapy is aimed at replacing the RPE cells – see lower blue box on the previous page.
➤ The work is at the clinical trial stage (2014–15).
➤ Human embryonic stem cells (ESCs) were induced to develop into RPE cells.
➤ These were injected directly into the affected area in the eye.
➤ Results from the trials showed that the cells survived and multiplied.
➤ This lead to some improvement in vision in the patients.

Leukemia

Key points

➤ Leukaemia is a cancer of white blood cells or leucocytes.
➤ Leucocytes are made in the bone marrow from multipotent adult stem cells.
➤ The leucocytes are released into the blood stream to fight off infection.
➤ Leukaemia is when these cells grow abnormally.
➤ Chemotherapy is used to kill all the bone marrow cells, the normal cells as well as the abnormal ones.
➤ Stem cells can be obtained from donor bone marrow or umbilical cord blood.
➤ These are introduced into the patient's blood and the stem cells migrate to the bone marrow and start to produce healthy leucocytes.

Ethics of the therapeutic uses of stem cells

Key points

❖ **Adult tissues**
➤ Autologous harvesting (see upper blue box on previous page) is the least controversial since the cells come from the patient and the person is not harmed.
➤ If harvested from the patient rejection problems do not occur as they are a perfect tissue match.
➤ They are less likely to develop malignant tumours compared to embryonic stem cells.
➤ In other cases the cells come from a donor who has made the decision to donate their cells. This is usually the situation with leukaemia – see purple box above.

❖ **Umbilical cord blood**
➤ After a baby is born the umbilical cord is clamped and cut close to the baby.
➤ Within the umbilical cord there is still a quantity of the baby's blood which contains blood stem cells.
➤ The blood is easily collected and no harm is done to either baby or mother.
➤ The blood can be frozen for long term storage.
➤ Stem cells are likely to be genetically different from the patient leading to rejection if not treated.

> Umbilical cord blood can be used to treat children with cancerous blood disorders such as leukaemia or certain genetic blood diseases such as Fanconi anaemia.

❖ **Embryonic stem cells**
➤ This is the most controversial.
➤ Embryonic stem cells (ESCs) are pluripotent (see the Stem cell glossary on page 102) and therefore have great potential for therapy.
➤ They will not have accumulated any mutations compared to adult cells.
➤ There is a risk of them developing into tumours.
➤ They are likely to be genetically different from the patient leading to rejection if not treated.
➤ During IVF treatment (see page 195) more embryos are produced than are used.
➤ Unused embryos could be used for another childless couple, for research, for ESCs, or destroyed.
➤ The embryos have been created in order to produce a baby.
➤ Many people feel destroying an embryo to collect ESCs is morally unacceptable.
➤ If though an embryo is created specifically using SCNT (somatic cell nuclear transfer) as a source of ESCs then the ethical issues become even more complex. See blue box below.
➤ The controversy arises over whether the pre-14 day embryo has 'rights' with respect to life. (An embryo older than 14 days cannot be used).

> SCNT was the method developed by Dr Ian Wilmut and used to create Dolly the sheep – see page 252.

> Follow these links to read articles on the ethics of using embryonic stem cells:
> http://www.eurostemcell.org/factsheet/embyronic-stem-cell-research-ethical-dilemma
> http://www.eurostemcell.org/factsheet/origins-ethics-and-embryos-sources-human-embryonic-stem-cells

5. What happens to the surface area to volume ratio as a cell increases in size?

6. Give one example of how a cell can avoid this problem.

7. What is the function of the surface area of a cell?

8. State three sources where stem cells can be obtained.

9. List the 7 functions of life and state briefly what each one means.

10. State two significant features about stem cells that make them suitable for stem cell therapy.

11. State three points about how stem cells are used to treat Stargardts's disease.

Electron microscopes

Key points

> Electron microscopes have a much higher resolution than light microscopes.
> This means they can see very small objects such as cell organelles, membranes and viruses, and even large molecules.
> The images can only be in shades of grey.
> Images can though be artificially coloured to make parts more clear.
> The object has to be non-living.

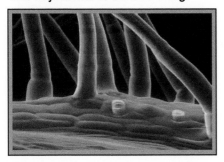

3.10 Artificially coloured scanning electron micrograph of a leaf surface

Microscopes

There are two main types – light and electron.
There are two types of electron microscope:
  • transmission,
  • scanning.
Key features of light microscopes:
  • low resolution,
  • can observe colour,
  • can observe living structures.
Key features of electron microscopes:
  • high resolution,
  • scanning em can observe in 3D.

3.9 A transmission electron microscope

Resolution

The resolving power of a microscope is the smallest distance between two objects so that they can be seen as two objects. This is determined by the wavelength of the beam being use to see the object – the shorter the wavelength the smaller the distance between the two objects. Electrons have a very much shorter wavelength compared to visible light.

Prokaryotic cells
Key points
- ➤ Prokaryotic cells are cells with a simple structure and no membrane bound nucleus.
- ➤ They do not have membrane bound organelles, i.e. they are without compartmentalisation.
- ➤ They divide by binary fission.

Ribosomes
There are two sizes called 70S and 80S. (You do not need to know what these mean.) Prokaryotic cells contain 70S ribosomes and eukaryotic cells contain 80S ribosomes. However mitochondria and chloroplasts contain 70S ribosomes suggesting their prokaryotic origin in evolution see page 89.

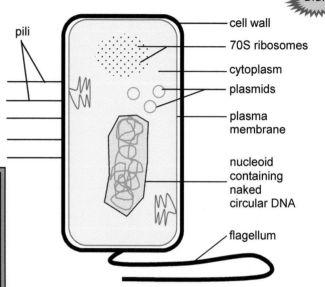

Draw

pili — cell wall
— 70S ribosomes
— cytoplasm
— plasmids
— plasma membrane
— nucleoid containing naked circular DNA
— flagellum

Example – *Escherichia coli* or *E. coli*

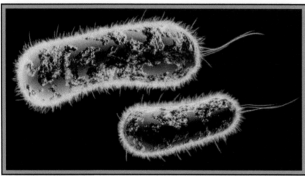

3.11 Artificially coloured scanning electron micrograph of bacteria showing pili and flagellae

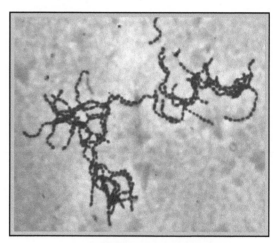

3.12 Streptococcus bacteria.
Note that these bacteria are round whereas *E. coli* is rod shaped

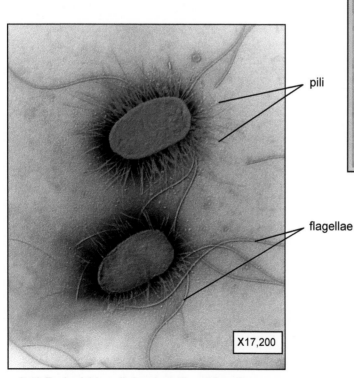

pili

flagellae

X17,200

3.13 *Escherichia coli* showing pili and flagellae.
Note the distinct difference in length and thickness

Electron micrographs of prokaryotic cells

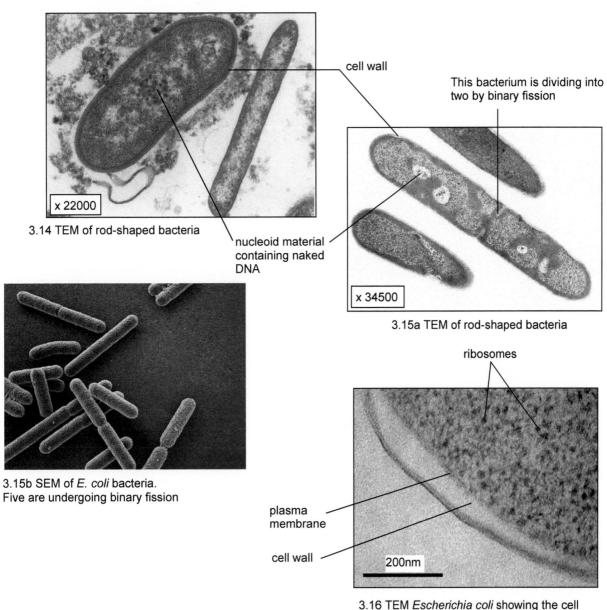

cell wall

3.14 TEM of rod-shaped bacteria

This bacterium is dividing into two by binary fission

x 22000

nucleoid material containing naked DNA

x 34500

3.15a TEM of rod-shaped bacteria

3.15b SEM of *E. coli* bacteria.
Five are undergoing binary fission

ribosomes

plasma membrane

cell wall

200nm

3.16 TEM *Escherichia coli* showing the cell wall, plasma membrane and ribosomes

12. What is the size of prokaryote ribosomes?	13. What is the name of the small circular pieces of DNA that are found in the cytoplasm of bacteria?
14. Distinguish between flagella and pili.	
	15. What is the name given to the type of bacterial cell division?
	16. Use the scale bar in the photograph above to determine the magnification.
17. State one advantage and one disadvantage of an electron microscope.	

Eukaryotic cells

➢ Eukaryotic cells contain membrane bound organelles, i.e. they are compartmentalised.
➢ Organelles carry out specific functions.

Animal cells

➢ Have centrioles.
➢ May have glycogen granules.
➢ May have phagocytic vesicles.

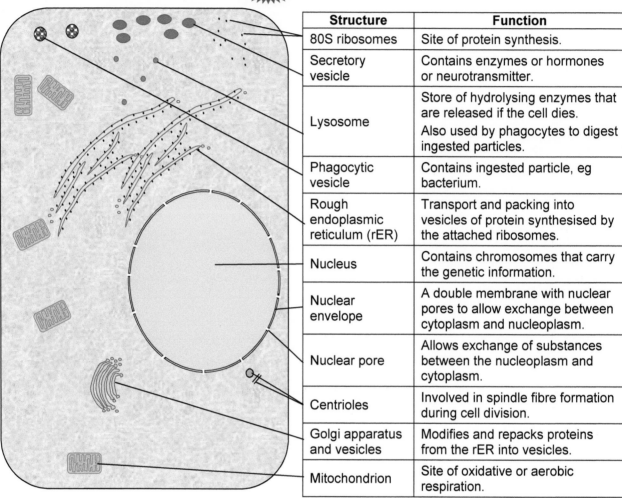

Structure	Function
80S ribosomes	Site of protein synthesis.
Secretory vesicle	Contains enzymes or hormones or neurotransmitter.
Lysosome	Store of hydrolysing enzymes that are released if the cell dies. Also used by phagocytes to digest ingested particles.
Phagocytic vesicle	Contains ingested particle, eg bacterium.
Rough endoplasmic reticulum (rER)	Transport and packing into vesicles of protein synthesised by the attached ribosomes.
Nucleus	Contains chromosomes that carry the genetic information.
Nuclear envelope	A double membrane with nuclear pores to allow exchange between cytoplasm and nucleoplasm.
Nuclear pore	Allows exchange of substances between the nucleoplasm and cytoplasm.
Centrioles	Involved in spindle fibre formation during cell division.
Golgi apparatus and vesicles	Modifies and repacks proteins from the rER into vesicles.
Mitochondrion	Site of oxidative or aerobic respiration.

You need to be able to interpret electron micrographs to identify organelles and deduce the function of specialised cells.
Examples.
- Large number of mitochondria – the cell is producing a lot of energy, perhaps for active transport.
- Large amount of rER – the cell is synthesising a lot of protein for export, perhaps digestive enzymes, or a hormone, or antibodies.
- Large number of vesicles – the cell is a secretory cell, again possibly producing digestive enzymes, or maybe they are neurosecretory vesicles.
- Large numbers of chloroplasts – photosynthesising cell such as a leaf palisade cell.

Electron micrographs of eukaryotic cells

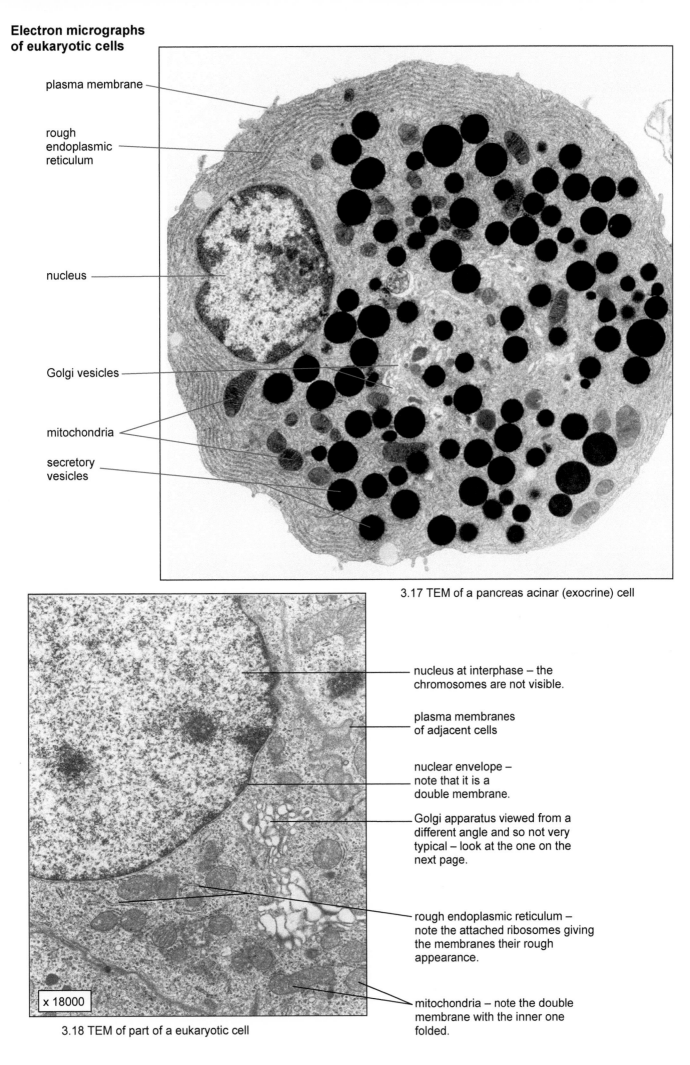

plasma membrane

rough endoplasmic reticulum

nucleus

Golgi vesicles

mitochondria

secretory vesicles

3.17 TEM of a pancreas acinar (exocrine) cell

x 18000

3.18 TEM of part of a eukaryotic cell

nucleus at interphase – the chromosomes are not visible.

plasma membranes of adjacent cells

nuclear envelope – note that it is a double membrane.

Golgi apparatus viewed from a different angle and so not very typical – look at the one on the next page.

rough endoplasmic reticulum – note the attached ribosomes giving the membranes their rough appearance.

mitochondria – note the double membrane with the inner one folded.

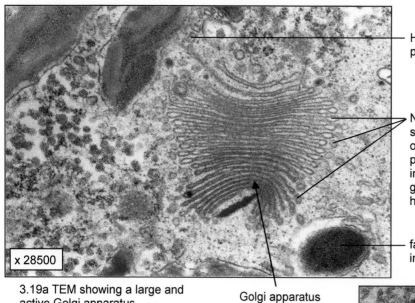

Here vesicles containing unprocessed proteins from the rER are joining on.

Note the vesicles budding off on both sides. These will either become lysosomes or they will be transporting processed proteins to the plasma membrane either for incorporation into the membrane (e.g. glycoproteins), or for exocytosis (e.g. hormones, digestive enzymes).

fat droplet – these usually stain black in electron micrographs.

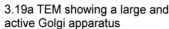

3.19a TEM showing a large and active Golgi apparatus

Golgi apparatus

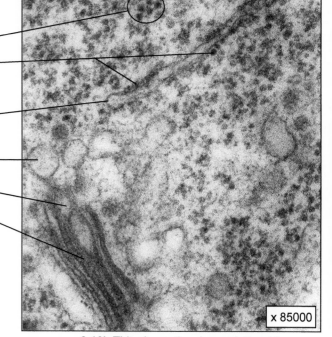

cluster of free ribosomes

ribosomes on rER

Note the swollen end of the rER where a vesicle is forming.

Vesicles then move to, and fuse with, the Golgi apparatus.

3.19b This shows the close relationship between rER and the Golgi apparatus

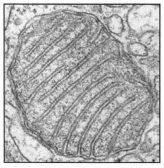

3.20 A mitochondrion. Note the cristae formed from the folded inner membrane

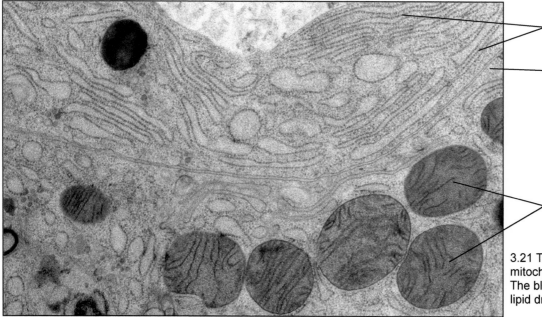

rough endoplasmic reticulum

plasma membranes of adjacent cells

mitochondria with cristae

3.21 TEM showing rER and mitochondria.
The black spot upper left is a lipid droplet.

Plant cells

Key points

➤ Have a cellulose cell wall.
➤ Mature cells may have a large central vacuole.
➤ Photosynthesising cells have chloroplasts.
➤ May have starch grains.

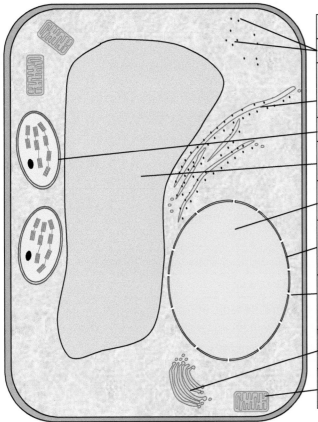

Structure	Function
80S ribosomes	Site of protein synthesis.
Rough endoplasmic reticulum (rER)	Transport and packing into vesicles of protein synthesised by the attached ribosomes.
Chloroplast	Site of photosynthesis.
Vacuole	Contains water, salts and waste products.
Nucleus	Contains chromosomes that carry the genetic information.
Nuclear envelope	A double membrane with nuclear pores to allow exchange between cytoplasm and nucleoplasm.
Nuclear pore	Allows exchange of substances between the nucleoplasm and cytoplasm.
Golgi apparatus and vesicles	Modifies and repacks proteins from the rER into vesicles.
Mitochondrion	Site of oxidative or aerobic respiration.

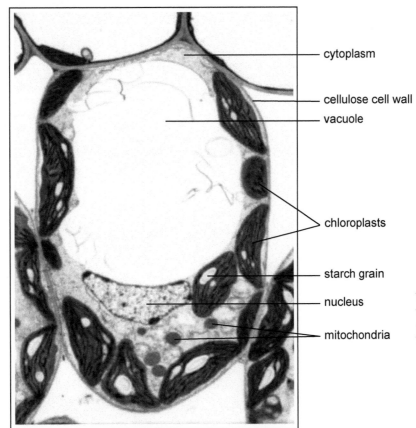

— cytoplasm

— cellulose cell wall
— vacuole

— chloroplasts

— starch grain

— nucleus

— mitochondria

The nucleus appears to be very small. This is because only the end has been cut through.

3.22 A palisade mesophyll cell in a soy bean leaf

Comparing prokaryotic and eukaryotic cells

Prokaryotic Cell	Eukaryotic Cell
Naked DNA.	DNA wrapped around histone proteins to form nucleosomes – see page 43.
DNA in cytoplasm.	DNA enclosed by a nuclear envelope *.
DNA circular.	DNA linear.
No membrane bound structures.	Membrane bound structures such as mitochondria, endoplasmic reticulum and Golgi apparatus present which compartmentalise functions.
Plasmids present.	No plasmids.
Ribosomes smaller (70S).	Ribosomes larger (80S).

* Note – it is a nuclear envelope – there are 2 membranes.

Comparing plant and animal cells

Although both are eukaryotic cells they show some distinct differences.

Plant Cells	Animal Cells
Cellulose cell wall.	No cellulose cell wall.
Mature cells usually contain a large central vacuole	No large central vacuole but small vacuoles may be present in the cytoplasm.
No cholesterol in the plasma membrane.	Cholesterol in the plasma membrane.
No centrioles.	Centrioles present.
Store starch.	Store glycogen.
May contain chloroplasts.	Never contain chloroplasts.

18. What is the size of eukaryotic ribosomes?

19. Complete the 9 shaded boxes below.

Feature	Prokaryotic cell	Eukaryotic cell
DNA	Enclosed in envelope or not enclosed?	Enclosed in envelope or not enclosed?
DNA	Naked.	
DNA	Circular or linear?	Circular or linear?
Mitochondria	Present or Absent?	Present or Absent?
Size of ribosomes		

20. State the storage carbohydrate in plant cells.

21. State the storage carbohydrate in animal cells.

22. Name three eukaryotic cell organelles that have a double membrane around them.

23. What is the name given to this double membrane?

24. What does the term 'compartmentalisation' mean when applied to eukaryotic cells?

25. List four differences between plant and animal cells.

26. Animal cells – complete the 6 shaded boxes.

Structure	Function
Nucleus	
	Site of protein synthesis.
	Contains hydrolytic enzymes.
Golgi apparatus	
	Transport and packing into vesicles of newly synthesised protein.
Mitochondrion	

Membranes

Key points
➢ The cytoplasm of both prokaryotic and eukaryotic cells is surrounded by a membrane called the plasma membrane.
➢ Eukaryotic cells contain several membranous or membrane bound structures providing compartments.
➢ In eukaryotic cells the nucleus, mitochondria and chloroplasts are bound by two membranes.
➢ This double membrane is called an envelope.
➢ Membranes are partially permeable.

Membrane structure

Key components
➢ Phospholipids,
➢ Proteins,
➢ Cholesterol (animal cells only),
➢ Glycoproteins.

Phospholipids
Phospholipids have a hydrophilic head and 2 hydrophobic tails – see page 26.
This property is called amphipathic; Thus they have to form a bilayer.

Proteins
These are highly variable in their structure, position and function. Some have a carbohydrate chain attached – these are glycoproteins.

Cholesterol
This is a characteristic of animal cell membranes.
It can comprise up to 50% of the membrane.
It reduces membrane fluidity by reducing the movement of the phospholipid tails.
It reduces permeability to some solutes.

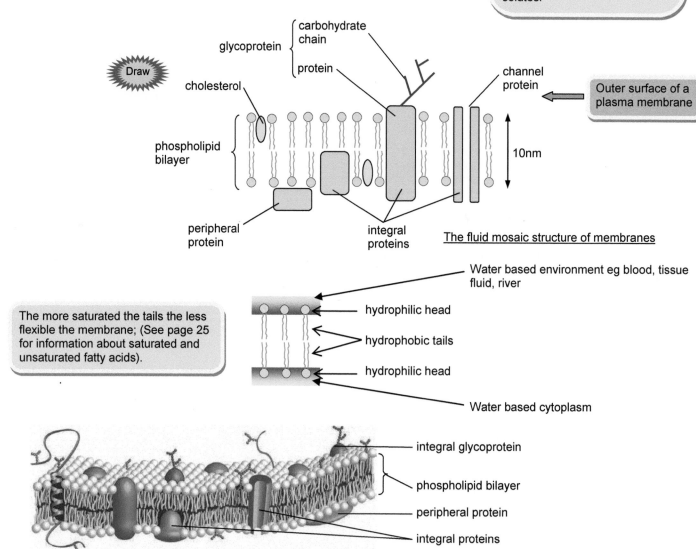

Draw

carbohydrate chain
glycoprotein
protein
channel protein
Outer surface of a plasma membrane
cholesterol
phospholipid bilayer
10nm
peripheral protein
integral proteins

The fluid mosaic structure of membranes

Water based environment eg blood, tissue fluid, river
hydrophilic head
hydrophobic tails
hydrophilic head
Water based cytoplasm

The more saturated the tails the less flexible the membrane; (See page 25 for information about saturated and unsaturated fatty acids).

integral glycoprotein
phospholipid bilayer
peripheral protein
integral proteins

3.23 3D drawing of the fluid mosaic model

IBHL Biology 2016 © Ashby Merson-Davies

The phospholipid bilayer

Key points
- Phospholipids are amphipathic – see pages 20 and 25 for structure and properties of phospholipids.
- The phospholipids form a bilayer.
- There is always a water solution on each side of a membrane and so there must be a hydro**philic** part next to the solution.
- If there was only one phospholipid molecule then the hydrophobic tails would be next to water.
- The hydrophilic part will always want to remain in contact with the water solution due to the hydrogen bonds which form between the head and water molecules.
- The hydrophobic tails will want to remain in contact with each other due to the hydrophobic interactions and therefore form a lipid bilayer.
- The major force causing the formation of the bilayer is the hydrophobic interaction.
- Since the molecules are held together solely by forces of mutual attraction and not chemical bonds it allows the bilayer to be very flexible and to break and re-join easily – see page 87.
- The hydrophobic tails are flexible.
- Saturated fatty acid chains make a membrane less fluid because they pack more tightly – see pages 24 and 29.
- Cholesterol makes some animal membranes less fluid by reducing the movement of the hydrophobic tails.

The proteins
Key points
- Position
  - Proteins on the surface are **peripheral** proteins.
  - Proteins partially embedded in the phospholipid bilayer or passing through it are **integral** proteins.
  - From above the proteins appear dotted around in the 'sea' of phospholipids looking like a mosaic.
- Structure
  - Mainly tertiary level but some transmembrane ones are often α-helix – see page 37.
  - Some proteins on the outer surface are glycoproteins.
- Functions
  - Hormone receptor,
  - Active transport,   } can be glycoproteins
  - Facilitated diffusion channel,
  - Electron carriers,
  - Immobilised enzymes,
  - Cell adhesion,
  - Cell-to-cell communication.

Models of membrane structure

❖ **Davson–Danielli model**
- The sandwich model – proposed in 1935.
- Phospholipid bilayer in the centre.
- Proteins coat both surfaces forming a protein – phospholipid – protein sandwich.
- Evidence for this came from electron micrographs done by Robertson in 1959 using a potassium permanganate stain which showed two dark lines with a pale line between.
- Danielli later added that protein lined channels passed through the phospholipid bilayer.
- Key problems with the Davson–Danielli model:
  - The proteins would be exposed to hydrophilic surfaces on both sides which is unstable.
  - Lipid soluble substances could not pass through.
  - Membranes around different organelles had different functions which would not be possible if all membranes had the same structure.
  - Membranes are bifacial, i.e. they have different inner and outer surfaces.

❖ **Singer–Nicholson model**
- The fluid mosaic model – proposed in 1972.
- It was supported by observations from the now more powerful electron microscope.
- Proteins were present on the surface of the phospholipid bilayer but not as a continuous layer.
- Other studies using dye marked proteins showed that these moved freely over the surface.
- Some proteins crossed the membrane from one side to the other.

27. What is a glycoprotein?

28. Distinguish between an integral membrane protein and a peripheral membrane protein.

29. What is the width of the phospholipid bilayer?

30. Which type of membrane protein forms channels?

31. Name the two molecules which reduce membrane fluidity.

32. Phospholipids are both hydrophobic and hydrophilic. What is the name given to this property?

33. Which part of a phospholipid is hydrophobic?

34. What is the major force causing the formation of the membrane bilayer?

35. Why do phospholipids have to form a bilayer in a membrane?

36. What is the property of a phospholipid bilayer that allows it to break and reform?

37. List 5 functions of membrane proteins.

38. Which type of eukaryotic cell does not have cholesterol as a membrane component?

39. Distinguish between the two models of membrane structure, naming both models.

Transmembrane transport

Simple diffusion
Key facts
➤ Many substances move through air and liquids such as cytoplasm, blood and tissue fluid by diffusion.
➤ Simple diffusion across the membrane is when substances such as oxygen, lipids and steroid hormones move through the phospholipid bilayer.
➤ Passive, therefore no energy from ATP is used.
➤ Particles are always moving in a random way.
➤ The substance always moves from a region of high concentration to a region of lower concentration using molecular kinetic energy.

Facilitated diffusion
Key facts
➤ Substances that cannot pass through the phospholipid bilayer have to pass through integral protein channels that have a hydrophilic core.
➤ This is called facilitated diffusion.
➤ The channels are specific and so have a binding site for the substance being transported.
➤ Sometimes these channels are gated to control the flow of the particular substance.
➤ Neurons contain both open and voltage gated facilitated channels for potassium – see pages 165-6.

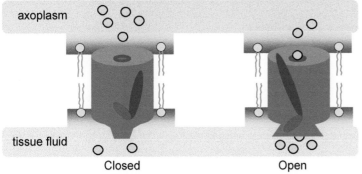

Pore facilitated.
A simple protein channel with a hydrophilic core

Carrier facilitated.
A more complex protein channel with the ability to regulate transport by opening and closing.

Facilitated diffusion. Both types of channel are specific.

➤ The voltage gated potassium channel consists of four polypeptides arranged so that there is a central transmembrane pore.
➤ Each one is composed of 6 transmembrane alpha helices.

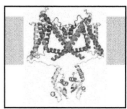

Central pore viewed from above

In this simplified model the two key components are the voltage sensing region (purple) and the paddle (red). (There are four of these but only one is shown). When there is a voltage change in the axoplasm the voltage sensing region is moved and this causes the paddle to move. This conformational change opens or closes the channel. The ball and chain model temporally inactivates an open channel until the paddle closes it.

axoplasm

tissue fluid

Closed   Open

The Voltage Gated Potassium Channel.

➤ One helix (red) on each is a voltage sensing region.

Side view of the channel embedded in the membrane (only 2 polypeptides shown)

3.24 Structure of the voltage gated potassium channel

Osmosis
Key facts
➤ Diffusion of water.
➤ Passive, therefore no energy is used.
➤ The water always moves from a higher water potential (lower solute concentration) to a lower water potential (higher solute concentration).
➤ A membrane is essential.
➤ Water moves only by osmosis, **never** by active transport.
➤ Water can move by simple diffusion through the phospholipid bilayer due to its small size.
➤ Water can also move by facilitated diffusion through specific channels called aquaporins – see page 177.

Tissues and organs to be used in medical procedures must be bathed in a solution with the same osmolarity as the cytoplasm to prevent osmosis occurring which would damage the tissues.

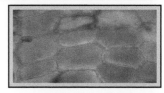

3.25a Rhubarb cells in distilled water

Determining the osmolarity of a tissue
Key principles
➤ Cells placed in a hypertonic solution will lose water by osmosis and shrink.
➤ In plant cells the cytoplasm pulls away from the cell wall. This is **plasmolysis**.
➤ Cells placed in a hypotonic solution will gain water by osmosis and swell.
➤ Animal cells may burst in a hypotonic solution (see blue box) but with plan cells the cellulose cell wall prevents this.
➤ Cells placed in an isotonic solution will remain unchanged as no osmosis takes place

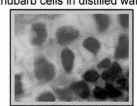

3.25b Plasmolysed rhubarb cells in a 5% sugar solution

Method

A tissue, such as fresh potato chips, is placed in a range of concentrations of salt or sugar solutions.

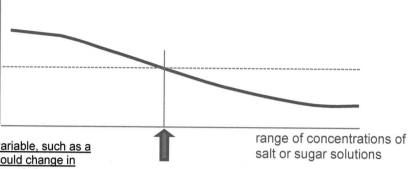

The dependent variable could be change in percentage mass or volume of the tissue, or change in volume of the solution.

range of concentrations of salt or sugar solutions

Graph illustrating how a dependent variable, such as a change in % mass of potato tissue, could change in varying concentrations of salt or sugar solutions

➤ The osmolarity of the tissue is the concentration of the sugar or salt solution (blue arrow) where there is no change in the dependent variable.
➤ Water has neither entered nor left the tissue.
➤ The tissue cells are in osmotic equilibrium with the surrounding solution.
➤ The salt or sugar solution is isotonic to the cell cytoplasm.

Kidney dialysis

In an artificial kidney machine the blood from the patient is passed on one side of a partially permeable membrane and on the other side is a fluid with a special composition.
Substances that need to be retained in the blood e.g. glucose, are the same concentration in the fluid so that they do not leave the blood.
Substances that need to leave the blood, e.g. urea, are not present in the fluid so that they will diffuse out of the blood – see page 179.

Active transport
Key facts

➤ Always uses energy from ATP which is hydrolysed to ADP + Pi.
➤ Transports against a concentration gradient.
➤ Requires an integral protein transporter in the membrane.
➤ Transport of substance requires a change in shape of the protein.
➤ The protein transporter has a specific binding site for the substance being transported.

Some pumps transport two or more substances together, either in the same direction (symport) or in opposite directions (antiport). An example of a symport is the $Na^+:Cl^-$ pump in the kidney – see page 176. An example of an antiport is the $Na^+:K^+$ pump in neurons – see below and page 165.

Inside of axon

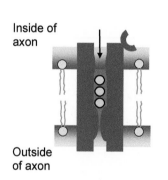 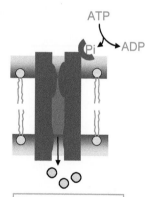 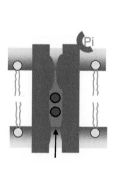 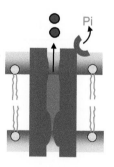

Outside of axon

Mechanism of the neuron sodium – potassium antiport pump.

Stage I
- Three sodium ions from the axoplasm enter and attach to specific binding sites.

Stage 2
- ATP binds and is hydrolysed to ADP + Pi.
- This causes a conformational change.
- Sodium ions released.
- Pi remains bound to transporter.

Stage 3
- Two potassium ions enter and bind to specific binding sites.

Stage 4
- Binding of the potassium causes the Pi to be released.
- This causes a conformational change.
- The potassium ions are released.

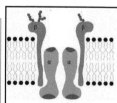

3.26 Diagram of the neuron Na+/K+ pump in the neuron membrane. There are two alpha, α, chains and two beta, β, chains.
The beta chains are glycoproteins.

IBHL Biology 2016 © Ashby Merson-Davies

Endocytosis

Key facts
- Endocytosis means taking substance into the cell.
- Phagocytosis takes in particles.
- Pinocytosis takes in solution.
- Energy from ATP is required.
- The plasma membrane folds inwards to form a vesicle which buds off.

> Endocytosis and exocytosis can occur due to the fluidity of the phospholipid bilayer.

Exocytosis

Key facts
- Exocytosis removes substances from the cell.
- This includes secretion of useful substances (enzymes, hormones, neurotransmitters), or excretion of waste.
- A vesicle in the cytoplasm joins to the plasma membrane and bursts.

> Take care to distinguish between secretion and excretion – see Glossary.

Transport vesicles

Key facts
- Vesicles bud off rER.
- Vesicles move through cytoplasm and join onto one side of the Golgi apparatus.
- Vesicles bud off other side of Golgi apparatus.
- Vesicle may move to plasma membrane for secretion of contents.
- Vesicle may remain in cytoplasm as a lysosome and fuse with a phagocytic vesicle.

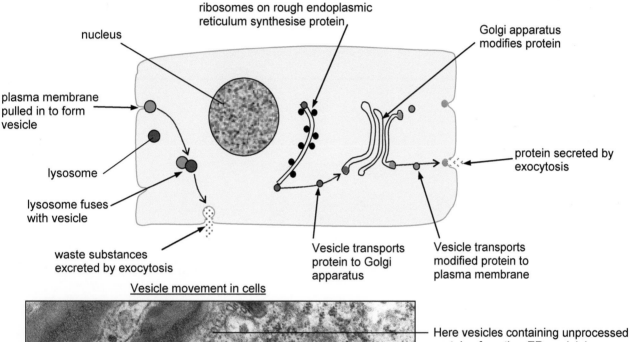

ribosomes on rough endoplasmic reticulum synthesise protein

nucleus

Golgi apparatus modifies protein

plasma membrane pulled in to form vesicle

lysosome

protein secreted by exocytosis

lysosome fuses with vesicle

waste substances excreted by exocytosis

Vesicle transports protein to Golgi apparatus

Vesicle transports modified protein to plasma membrane

Vesicle movement in cells

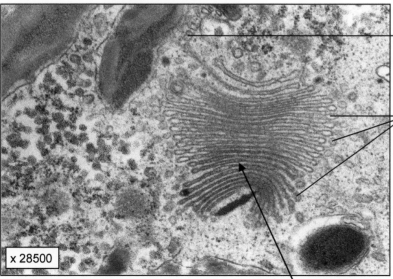

x 28500

Here vesicles containing unprocessed proteins from the rER are joining on.

Note the vesicles budding off on both sides. These will either become lysosomes or they will be transporting processed proteins to the plasma membrane either for incorporation into the membrane (e.g. glycoproteins), or for exocytosis (e.g. hormones, digestive enzymes).

3.27 TEM of a Golgi apparatus

Golgi apparatus

The origin of cells

Key points

➤ Cells can only be formed from pre-existing cells.
➤ The first cells must have arisen from non-living material.
➤ The origin of eukaryotic cells can be explained by the endosymbiotic theory.

The endosymbiotic theory

Points for discussion

➤ This theory is that eukaryotic cells arose from combinations of different types of prokaryotic cell.
➤ Usually, if one type of bacterial cell gets inside another, one of two things happens:
  • the host cell digests the invader,
  • the invader multiplies and kills the host cell.
➤ Thus, there is a battle between host and invader.
➤ The endosymbiotic theory imagines a drawn result – neither host nor invader wins and they settle down to work together.
➤ Suppose three types of imaginary prokaryotic cell which we will call 'Eater', 'Eliminator', and 'Sunshine':

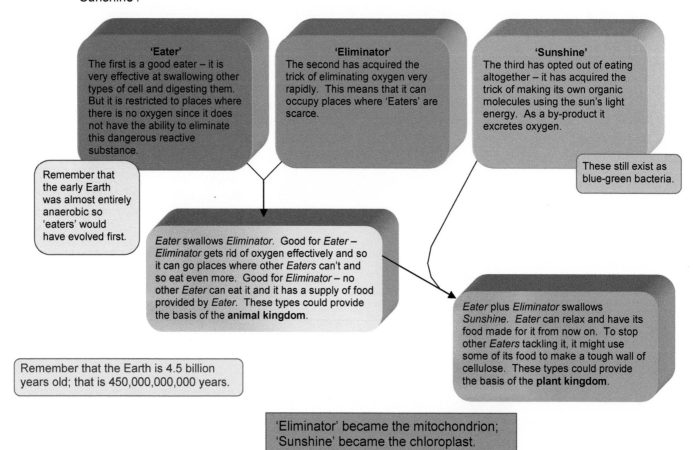

'Eater'
The first is a good eater – it is very effective at swallowing other types of cell and digesting them. But it is restricted to places where there is no oxygen since it does not have the ability to eliminate this dangerous reactive substance.

'Eliminator'
The second has acquired the trick of eliminating oxygen very rapidly. This means that it can occupy places where 'Eaters' are scarce.

'Sunshine'
The third has opted out of eating altogether – it has acquired the trick of making its own organic molecules using the sun's light energy. As a by-product it excretes oxygen.

These still exist as blue-green bacteria.

Remember that the early Earth was almost entirely anaerobic so 'eaters' would have evolved first.

Eater swallows *Eliminator*. Good for *Eater* – *Eliminator* gets rid of oxygen effectively and so it can go places where other *Eaters* can't and so eat even more. Good for *Eliminator* – no other *Eater* can eat it and it has a supply of food provided by *Eater*. These types could provide the basis of the **animal kingdom**.

Eater plus *Eliminator* swallows *Sunshine*. *Eater* can relax and have its food made for it from now on. To stop other *Eaters* tackling it, it might use some of its food to make a tough wall of cellulose. These types could provide the basis of the **plant kingdom**.

Remember that the Earth is 4.5 billion years old; that is 450,000,000,000 years.

'Eliminator' became the mitochondrion; 'Sunshine' became the chloroplast.

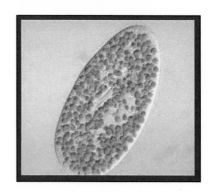

3.28 This photo is a Paramecium (a single celled organism) that has taken in Chlorella cells but not digested them. The Chlorella cells now provide sugars to the Paramecium. This is similar to the probable process that occurred in the evolution of the eukaryotic cell.

IBHL Biology 2016 © Ashby Merson-Davies

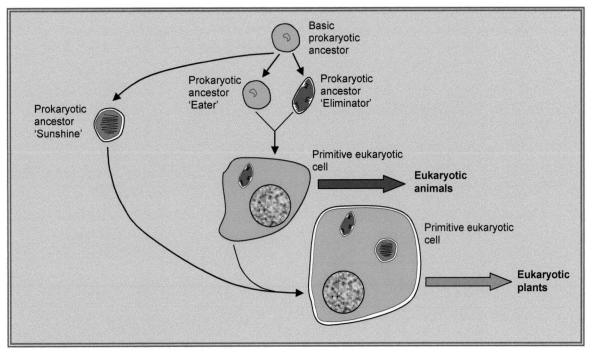

A possible origin for eukaryotic cells

Evidence for the endosymbiotic theory

➢ Chloroplasts and mitochondria both have envelopes (double membranes). The inner membrane would be that of the prokaryote that had been eaten, and the outer membrane would be formed around it from the plasma membrane of the eating prokaryote – see endocytosis – phagocytosis on page 87.

➢ Proteins on the outer membrane are largely produced by the cell DNA, whereas the proteins on the inner membrane are largely produced by the chloroplast / mitochondrial DNA.

➢ Chloroplasts and mitochondria have a loop of naked DNA as in prokaryotes.

➢ Chloroplasts and mitochondria can divide independently from the cell.

➢ When the eukaryotic cell divides there is a chance that the cytoplasm of the daughter cells will contain chloroplasts and / or mitochondria.

double membrane

➢ The ribosomes in chloroplasts and mitochondria are the same size as those in prokaryotes (70S), and smaller than those in eukaryote cytoplasm (80S).

➢ Thylakoids are similar to the structures found in blue-green bacteria.

➢ Chlorophyll *a* is the main photosynthetic pigment for both prokaryotes and eukaryotes.

➢ Mitochondrial cristae are similar to mesosomes, folded structures formed from the plasma membrane of prokaryotes and where respiration takes place.

➢ The 64 codons in the genetic code nearly always code for the same amino acid and the few exceptions have probably arisen since the common origin of life – see page 36.

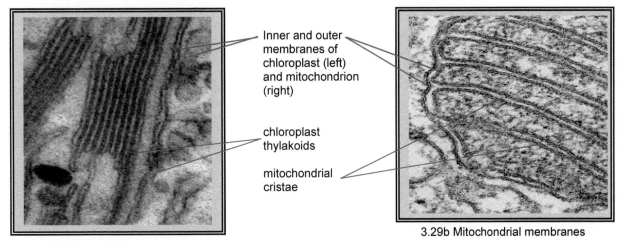

Inner and outer membranes of chloroplast (left) and mitochondrion (right)

chloroplast thylakoids

mitochondrial cristae

3.29a Chloroplast membranes

3.29b Mitochondrial membranes

Note that the inner membrane of chloroplasts is not folded whereas the inner membrane of mitochondria is.

40. Distinguish between simple and facilitated diffusion.

41. What feature of a facilitated diffusion channel makes it selective?

42. How is a facilitated diffusion channel modified in order to control the flow of the substance through the channel?

43. State one example of a facilitated transport channel.

44. State four features about osmosis.

45. Which type of membrane protein is required for active transport?

46. Why is energy necessary for active transport?

47. State one example of an active transport pump.

48. Distinguish between endocytosis and exocytosis.

49. Which one requires energy?

50. State the two types of endocytosis and distinguish between them.

51. Name the cell organelle that produces the vesicles containing protein for export.

52. Name the cell organelle that synthesises proteins for export.

IBHL Biology 2016 © Ashby Merson-Davies

53. If the percentage change in mass of potato tissue is measured in solutions of different concentration and a graph plotted of this data, how is the osmolarity of the tissue determined from the graph?
Explain your reasoning.

54. Complete the 8 white boxes of key features for each of the three types of transport.

Diffusion	Osmosis	Active transport
With the concentration gradient.		
	Transports water.	
		Requires a membrane
	Does not require ATP.	

55. What is meant by the endosymbiotic theory?

56. State the two organelles that could have resulted from endosymbiosis.

57. State four pieces of evidence for the endosymbiotic theory.

Cell division

> ➤ **Cell** division is a process called cytokinesis.
> ➤ It is preceded by **nuclear** division, either mitosis or meiosis.
> ➤ Cyclins are involved in the control of the cell cycle.

Cyclins
The cell cycle is divided into three phases – interphase, mitosis, cytokinesis.
Interphase is divided into three sub-phases.
Each phase has to be regulated to ensure everything is ready before progression to the next phase.
Regulation is carried out by enzymes called cyclin-dependent kinases, CDKs.
CDKs are controlled by a group of non-enzyme proteins called cyclins.
Each CDK has its own specific cyclin.
The CDKs are present throughout the cell cycle but the specific cyclins are synthesised and broken down at specific points in each part of the cycle.

The cell cycle

Consists of:
- Interphase,
- Mitosis,
- Cytokinesis.

DNA replication occurs towards the end of interphase in preparation for mitosis.

Nuclear division – the replicated chromosomes are separated into two nuclei.

Cell division – the cell is split into two, one nucleus in each part.

One cell continues in the cycle and the other may differentiate into a specialised cell.

Cell activities

Mitosis is division of the nucleus into two genetically identical daughter nuclei.

Interphase is an active period in the life of a cell when many cell activities occur, including transcription, translation, synthesis of other molecules, DNA replication and an increase in the number of mitochondria and chloroplasts.

Cytokinesis is division of the cell into two. The division may be equal or unequal – see page 189.
Cytokinesis is different in plant and animal cells.

Mitosis is involved in:
- ◆ Asexual reproduction,
- ◆ Embryonic development,
- ◆ Growth,
- ◆ Tissue repair.

Mitosis

Phase	Key points
Prophase	• Replicated DNA condenses by supercoiling (multiple coiling) and becomes visible under the light microscope. • Spindle microtubules start to form. • Nuclear envelope breaks down.
Metaphase	• Microtubule network completed. • Microtubules attach to centromeres. • Chromosomes move to equator of cell.
Anaphase	• Centromeres split. • Microtubules contract. • Chromosomes pulled to opposite poles.
Telophase	• Chromosomes uncoil. • Microtubules break down. • Nuclear envelope reforms. (*This is effectively the opposite of prophase*)

Note –
There are three key points for each phase.

The difference between chromosome and chromatid

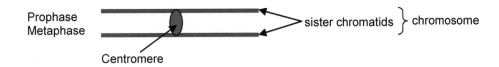

Prophase
Metaphase

sister chromatids } chromosome

Centromere

Note
The two DNA molecules formed by replication are called sister chromatids until the centromere splits at the start of anaphase. After this they are individual chromosomes.

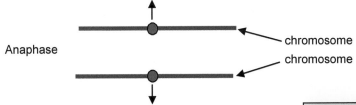

Anaphase

chromosome
chromosome

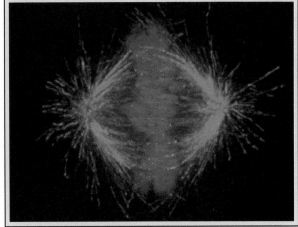

3.30 A human cell at metaphase. Chromosomes are blue, centromeres red and the spindle microtubules are green

Cell with one pair of chromosomes at interphase

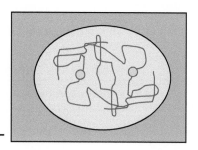

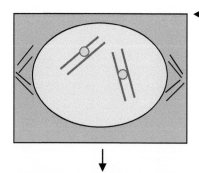

Prophase
⇒ Replicated DNA condenses by supercoiling and becomes visible under the light microscope.
⇒ Spindle microtubules start to form (from centrioles in animal cells).
⇒ Nuclear envelope breaks down.

> Remember –
> **There are three key points for each phase.**

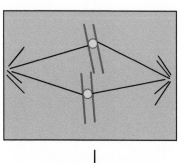

Metaphase
⇒ Microtubule network completed.
⇒ Microtubules attach to centromeres.
⇒ Chromosomes move to equator of cell.

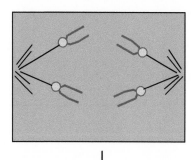

Anaphase
⇒ Centromeres split.
⇒ Microtubules contract.
⇒ Chromosomes pulled to opposite poles.

> A chromosome consists of a pair of sister chromatids, but as soon as the centromere splits the chromatids become chromosomes.

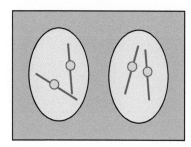

Telophase
⇒ Chromosomes uncoil.
⇒ Spindle microtubules break down.
⇒ Nuclear envelope reforms.

Cytokinesis

Two cells each with one pair of chromosomes.

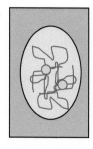 

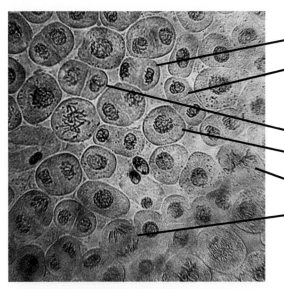

early telophase – the chromosomes are still visible

later telophase – the nuclear envelope has reformed and the start of cytokinesis can be seen

cytokinesis continues – the developing cell wall is clearly visible

prophase – the nuclear envelope is still present

metaphase

anaphase

Mitosis in plant cells

3.31 Mitosis in plant cells

Mitotic Index
This gives an indication of the amount of mitotic activity in the tissue;
The calculation is:

$$\frac{\text{number of cells at any phase of mitosis}}{\text{total number of cells}}$$

The mitotic index is a way of measuring the dividing activity of a tissue. It is especially important in assessing the effectiveness of cancer chemotherapy. The index is determined before and during treatment. If it has fallen then that indicates the treatment is working.

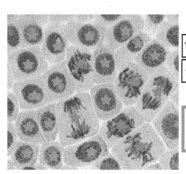

★ cells in mitosis: 6

★ cells in interphase: 16

Index $\dfrac{6}{6 + 16} = 0.27$

3.32 Calculating mitotic index

58. List the sequence of stages in the cell cycle.	59. In which phase of mitosis does the centromere split?	60. What structures attach to the centromere?
	62. In which phase of mitosis does the nuclear envelope break down?	63. When does a chromatid become a chromosome?
61. Name the phase in the cell cycle when the cell divides into two.		
64. List the sequence of phases in mitosis.	65. In which phase of mitosis does the nuclear envelope reform?	67. List four situations which involve mitosis.
	66. Name the group of chemical substances involved in the control of the cell cycle.	

68. Label the diagram.

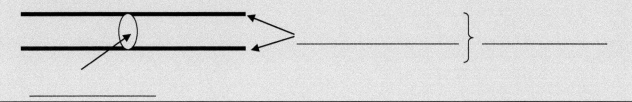

_____

_____ } _____

Cell division and cancer
- Uncontrolled cell division results in a cancerous tumour.
- Tumours can spread via both blood and lymph.
- Mutagens, oncogenes and metastasis are involved in the development of primary and secondary tumours.

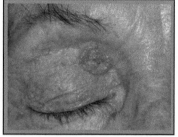

3.33 A typical appearance of nodulo-ulcerative BCC (basal cell carcinoma)

Mutagens
This is anything that causes a mutation of a cell's genome.
This could be by:
- directly affecting the structure of DNA such as a thymine dimer.
- affecting the replication of DNA.
- affecting nuclear division by damaging the microtubule mechanism or cyclin regulation.
- radiation in the electromagnetic spectrum of UV and above such as X-rays, gamma rays.
- a wide range of chemicals such as Aldrin, an organochlorine insecticide, and benzene, an industrial solvent.
- Reactive oxygen species (ROS), e.g. hydrogen peroxide. These are often natural by-products of metabolism in cells but are normally removed by the cellular antioxidants.
- Certain metals such as nickel.
- Certain viruses.

Metastasis
- The spread of cancer from one part of the body to another.
- A primary tumour develops in one part of the body but may remain there.
- It may though become metastatic where cells enter the blood or lymphatic system.
- These can lodge in another part of the body and form a secondary tumour.
- The secondary tumour has the same name as the primary, i.e. a primary tumour in the breast which spreads to the lungs is still called a breast cancer.

Oncogenes
- These are genes that, when mutated or expressed at high level, can turn a normal cell into a tumour cell.
- They are usually the genes involved in the control of the cell cycle.
- Cells that have been damaged in some way usually undergo programmed cell death called apoptosis.
- Oncogenes prevent cell death and allow the cell to survive and divide.
- Most oncogenes require an additional step such as a mutation in another gene or a viral infection to cause cancer.

The correlation between smoking and the incidence of cancer

- Smoking accounts for nearly one fifth of all cancer cases.
- Smoking causes more than four in five cases of lung cancer.
- Other cancers related to smoking include:

Tobacco smoke includes over 70 different carcinogenic (cancer causing) chemicals.

- mouth
- nose
- larynx
- oesophagus
- stomach
- bowel
- bladder
- kidney
- cervix
- ovary
- one type of breast

Graph showing the relative risk of lung cancer for men based on duration and intensity of smoking

(Graph legend)
- <10 cigarettes per day
- 10-19 cigarettes per day
- >20 cigarettes per day

(Graph: Relative risk % vs Years of smoking, x-axis: <20, 20-29, 30-39, 40-49, >50; y-axis: 0 to 40)

Between 2005 and 2010, an average of 130,659 Americans (74,300 men and 56,359 women) died of smoking attributable lung cancer each year. Exposure to second-hand smoke causes approximately 7330 lung cancer deaths among non-smokers every year.
Non-smokers have a 20-30% greater chance of developing lung cancer if they are exposed to second-hand smoke at home or at work.

Meiosis

Key points
- Most cells are diploid, i.e. they have two sets of chromosomes in each cell nucleus.
- The chromosomes are in pairs.
- Each parent contributed one of the pair.
- A haploid cell only has only one set of chromosomes.
- Meiosis is a reduction division, i.e. halves the number of chromosomes from diploid to haploid.
- One parent nucleus results in 4 daughter nuclei.
- One or more of these nuclei differentiate into a gamete.
- Halving of the chromosome number allows for a sexual life cycle with fusion of gametes.
- It results in genetic variety.

> Since you have studied mitosis you already know most of meiosis. Meiosis has two phases, but the names are the same as in mitosis with I or II added. Likewise the key facts for each stage are very similar. On the diagrams the pattern is the same as in mitosis but the purple text indicates where the five differences are.

Phase	Key points
Prophase I	Replicated DNA starts to condense by supercoiling. Spindle microtubules start to form. Homologous chromosomes line up as pairs called bivalents Crossing over may occur between non-sister chromatids within the bivalent leading to exchange of genetic material. Supercoiling / condensation completed. Nuclear envelope breaks down.
Metaphase I	Microtubule network completed. Microtubules attach to centromeres. Bivalents move to equator. Alignment is random.
Anaphase I	Centromeres do **not** split. Microtubules contract. Homologous chromosomes pulled to opposite poles. The chromosome number is halved.
Telophase I	These stages often merge with each other because they are opposite. The spindle fibre network breaks down and two new ones begin to form, often at right angles to the first one.
Cytokinesis I	*First cell division starts.*
Prophase II	
Metaphase II	Microtubule network completed. Microtubules attach to centromeres. Chromosomes move to equator.
Anaphase II	Centromeres **do** split. Microtubules contract. Chromosomes pulled to opposite poles.
Telophase II	Chromosomes uncoil. Spindle fibre network breaks down. Nuclear envelope reforms.
Cytokinesis II	*Second cell division into four haploid cells.*

Cell with one homologous
pair of chromosomes

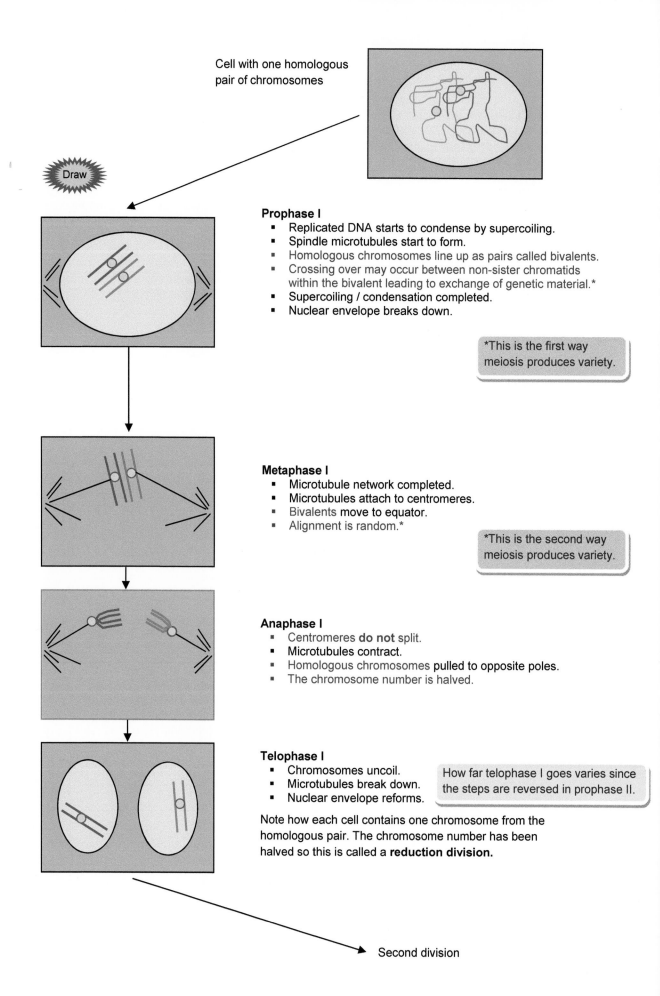

Draw

Prophase I
- Replicated DNA starts to condense by supercoiling.
- Spindle microtubules start to form.
- Homologous chromosomes line up as pairs called bivalents.
- Crossing over may occur between non-sister chromatids within the bivalent leading to exchange of genetic material.*
- Supercoiling / condensation completed.
- Nuclear envelope breaks down.

*This is the first way meiosis produces variety.

Metaphase I
- Microtubule network completed.
- Microtubules attach to centromeres.
- Bivalents move to equator.
- Alignment is random.*

*This is the second way meiosis produces variety.

Anaphase I
- Centromeres **do not** split.
- Microtubules contract.
- Homologous chromosomes pulled to opposite poles.
- The chromosome number is halved.

Telophase I
- Chromosomes uncoil.
- Microtubules break down.
- Nuclear envelope reforms.

How far telophase I goes varies since the steps are reversed in prophase II.

Note how each cell contains one chromosome from the homologous pair. The chromosome number has been halved so this is called a **reduction division.**

Second division

Cytokinesis I

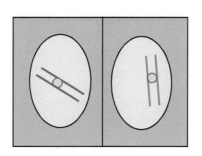

Each of these cells then undergoes the
second division of meiosis.
Only one is shown below for simplicity.
The second division is very similar to mitosis.

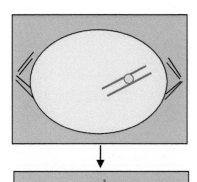

Prophase II
- Chromosomes undergo supercoiling.
- Microtubules start to form.
- Nuclear envelope breaks down.

> The amount of supercoiling
> required depends on how much
> they uncoiled during telophase I.

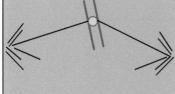

Metaphase II
- Microtubule network completed.
- Microtubules attach to centromeres.
- Chromosomes move to equator of cell.

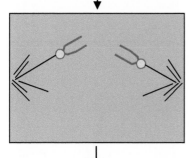

Anaphase II
- Centromeres **do** split.
- Microtubules contract.
- Chromosomes pulled to opposite poles.

> Remember – a chromosome
> consists of a pair of sister
> chromatids, but as soon as the
> centromere splits the chromatids
> become chromosomes – see
> page 94.

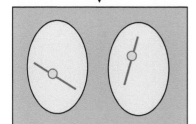

Telophase II
- Chromosomes uncoil.
- Microtubules break down.
- Nuclear envelope reforms.

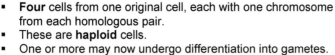

Cytokinesis II in
both cells

- **Four** cells from one original cell, each with one chromosome
  from each homologous pair.
- These are **haploid** cells.
- One or more may now undergo differentiation into gametes.
- In spermatogenesis all four differentiate into sperms.
- In oogenesis only one differentiates into a secondary oocyte
  – see page 189.

Genetic variety

Key points

➢ Sexual reproduction allows for genetic variety.
➢ Meiosis produces variety in two ways:
  • Crossing over in prophase I resulting in exchange of maternal and paternal alleles between non-sister chromatids of homologous chromosomes – see page 265.
  • Bivalents line up on equator in a random way in metaphase I – see diagram below.
➢ Variety is also produced by random fertilisation of gametes.

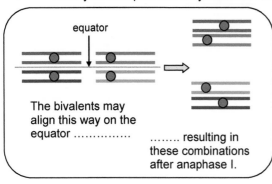
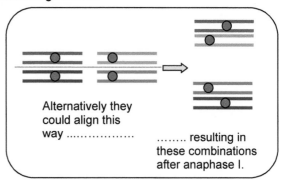

The bivalents may align this way on the equator .... resulting in these combinations after anaphase I.

Alternatively they could align this way .... resulting in these combinations after anaphase I.

How random alignment produces variety

Non-disjunction

Normally at meiosis the cell would split into four cells.

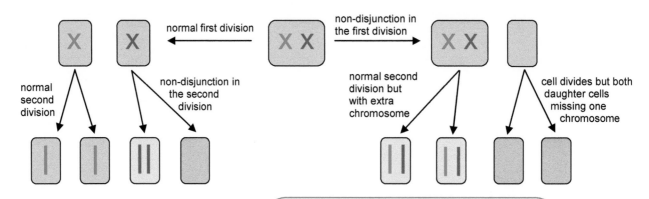

Key points

➢ Non-disjunction is when separation of homologous chromosomes or sister chromatids fails to occur.
➢ This can happen at anaphase of either the first or the second division.

normal first division

non-disjunction in the first division

normal second division

non-disjunction in the second division

normal second division but with extra chromosome

cell divides but both daughter cells missing one chromosome

If a yellow gamete is fertilised then the zygote will have one extra chromosome.
An example in humans is Down syndrome where the extra chromosome is number 21. This is called trisomy 21.

If a brown gamete is fertilised then the zygote will be missing a chromosome. An example is Turner's syndrome which has a single X chromosome.

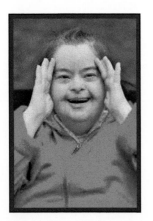

3.34 A woman with Down syndrome

Age and non-disjunction

Key points
➢ Studies have shown the significant association between advanced maternal age and chromosome 21 non-disjunction was restricted to meiotic errors in the egg.
➢ The association was not observed in sperm or in post-zygotic mitotic errors.
➢ Advanced maternal age was significantly associated with both meiosis I and meiosis II errors.
➢ Meiosis I errors were 8.5 times more likely in mothers 40 or more years old compared to mothers 20-24 years old.
➢ Meiosis II errors were 15 times more likely in mothers 40 or more years old compared to mothers 20-24 years old.

Karyotyping

 Pair of chromosomes showing matching banding pattern.

> Karyotyping is arranging the chromosomes according to their size and banding pattern to form a karyogram for that cell.

Key facts
➢ Used in pre-natal diagnosis of chromosome abnormalities.
➢ Observing major changes in chromosome structure due to mutations such as translocation or duplication.
➢ Observing changes in chromosome number as in Down syndrome.
➢ Foetal cells are collected using:
  • amniocentesis or
  • chorionic villus sampling.
➢ Risks – there is a small risk of injuring the fetus or causing a miscarriage.

⬅ The upper row is the standard banding pattern.

⬅ The lower row is a cut-out of the chromosomes from a photograph of prophase using the standard banding pattern to match the pairs.

A karyogram of a normal male

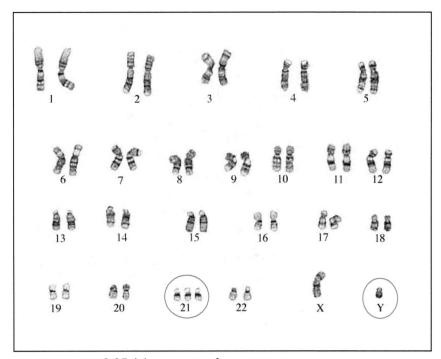

3.35 A karyogram of a person.
They are male – they have a Y chromosome.
They have Down syndrome – 3x chromosome 21.

69. How many chromosomes are there in each body cell of a person with Down syndrome?	70. What is karyotyping?	71. What is the purpose of karyotyping?
72. State two ways cells are collected for karyotyping?		

73. What is non-disjunction?

74. Identify these stages of the cell cycle.

3.35

Glossary

ASEPTATE	A septum is a dividing wall: aseptate means without a septum.
CONTRACTILE VACUOLE	A special structure found in some simple fresh water organisms that collects the water entering the cell via osmosis and then pumps it out of the cell.
EXCRETION	Removal of the waste products of metabolism.
FACILITATE	To make easier.
GENOME	In prokaryotes it is all the information in the single circular chromosome plus plasmids. In eukaryotic animals it is all the information in a haploid set of chromosomes plus mitochondrial DNA. In eukaryotic plants it is all the information in a haploid set of chromosomes plus mitochondrial DNA plus chloroplast DNA.
HYDROPHILIC	Water loving.
HYDROPHOBIC	Water hating.
HYPERTONIC	A solution that has a higher solute concentration than the one it is being compared with.
HYPOTONIC	A solution that has a lower solute concentration than the one it is being compared with.
ISOTONIC	A solution that has the same solute concentration as the one it is being compared with.
KINETIC ENERGY	The energy an object possesses due to its motion.
MESOSOME	In prokaryotic cells the plasma membrane extends inwards to form a folded structure containing the enzymes for respiration.
OSMOLARITY	A measure of the concentration of osmotically active solutes in a solution.
PARTIALLY PERMEABLE	Some substances are able to diffuse through the membrane.
SECRETION	Release from a cell by exocytosis of a useful substance e.g. hormone.
SEM : TEM	Scanning electron micrograph : Transmission electron micrograph.
SOLUTE	A substance that dissolves in a solvent to form a solution.
SOLVENT	A liquid that dissolves a solute.
WATER POTENTIAL	The tendency of water to move from one region to another. The more dilute the solution the higher the water potential.

Stem cell glossary

TOTIPOTENT	Cells which can differentiate into all cell types because all their genes are functional. This can lead to development of a complete living organism.
PLURIPOTENT	Cells which can differentiate into nearly all cell types and arise from totipotent cells as a result of some genes being switched off. This makes them valuable for stem cell therapy. Read about how adult cells can be turned into pluripotent cells - induced pluripotent cells - by following this link. http://stemcells.nih.gov/info/basics/pages/basics10.aspx
MULTIPOTENT	Cells which can differentiate into a small range of closely related cell types. An example is haematopoietic stem cells (HSCs) found in bone marrow which can make every type of blood cell – red cells, white cells and platelets.
OLIGOPOTENT	Cells which can only differentiate into a few cell types.
UNIPOTENT	Cells which can produce only one cell type, their own, but have the property of being able to keep dividing which distinguishes them from non-stem cells. An example would be the germinal epithelial cells in the testis.

Answers to Grey Box Questions   **Underlined words are required.**

1. a. Cells are the smallest units of life. b. Living organisms are composed of one or more cells.
    c. Cells come from pre-existing cells.
2. See text page for 68 examples.
3. Boiled broth and sealed flask – broth remained sterile. Opened flask – broth went bad.
4. Life could not arise spontaneously.
5. Decreases.
6. Large central vacuole. microvilli. becoming columnar or flattened.
7. Act as an exchange surface between the cytoplasm and the cell's environment.
8. Adult tissues (e.g. bone marrow). Embryos. Umbilical cord blood.
9. age 70.
10. They are able to differentiate into specialised cell types. They can continue to divide.
11. See page 72.   12. 70S.   13. Plasmids.
14. Flagella are long, attached at one end and few in number. Pili cover the surface and are short.
15. Binary fission.
16. 22mm = 22,000,000nm   22,000,000 ÷ 200 = 110,000× magnification.
17. See page 73.
18. 80S.
19. Not.   Enclosed.
    –   Attached to proteins.
    Circular.   Linear.
    Absent.   Present.
    70S.   80S.
20. Starch.   21. Glycogen.   22. Mitochondrion. Chloroplast. Nucleus.   23. Envelope.
24. The cell contains membrane bound structures that carry out specific functions.
25. See table on page 80.
26. Contains genetic material. Ribosomes. Lysosome. Modifies and packs proteins into vesicles.
    Rough endoplasmic reticulum. Release of energy through <u>aerobic</u> respiration.
27. Protein + carbohydrate.
28. Integral protein – partially or completely embedded in the membrane. Peripheral protein – on the
    surface of the phospholipid bilayer.
29. 10nm.   30. Integral.   31. Cholesterol. <u>Saturated</u> fatty acids.   32. Amphipathic.
33. Fatty acid chains.   34. Mutual attraction between the hydrophobic tails.
35. One end is hydrophilic and the other end hydrophobic. Each side of the membrane must be hydrophilic.
36. Its fluidity – there are no chemical bonds between the phospholipids.
37. See the list on page 83.
38. Plant.
39. Davson-Danielli model – sandwich, phospholipid bilayer between two layers of protein.
    Singer-Nicholson model – fluid mosaic, phospholipid bilayer with integral and peripheral proteins
    dotted around.
40. Simple – diffusion through the phospholipid bilayer. Facilitated – diffusion through specific integral
    channel proteins.
41. Specific binding site for the substance being transported.   42. Gated.
43. Sodium ion / potassium ion channel in neuron membrane.
44. Diffusion of water; with the concentration gradient; membrane required; no energy required / passive.
45. Integral.   46. Transport is against the concentration gradient.
47. Sodium – potassium pump in neuron membrane / sodium – potassium – chloride pump in kidney.
48. Endocytosis is taking substances into the cell; exocytosis is removing substances from the cell.
49. Endocytosis.
50. Pinocytosis – taking in water / solution. Phagocytosis – taking in particles.
51. Golgi apparatus.
52. Rough endoplasmic reticulum.
53. The osmolarity is the point where the change in mass is zero. This is because no water is
    entering or leaving the cell by osmosis – the external solution therefore has the same
    concentration as the cytoplasm.

54. Diffusion column – transports a range of substances; does not require a membrane; does not require ATP.
Osmosis column – with the concentration gradient; requires a membrane.
Active transport column – against the concentration gradient; transports a range of substances; Requires ATP.

55. Eukaryotic cells have evolved from ancestral prokaryotic cells that have joined together to co-operate.

56. Chloroplasts and mitochondria.

57. Chloroplasts and mitochondria have 70S ribosomes. These ribosomes synthesise several proteins used by the organelle. They have envelopes. They replicate themselves. They have their own ring of DNA.

58. Mitosis – cytokinesis – interphase. 59. Anaphase. 60. Spindle microtubules.
61. Cytokinesis. 62. Prophase. 63. When the centromere splits.
64. Prophase – metaphase – anaphase – telophase.
65. Telophase. 66. Cyclins.
67. Growth; asexual reproduction; tissue repair; embryonic development.
68. Sister chromatids. Chromosome. 69. 47.
70. Arranging photographs of the chromosomes in their pairs according to their size and banding pattern.
71. To look for abnormalities – prenatal diagnosis.
72. Amniocentesis. Chorionic villus sampling.
73. The failure of homologous chromosomes or sister chromatids to separate during anaphase I or II.

74.

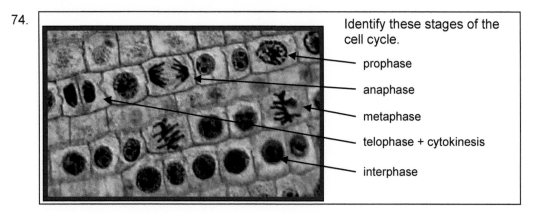

Identify these stages of the cell cycle.

- prophase
- anaphase
- metaphase
- telophase + cytokinesis
- interphase

Self-test Quiz

1. The cell theory states that:
   a. living organisms are composed of cells,
   b. cells come from pre-existing cells,
   c. cells are the smallest unit of life,
   d. all of the above.

2. A description of emergent properties could include:
   a. cell growth is in an outward direction,
   b. germinating seeds emerge above the soil,
   c. stem cells emerge by differentiating into specialised cells,
   d. specialised groups of cells interact to form a functional unit better than the individual cells.

3. Which of the following best describes stem cells?
   a. They are cells found in the stems of plants.
   b. They are cells able to divide and differentiate along different pathways.
   c. They are cells that have differentiated into specialised tissues.
   d. They are cells that have had part of their genome switched off.

4. Which of the following statements about Stargardt's disease is correct?
    a. It is a disease of the eye which may be treatable with stem cell therapy.
    b. Stem cells can be used to replace damaged light receptor cells.
    c. Treatment requires the use of adult stem cells.
    d. Embryonic stem cells injected into the blood stream migrate to the eye.

5. Which of the following best describes the function of the Golgi apparatus?
    a. It synthesises the proteins used in lysosomes.
    b. It buds off vesicles which combine with the rough endoplasmic reticulum.
    c. Vesicles from the rough endoplasmic reticulum fuse with it.
    d. Vesicles released from the tips fuse with the nuclear envelope.

6. Which of the following statements about prokaryotic cells is correct?
    a. They can divide by binary fission.
    b. Meiosis is an important phase in their life cycle.
    c. They have fewer organelles than eukaryotic cells.
    d. They do not have a cell wall.

7. A characteristic of both prokaryotic and eukaryotic cells is:
    a. possession of a nucleus,
    b. compartmentalisation,
    c. ribosomes in the cytoplasm,
    d. presence of membranous cytoplasmic organelles.

8. In a prokaryotic cell:
    a. the ribosomes are found on the rough endoplasmic reticulum,
    b. the ribosomes are smaller than in the eukaryotic cell,
    c. the lysosomes contain digestive enzymes,
    d. the nucleus contains a single linear molecule of naked DNA.

9. The diagram below shows part of a cell membrane. Which molecule is an integral protein?
    a. One,
    b. Two ,
    c. Three,
    d. Four.

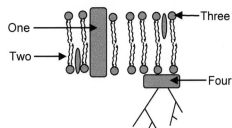

10. The main molecules forming membranes are:
    a. phospholipids and proteins,
    b. lipids and polysaccharides,
    c. carbohydrates and lipids,
    d. lipids.

11. The function of cholesterol in a membrane is to:
    a. make it more fatty,
    b. increase the hydrophobic property of the membrane,
    c. help to hold the peripheral proteins in place,
    d. reduce the permeability of the membrane to certain solutes.

12. The diagram below shows part of a cell membrane. Which molecule is a glycoprotein?
    a. One,
    b. Two,
    c. Three,
    d. Four.

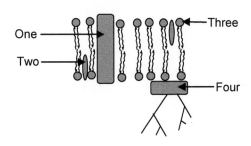

13. Which of the following statements is correct?
    a. Active transport uses energy from ATP to transfer molecules across a membrane against a concentration gradient.
    b. Diffusion is the movement of water from a concentrated solution to a weak solution.
    c. Osmosis requires energy from ATP.
    d. Molecules can only diffuse across a membrane.

14. Which of the following statements is correct?
    a. A phospholipid has hydrophobic regions at both ends of the molecule.
    b. A membrane is made up of two layers of protein with a hydrophobic core.
    c. Proteins embedded in a membrane can act as transport channels.
    d. The presence of cholesterol in a membrane is harmful.

15. Which is the best description of vesicle movement within a cell?
    a. from the plasma membrane to the Golgi apparatus,
    b. from the Golgi apparatus to the rER,
    c. from the plasma membrane to the rER,
    d. from the rER to the Golgi apparatus.

16. Facilitated diffusion means:
    a. The transfer of substances through an integral protein channel in a membrane against a concentration gradient.
    b. Using ATP to facilitate the diffusion of substances from one part of a cell to another.
    c. Using a protein carrier and energy to diffuse substances rapidly down a concentration gradient.
    d. The diffusion of substances through an integral protein channel in a membrane.

17. As a cell increases in size:
    a. the surface area to volume ratio decreases,
    b. the surface area to volume ratio increases,
    c. the surface area to volume ratio does not change,
    d. the surface area to volume ratio begins to decrease only after the cell reaches a certain size.

18. If cells or tissues are going to be used in medical procedures then they must be bathed in a solution with the same osmolarity as the blood. This is:
    a. to allow osmosis to occur,
    b. to maintain the same ion concentrations in both cells and blood,
    c. to allow active transport of glucose and other nutrients into the cells,
    d. to prevent osmosis from occurring.

19. In an investigation, the osmolarity of the cells in a piece of potato tissue bathed in sucrose solutions of known concentration could be found when:
    a. the volume of the sucrose solution begins to decrease,
    b. when the mass of the potato tissue begins to decrease,
    c. when the mass of the potato tissue remains unchanged,
    d. the volume of the sucrose solution begins to increase.

20. In multicellular organisms cells differentiate because:
    a. some of their genes are expressed but not others,
    b. some genes are lost from the nucleus,
    c. not all genes are passed on when the cell reproduces,
    d. the nucleus is lost.

21. Which of the following statements is correct?
    a. Animal cells are round whereas plant cells are square.
    b. Plant cell walls are enclosed in membrane.
    c. Both plant and animal cells have 80S ribosomes.
    d. Animal cells contain more organelles than plant cells.

IBHL Biology 2016 © Ashby Merson-Davies

22. The data in the table below shows the normal concentration of two ions inside and outside the nerve cell of a squid.

| Ions | Concentration / mmoles dm^{-3} | |
	Inside	Outside
Potassium K$^+$	0.400	0.020
Chloride Cl$^-$	0.120	0.560

This information shows that:
   a. potassium ions diffuse into nerve cells whereas chloride ions diffuse out,
   b. osmosis creates diffusion gradients for these two ions,
   c. potassium ions are moved out of the cell by active transport whereas chloride ions are actively moved in,
   d. chloride ions are moved out of the cell by active transport whereas potassium ions are actively moved in.

23. Which of the following statements could be used as evidence for the endosymbiotic theory?
   a. Prokaryotic cells have 80S ribosomes whereas eukaryotic cells have 70S ribosomes.
   b. Both prokaryotic and eukaryotic cells have ribosomes.
   c. Chloroplasts and mitochondria have an envelope.
   d. Chloroplasts and mitochondria do not have organelles.

24. Which of the following events occurs during mitosis?
   a. DNA replication,
   b. replication of organelles,
   c. Splitting of the centromeres,
   d. Splitting of the cell.

25. During which phase of meiosis could crossing over occur?
   a. Prophase I,
   b. Prophase II,
   c. Metaphase I,
   d. Metaphase II.

26. Which one of the following molecules is involved in the control of the cell cycle?
   a. cyclins,
   b. cholesterol,
   c. carbohydrate,
   d. glycoprotein.

27. Several pieces of tissue from two different types of potato were bathed in salt solutions of differing concentrations and their percentage change in mass measured over a period of one hour.

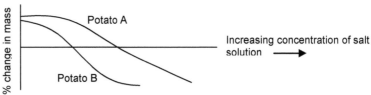

Which one of the following statements is correct?
   a. There were more pieces of potato A then potato B.
   b. The pieces of potato B were smaller than the pieces of potato A.
   c. The cytoplasm of potato A cells had a lower solute concentration than potato B cells.
   d. The cytoplasm of potato B cells had a lower solute concentration than potato A cells.

28. A root tip was stained and observed under the light microscope. In the field of view there were 22 cells that were in one of the four phases of mitosis and 88 that were in interphase. The mitotic index was:
    a. 0.25,
    b. 0.2,
    c. 5.0,
    d. 4.0.

29. Karyotyping is a process whereby:
    a. genes are sorted according to size,
    b. genetic abnormalities can be marked on chromosomes,
    c. the number of chromosomes can be counted,
    d. chromosomes are sorted according to size and structure.

30. Which of the following shows a correct sequence of stages of the first division of meiosis?
    a. Prophase I, metaphase I, telophase I, anaphase I,
    b. Prophase I, anaphase I, metaphase I, telophase I,
    c. Prophase I, metaphase I, anaphase I, telophase I,
    d. Prophase I, telophase I, metaphase I, anaphase I.

31. Non-disjunction occurs as a result of:
    a. the two parts of meiosis occurring in reverse order,
    b. a failure in the spindle fibre network of microtubules,
    c. genes becoming lost,
    d. a failure in the process of cytokinesis.

32. Down syndrome is:
    a. an example of a trisomy,
    b. a result of non-disjunction in the sex chromosomes,
    c. due to a gene mutation,
    d. an example of karyotyping.

33. A haploid cell is one in which:
    a. only one of each pair of chromosomes is present,
    b. there are 23 chromosomes,
    c. the sex chromosomes are missing,
    d. there is no nucleus.

Chapter Four

Cell Metabolism

Metabolism is the web of all the enzyme catalysed reactions in a cell or organism.

Two major metabolic pathways are photosynthesis and respiration. Photosynthesis stores energy from sunlight in organic compounds such as glucose, and respiration then releases this energy which can be used for metabolic work such as active transport or protein synthesis.

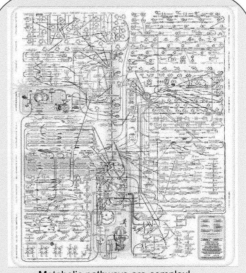

Metabolic pathways are complex!
Designed by Donald Nicholson
©2002 International Union of Biochemistry and Molecular Biology

Metabolism
Key points
➢ Life is based carbon compounds.
➢ Four major groups of carbon compounds are:
  • carbohydrates,
  • lipids,
  • proteins,
  • nucleic acids.
➢ Metabolic pathways consist of chains and cycles of enzyme catalysed reactions.
➢ Metabolism is the web of all the enzyme catalysed reactions in a cell or organism.
➢ Anabolism is:
  • the synthesis of complex organic molecules from simpler molecules,
  • including formation of macromolecules from monomers by condensation reactions.
➢ Catabolism is:
  • the breakdown of complex organic molecules into simpler molecules,
  • including hydrolysis of macromolecules into monomers.

> Glycolysis is a chain reaction,
> The Calvin cycle and Kreb's cycle are cyclic reactions.

Enzymes
Key points
➢ Enzymes are key molecules in metabolism.
➢ They lower the activation energy so that reactions can take place at physiological temperatures.
➢ The activity of an enzyme can be controlled by end-product inhibition – see pages 114–5.
➢ This allows metabolic pathways to be regulated.

Lock and key model of enzyme action

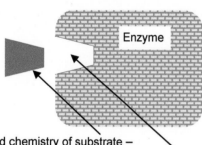

Shape and chemistry of substrate – corresponds to shape and chemistry of active site.

Key points
➢ Enzymes are large molecules folded to form a three-dimensional globular structure.
➢ Thus the minimum level is tertiary – see page 37.
➢ The folding creates a specifically shaped three-dimensional 'pocket', the active site, on the surface.
➢ The substrate or substrates fit into the active site.
➢ The chemical properties of the active site match those of the substrates so they are chemically attached.
➢ Both enzyme and substrate(s) are moving around randomly in solution.
➢ Thus they will collide and the substrate(s) enter the active site.
➢ The substrates are brought together in the correct orientation for catalysis to occur.
➢ Enzymes can catalyse both catabolic and anabolic reactions.

Calculating rates of reaction
Example
An investigation with yeast was carried out which measured the volume of carbon released over time and the data plotted.

Rate of reaction =
$$\frac{\text{volume of carbon dioxide released}}{\text{time}}$$
$$= \frac{40 - 15}{20}$$
$$= 1.25 \text{ cm}^3 \text{ s}^{-1}$$

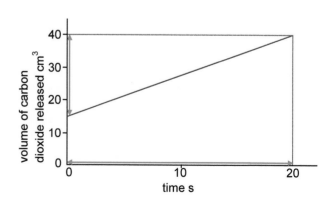

How to calculate a rate of reaction

Factors affecting enzyme action

Key background points

➢ Enzymes are proteins.
➢ They are large, complex folded molecules held in shape by, mostly, weak bonds.
➢ Increasing temperature makes atoms and molecules move more quickly.
➢ Hydrogen bonds and ionic bonds are affected by changes in pH – see page 39.

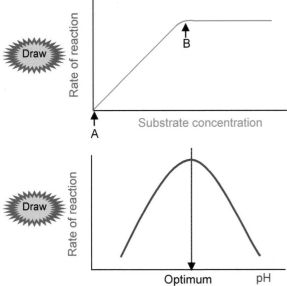

- We assume here that the amount of enzyme is fixed and therefore the number of active sites is constant.
- As substrate concentration increases between A and B more collisions occur with enzyme molecules and so more reactions occur.
- At point B all the active sites are occupied by substrate at any one time and so there can be no further increase in reaction rate.

- Enzymes are large protein molecules folded into a complex three-dimensional shape.
- This shape is held in place by bonds (see page 37) and these are strongest at the optimum pH.
- Changing the pH affects these bonds and so the shape of the molecule, and hence the active site, changes.
- If the substrate can no longer bind to the active site then the reaction rate drops.
- Note the symmetry of the curve.

- Note the asymmetry of this curve compared to the pH one.
- There is an approximately exponential increase up to the optimum temperature and then a sharp drop.
- Temperature increases the molecular movement and so in the solution the molecules collide more frequently and with more energy.
- This makes it more likely that the reaction occurs.
- However beyond the optimum temperature the amino acids within the protein are moving so much that weak bonds are broken and the molecule begins to fall apart.
- Once again the shape of the active site no longer fits the shape of the substrate and the reaction cannot take place.

Enzymes and activation energy

Key points

➢ In order for a chemical reaction to start it usually requires an input of energy.
➢ This is called the activation energy. (You might perhaps have done a practical using Benedict's reagent to test for sugar. This requires an input of heat energy).
➢ The activation energy is required to get the substrate into its transition state.
➢ The function of enzymes is to lower the activation energy so that the reaction takes place at physiological temperatures, generally between -5 and 45^0C.
➢ Remember:
  - enzyme **E** binds to substrate(s) **S** to form an enzyme-substrate complex **ES**;
  - reaction occurs resulting in an enzyme-product(s) complex **EP**;
  - product(s) **P** released from enzyme.

$$E + S \rightarrow ES \rightarrow EP \rightarrow E + P$$

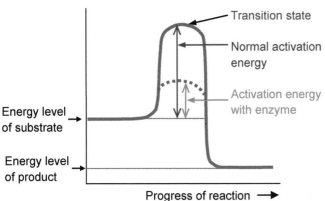

The graph shows an exothermic reaction, i.e. energy is given out.

Enzyme inhibition

1. Competitive

Key points
- ➤ Substrate and inhibitor have similar shapes.
- ➤ They compete for the active site.

An example is
shown in green

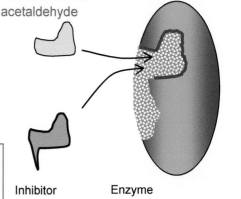

Normal substrate
acetaldehyde

---

* In the liver the metabolic pathway is:

$$ethanol \longrightarrow acetaldehyde \xrightarrow{\textit{aldehyde dehydrogenase}} acetate$$

Disulfiram is a drug used to help recovering alcoholics. Acetaldehyde is not broken down in the liver and its accumulation in the blood causes severe headache and nausea.

Inhibitor
Disulfiram *

Enzyme
aldehyde dehydrogena...

2. Non-competitive

Key points
- ➤ Inhibitor has its own binding site.
- ➤ Substrate and inhibitor do not compete for the active site.
- ➤ Binding of the inhibitor causes a conformational change in the active site, i.e. changes its shape, preventing binding of substrate.

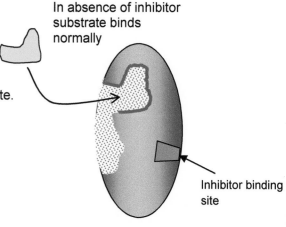

In absence of inhibitor
substrate binds
normally

Inhibitor binding
site

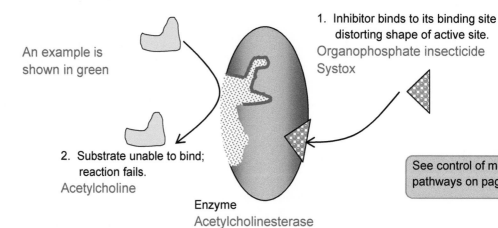

An example is
shown in green

1. Inhibitor binds to its binding site distorting shape of active site.
Organophosphate insecticide
Systox

2. Substrate unable to bind; reaction fails.
Acetylcholine

Enzyme
Acetylcholinesterase

See control of metabolic pathways on page 114.

Graphical representation of inhibition

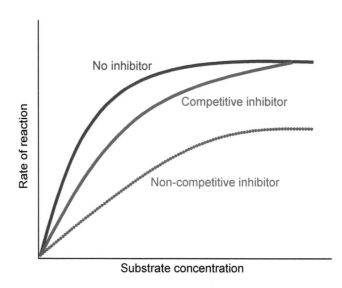

Graph showing the effect of a fixed concentration of inhibitor on the rate of a reaction when substrate concentration changes.

At higher substrate concentrations the relative amount of competitive inhibitor becomes so low it has no effect.

Since the non-competitive inhibitor binds to a different site it will always reduce the rate of reaction.

IBHL Biology 2016 © Ashby Merson-Davies

1. What is catabolism?

2. What is the minimum level of protein structure for an enzyme?

3. What is an ionic bond?

4. Explain why an ionic bond breaks when the pH decreases?

5. What is meant by the term 'denaturing'?

6. What is the name of the model of enzyme-substrate interaction?

7. State the region of an enzyme where the substrate binds.

8. What property must this region have for the substrate to bind?

9. Draw a graph to show the effect of substrate concentration on reaction rate.

10. Explain the shape of the graph.

11. What is the opposite of catabolism?

12. What is the characteristic feature of molecules in solution which allows catalysis to take place?

13. What do enzymes do to activation energy?

14. Distinguish between competitive and non-competitive inhibition.

15. Why does a competitive inhibitor have no effect on reaction rate at higher substrate concentrations?

Enzymes in biotechnology

> ➢ Enzymes are widely used in industry.
> ➢ It is often useful to immobilise the enzyme by fixing it to an inactive substance.
> ➢ An example is the production of lactose-free milk.

Production of lactose-free milk

Key points
- ➢ Many adults are intolerant of the lactose in milk.
- ➢ This is because as they get older the gene producing lactase gets switched off.
- ➢ Lactose is a disaccharide and cannot be absorbed by the gut.
- ➢ The lactose then gets fermented by bacteria in the large intestine resulting in nausea, abdominal pain and diarrhoea.
- ➢ Milk is treated with lactase and this breaks down the lactose to the monosaccharides glucose and galactose which are easily absorbed by the gut.
- ➢ Lactase is obtained from the fungus *K.lactis*.
- ➢ The lactase is often immobilised in alginate beads and the milk passed over it.

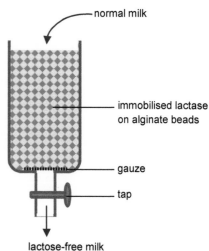

normal milk

immobilised lactase on alginate beads

gauze

tap

lactose-free milk

A simple laboratory set-up for producing lactose-free milk

Advantages of immobilised enzyme

Key points
- ➢ It can be used in a continuous flow system making it very efficient.
- ➢ The product is not mixed with the enzyme so no purification process is needed.
- ➢ Since enzyme is not lost production time can be prolonged.
- ➢ The enzyme can be recovered to use again making the process more economical.

Uses of lactose-free milk

Key points
- ➢ The milk can be drunk by lactose-intolerant people as a source of calcium and vitamins.
- ➢ It is used in the production of ice cream as lactose crystallises when cold and makes the ice cream granular. The glucose and galactose remain dissolved and so the ice cream is smoother.
- ➢ In yoghurt production bacteria ferment lactose slowly but ferment glucose and galactose much more quickly making production faster.
- ➢ Lactose is not a sweet tasting sugar whereas glucose and galactose are. By changing the lactose into these two sugars foods such as yoghurt and ice cream made from lactose-free milk need less added sugar to make them taste sweet.

Controlling metabolic pathways by end-product inhibition

> Refer back to non-competitive inhibition on page 112.

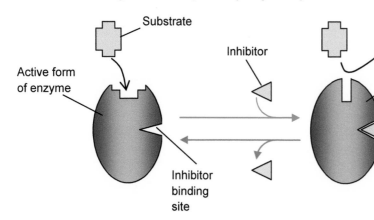

Substrate

Inhibitor

Enzyme inactivated

Active form of enzyme

Inhibitor binding site

Key points
- ➢ The inhibitor binds to the inhibitor binding site.
- ➢ This causes a conformational change which distorts the shape of the active site.
- ➢ The substrate cannot bind.
- ➢ If the inhibitor is removed the shape of the active site is restored.

IBHL Biology 2016 © Ashby Merson-Davies

Example

- Threonine and isoleucine are amino acids.
- Threonine is converted to isoleucine.
- The first enzyme in the pathway is threonine deaminase.
- When isoleucine is being used the synthesis pathway continues.
- If isoleucine demand drops then it accumulates.
- It binds to threonine deaminase and inhibits it.
- If demand rises again the inhibition is removed and the pathway is reactivated.

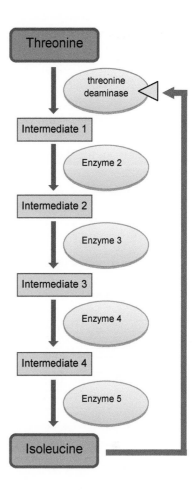

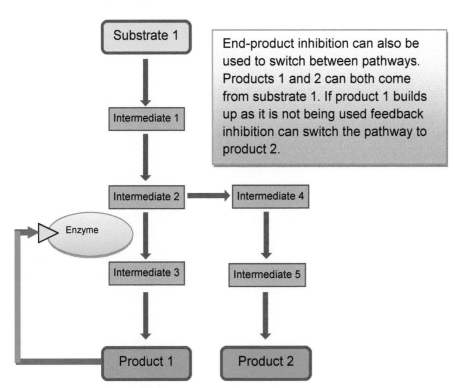

End-product inhibition can also be used to switch between pathways. Products 1 and 2 can both come from substrate 1. If product 1 builds up as it is not being used feedback inhibition can switch the pathway to product 2.

Oxidation and reduction

Key points

➢ Oxidation and reduction are two common pathways in metabolism.
➢ The reactions always go together as two reactants are involved – as one reactant is oxidised the other is reduced.

Remember OIL RIG for electrons.
Oxidation **I**s **L**oss of electrons;
Reduction **I**s **G**ain of electrons.

Oxidation is also gain of oxygen or loss of hydrogen.
Reduction is also loss of oxygen or gain of hydrogen.

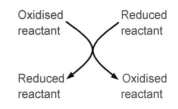

Biochemical pathways

In Biology the biochemical pathways can be much simplified by focusing just on the number of carbon atoms in the molecule. Remember though that the hydrogen and oxygen atoms are still there but are not shown.

This means that in an oxidation or reduction reaction nothing appears to happen as the number of carbon atoms remains the same, for example, the oxidation of lactate to pyruvate can be written simply as ....

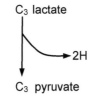

though what has actually happened is ......

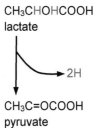

The phosphate group

This occurs frequently in pathways. When it is part of a molecule it is written simply as P, e.g. glucose phosphate is C_6P; when it is a free phosphate ion it is written as Pi – **P**hosphate **i**on.

Use of the terms diphosphate and bisphosphate

Both mean that the molecule has two phosphate groups attached to it. Di- means the two phosphates are attached to each other; bis- means the two phosphates are attached to different parts of the molecule.

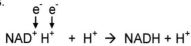

Adenosine diphosphate

$$\begin{array}{ccc} P & & P \\ | & & | \\ C-C-C-C-C-C \end{array}$$

Hexose 1, 6-bisphosphate

Electron carriers – hydrogen carrying coenzymes

There are several reactions where oxidation of the substrate occurs by dehydrogenation. When the hydrogen is removed it is transferred to a hydrogen-carrying coenzyme. Three of these are used.

Oxidised state	Reduced state
NAD^+ ⟷	$NADH + H^+$
$NADP^+$ ⟷	$NADPH + H^+$
FAD ⟷	$FADH_2$

The reduced state can also be simply described as reduced NAD, reduced NADP and reduced FAD.
The reaction is reversible.

Remember that a hydrogen atom consists of a proton H^+ and an electron e^-. The reduction reaction
$NAD^+ + 2H \rightarrow NADH + H^+$ can be re-written as $NAD^+ + 2H^+ + 2e^- \rightarrow NADH + H^+$
What has happened is:

$$\begin{array}{c} e^- \quad e^- \\ \downarrow \quad \downarrow \\ NAD^+ H^+ \; + \; H^+ \rightarrow NADH + H^+ \end{array}$$

---

16. Is oxidation loss or gain of electrons?

17. Is reduction loss or gain of hydrogen?

18. Which type of inhibition is used for control of metabolic pathways?

19. Give an example of feedback control stating the starting substrate, the final product and the enzyme that is inhibited.

20. What is meant by the term conformational change?

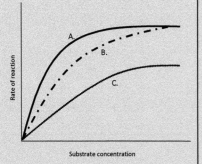

21. The graph on the left shows the effect of inhibitors. What are the lines A, B and C?

A.

B.

C.

22. What is an immobilised enzyme?

23. State one example of industrial use of an immobilised enzyme.

24. State two reasons why your example is of commercial value.

25. State two advantages of using an immobilised enzyme.

Photosynthesis

> *In all of the biochemical pathways in this chapter the biochemistry has been simplified to show only the key stages. Intermediate steps have been missed out in several places but you do not need to know these.*

Key points

- Photosynthesis is the production of carbon compounds in cells using light energy.
- Visible white light from the sun is composed of a range of wavelengths (colours).
- Red has the longest wavelength and violet the shortest.
- Chlorophyll absorbs red and blue light most effectively and reflects green light.
- Visible light has wavelengths between 400 and 700nm.

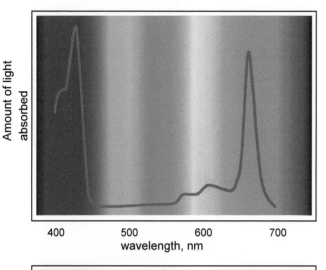

The **absorption spectrum** of chlorophyll shows how much of a particular wavelength is absorbed by the pigments.

Draw

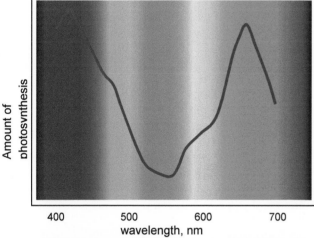

An **action spectrum** shows how much photosynthesis takes place at a particular wavelength.

Draw

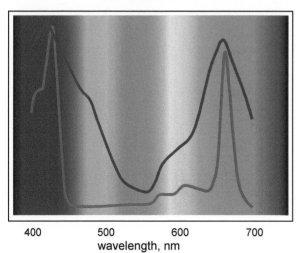

If the two are superimposed this clearly shows the close correlation, indicating that the light energy absorbed is used in the process of photosynthesis.

The difference between the two is because there are additional pigments in chloroplasts which absorb other wavelengths.

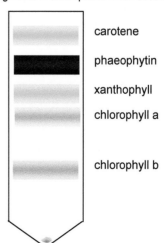

carotene

phaeophytin

xanthophyll

chlorophyll a

chlorophyll b

Diagram of chloroplast pigments separated by simple paper chromatography

Factors affecting the rate of photosynthesis

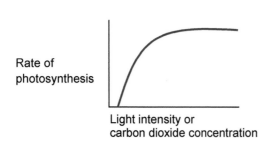

Rate of photosynthesis

Light intensity or
carbon dioxide concentration

1. **Light intensity**
   As the intensity increases there comes a point when all the chlorophyll molecules are saturated and cannot accept any more light.
   A minimum intensity is required before photosynthesis starts.

2. **Carbon dioxide**
   This is a substrate for an enzyme controlled reaction, and once all the enzyme active sites are used up the reaction cannot go faster. Refer back to the section on enzymes on page 110.
   A minimum concentration of carbon dioxide is required before photosynthesis starts.

3. **Temperature**
   The shape of the graph should be familiar. (Refer back to the section on enzymes.) Many of the reactions of photosynthesis are enzyme controlled and hence the rate of photosynthesis shows the same shape.

Rate of photosynthesis

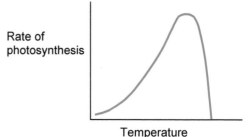

Temperature

Limiting factors

Key point

➢ When a chemical process depends on more than one essential condition being favourable, its rate is limited by that factor which is nearest its minimum value.

Imagine a pizza production line. To make 10 pizzas requires:

10 bases	4 mushrooms
10 tomatoes	25 anchovies
150g grated cheese	20 olives

But suppose you only have 12 olives. This means that you can only make 6 pizzas, so the olives are the limiting factor.
Again suppose you have 12 olives but now only 5 tomatoes. Now you can only make 5 pizzas as this time it is the tomato that is the limiting factor.

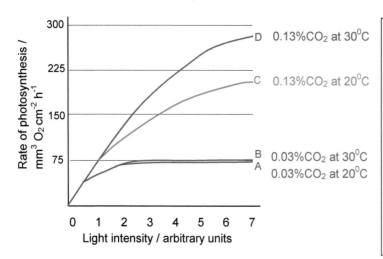

Curves A and B are identical even though the temperature for B is 10°C higher. This indicates that temperature is not the limiting factor.

If the carbon dioxide concentration is raised but the temperature kept at 20°C the curve rises to C, indicating that the limiting factor for A and B was CO_2 concentration.

If the temperature is now raised to 30°C the curve rises to D, indicating that the limiting factor for curve C was temperature.

The chloroplast

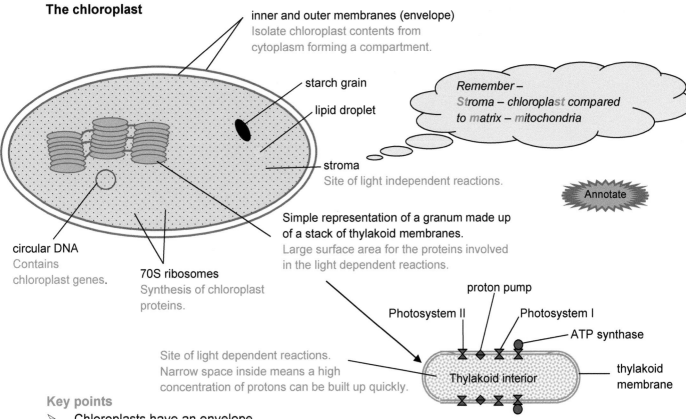

inner and outer membranes (envelope)
Isolate chloroplast contents from cytoplasm forming a compartment.

starch grain

lipid droplet

stroma
Site of light independent reactions.

Remember –
Stroma – chloroplast compared to matrix – mitochondria

Annotate

circular DNA
Contains chloroplast genes.

70S ribosomes
Synthesis of chloroplast proteins.

Simple representation of a granum made up of a stack of thylakoid membranes.
Large surface area for the proteins involved in the light dependent reactions.

proton pump

Photosystem II

Photosystem I

ATP synthase

Site of light dependent reactions.
Narrow space inside means a high concentration of protons can be built up quickly.

Thylakoid interior

thylakoid membrane

Key points

➤ Chloroplasts have an envelope.
➤ Thylakoid membranes form stacks called grana.
➤ These provide a large surface area for light absorption.
➤ Photosystems I and II contain a mixture of photosynthetic pigments but mainly chlorophyll – see page 117.
➤ The photosystems are embedded in the thylakoid membrane.
➤ Along with the photosystems are molecules for electron transport and proton pumping.
➤ ATP is generated using the chemiosmotic process – the principle is the same as in mitochondria but the molecules involved are slightly different – see page 131.

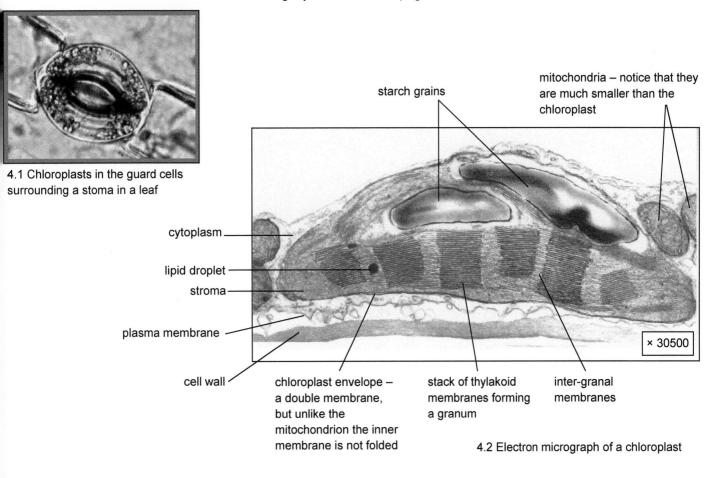

4.1 Chloroplasts in the guard cells surrounding a stoma in a leaf

starch grains

mitochondria – notice that they are much smaller than the chloroplast

cytoplasm

lipid droplet

stroma

plasma membrane

× 30500

cell wall

chloroplast envelope – a double membrane, but unlike the mitochondrion the inner membrane is not folded

stack of thylakoid membranes forming a granum

inter-granal membranes

4.2 Electron micrograph of a chloroplast

Photosynthesis pathways

➤ There are three processes:
- The light dependent reactions,
- ATP generation by chemiosmosis – photophosphorylation,
- The light independent reactions.

The light dependent reactions
Key points

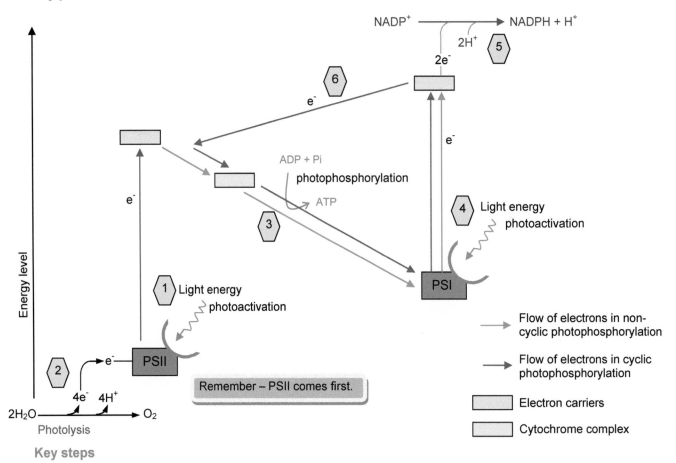

Key steps

① Photosystem II absorbs light energy and electrons are boosted to a higher energy level. This is **photoactivation**.

② The electrons lost from PSII are replaced by splitting water – **photolysis**. Oxygen gas is released and the protons remain in the thylakoid interior.

③ The electrons fall in energy level through a series of carriers. One of these is a cytochrome complex which acts as a proton pump resulting in the formation of ATP. This is called photophosphorylation.

④ The electrons fall into PSI and light energy is absorbed (photoactivation) to boost them to another electron carrier.

⑤ The electrons can pass to $NADP^+$ reducing it with the addition of $2H^+$.

⑥ Alternatively the electrons can fall back to PSI through the proton pump in a cyclic process that generates more ATP.

IBHL Biology 2016 © Ashby Merson-Davies

ATP generation by chemiosmosis – photophosphorylation

This is the synthesis of ATP using the energy from light that has been stored as electron energy in reduced $NADP^+$. This electron energy drives the proton pump.

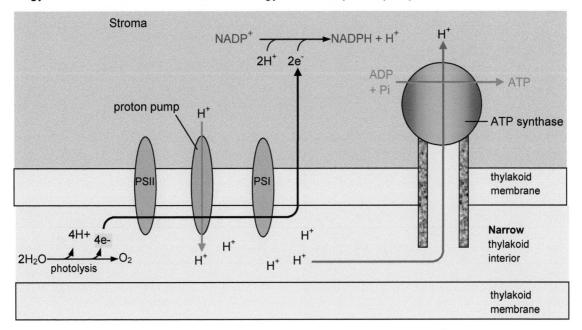

Key steps

➢ Electrons flow through the carriers, including photosystems II and I.
➢ As they pass through the cytochrome complex protons are **pumped** to the interior of the thylakoid.
➢ The thylakoid interior is narrow to increase the concentration of protons.
➢ The protons then flow back by **diffusion** down a concentration gradient into the stroma through the enzyme ATP synthase.
➢ ATP is generated.

Relate this diagram to the one on the previous page.

Also note how similar it is to the diagram on page 130.
On page 131 is a comparison of the two.

The flow of protons through the ATP synthase complex is called chemiosmosis – see yellow box below.

Difference between the cyclic and non-cyclic pathways:

• With non-cyclic the electrons continue on to join with protons and $NADP^+$ whereas with cyclic they are returned to the chlorophyll in photosystem I.

The cyclic pathway has two advantages:

1. It provides the additional ATP needed to drive the light independent reactions. The Calvin cycle requires more ATP than NADPH + H^+. Non-cyclic photophosphorylation gives a ratio of 1:1 so more ATP is needed. Cyclic photophosphorylation provides this additional ATP.
2. It provides ATP that can be used for other processes such as stomatal opening by guard cells – see page 216.

Why chemiosmosis? You remember that osmosis is the diffusion of water through a membrane from a high concentration of water to a lower concentration. The principles here are exactly the same, but instead of water it is another chemical, the hydrogen ion, diffusing from the high concentration in the thylakoid interior to the lower concentration in the stroma.

Summary	
Inputs	- Water
	- Light energy
Products	- Oxygen
	- ATP
	- NADPH + H^+

26. Which colours in the spectrum are absorbed most during photosynthesis?

27. What is the range of wavelengths of light in the visible spectrum?

28. List two factors, other than carbon dioxide, that affect the rate of photosynthesis.

29. Distinguish between an absorption spectrum and an action spectrum.

30. Draw a graph to show the effect of carbon dioxide concentration on the rate of photosynthesis.

33. Draw graphs using the same axes to show the absorption spectrum of chlorophyll and an action spectrum.

31. On your graph above draw an arrow to indicate where another factor becomes limiting.

32. State which one of the factors you gave in Q28 is likely to be the limiting factor.

34. Where does the light independent reaction take place?

35. Where does the light dependent reaction take place?

36. What is a granum?

37. What happens when light energy is absorbed by a photosystem?

38. Where are the two photosystems found?

39. Write the photolysis reaction.

40. What is photoactivation?

41. In which order are the two photosystems with respect to electron flow?

42. Which photosystem is used in cyclic photophosphorylation?

43. Why is the thylakoid interior narrow?

44. Where is the proton pump in relation to the two photosystems?

45. Which molecule could pick up the electrons after they have passed through the photosystems?

46. Write the chemical reaction catalysed by ATP synthase.

47. Why is cyclic photophosphorylation essential for the Calvin cycle?

Light dependent reactions

Fill in the dotted lines.

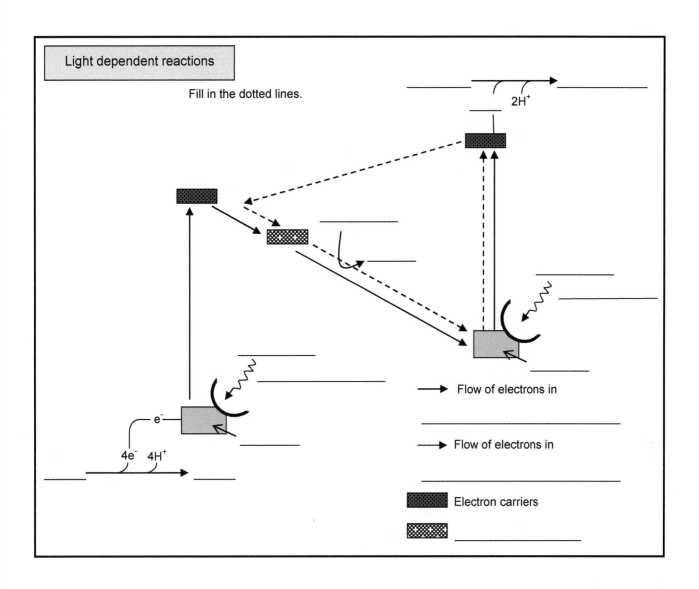

2H⁺

e⁻

4e⁻ 4H⁺

⟶ Flow of electrons in

⟶ Flow of electrons in

▓▓ Electron carriers

▒▒ _____

Photophosphorylation

Fill in the dotted lines.

This region is the _____

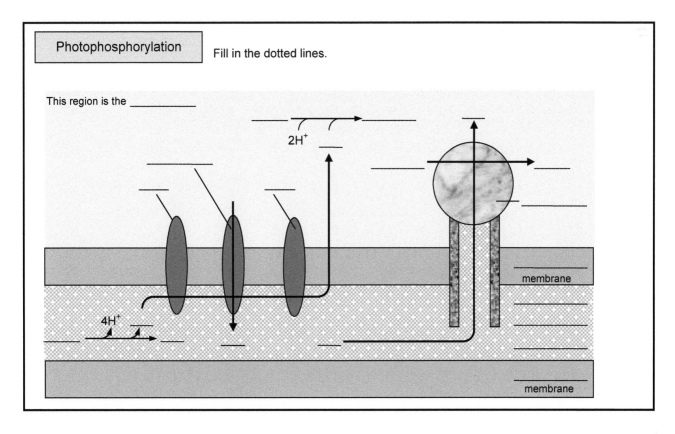

2H⁺

4H⁺

membrane

membrane

The light independent reactions

Key points

➢ The light independent reactions are driven by the ATP and NADPH + H⁺ made in the light dependent reactions. The important point to remember is that both sets of reactions continue **at the same time**.

➢ The light independent reactions occur in the stroma.

➢ It is a cyclic pathway called the Calvin cycle.

Each rotation of the Calvin cycle uses one molecule of carbon dioxide. The diagram below shows three cycles joined together. This is so that the three molecules of carbon dioxide entering emerge as one 3-carbon compound, triose phosphate.

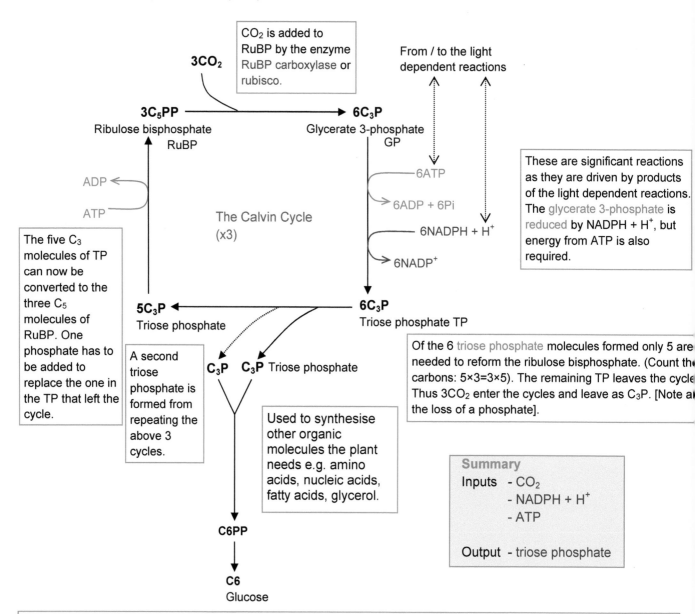

CO₂ is added to RuBP by the enzyme RuBP carboxylase or rubisco.

From / to the light dependent reactions

3CO₂

3C₅PP ⟶ **6C₃P**

Ribulose bisphosphate
RuBP

Glycerate 3-phosphate
GP

ADP ⟵
ATP

The Calvin Cycle
(x3)

6ATP
6ADP + 6Pi
6NADPH + H⁺
6NADP⁺

These are significant reactions as they are driven by products of the light dependent reactions. The glycerate 3-phosphate is reduced by NADPH + H⁺, but energy from ATP is also required.

The five C₃ molecules of TP can now be converted to the three C₅ molecules of RuBP. One phosphate has to be added to replace the one in the TP that left the cycle.

5C₃P ⟵ **6C₃P**

Triose phosphate

Triose phosphate TP

A second triose phosphate is formed from repeating the above 3 cycles.

C₃P   C₃P Triose phosphate

Used to synthesise other organic molecules the plant needs e.g. amino acids, nucleic acids, fatty acids, glycerol.

Of the 6 triose phosphate molecules formed only 5 are needed to reform the ribulose bisphosphate. (Count the carbons: 5×3=3×5). The remaining TP leaves the cycle. Thus 3CO₂ enter the cycles and leave as C₃P. [Note also the loss of a phosphate].

Summary
Inputs - CO₂
         - NADPH + H⁺
         - ATP

Output - triose phosphate

C6PP

C6
Glucose

Triose phosphate can be used as a precursor for conversion into other organic molecules the plant needs e.g. amino acids, nucleic acids, fatty acids, glycerol.
Alternatively two triose phosphate molecules can be joined to form glucose by a pathway similar to a reversal of the first few steps of glycolysis. (See page 127). Glucose can be converted to starch and stored or used to synthesise cellulose. (See pages 23/4).

- Ribulose is a sugar and sugars are metabolically stable compounds.
- Phosphorylating it to ribulose bisphosphate makes it less stable and more reactive to take part in a metabolic pathway.
- See also glycolysis on page 127.

All the biochemical pathways follow a standard colour code to help you learn them.

The basic carbon path is black.
Hydrogen transfers are blue.
Energy transfers are red.

Calvin's 'lollipop' experiment

This seemingly simple apparatus allowed Calvin to determine the steps in the light independent reactions.

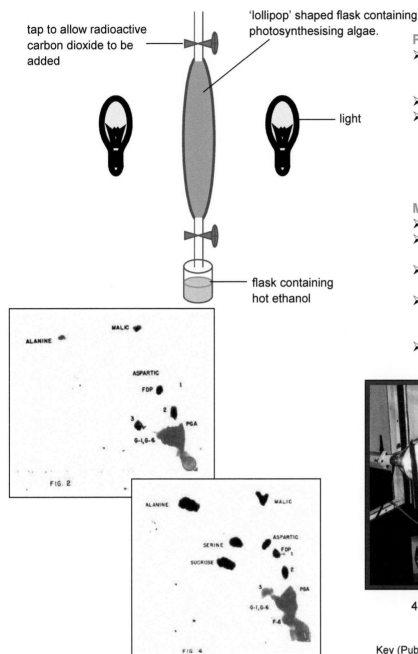

tap to allow radioactive carbon dioxide to be added

'lollipop' shaped flask containing photosynthesising algae.

light

flask containing hot ethanol

Principles
- ➤ The algae take up the radioactive carbon dioxide and build it into organic compounds.
- ➤ Hot ethanol inactivates enzymes.
- ➤ Samples taken at timed intervals after introduction of the carbon dioxide will show the sequence of steps in the pathway converting carbon dioxide to glucose.

Method
- ➤ Radioactive carbon dioxide introduced.
- ➤ After a few seconds sample drained into hot ethanol.
- ➤ Paper chromatography used to separate molecules.
- ➤ Paper dried and placed against photographic film to produce autoradiograph.
- ➤ Spots on paper analysed to determine actual molecule.

4.4 Calvin's lollipop apparatus

4.3 Autoradiograms obtained using the lollipop apparatus
These are the autoradiograms in Calvin and Benson's original paper published December 1948. Fig 2 is after 5 seconds and Fig 4 after 90 seconds.

Key (Published term / *modern term*)
FDP = fructose-1, 6-diphosphate (*fructose-1, 6-bisphosphate*); PGA = phosphoglyceric acid (*phosphoglycerate*); G-1 = glucose-1-phosphate; G-6 = glucose-6-phosphate; F-6 = fructose-6-phosphate; malic (*malate*); aspartic (*aspartate*).

Atmosphere, oceans, rocks and photosynthesis

Key points
- ➤ The early Earth's atmosphere was anaerobic so any organisms had to use inefficient anaerobic respiration.
- ➤ About 3.5 million years ago some prokaryotic organisms evolved the ability to harvest sunlight energy using a form of photosystem I.
- ➤ The source of electrons was sulphur compounds which limited them to volcanic areas.
- ➤ About 2.5 million years ago another group of prokaryotes modified PSI to produce PSII which extracted electrons from water.

- ➢ These were the cyanobacteria.
- ➢ They were now able to exploit the vast areas covered by ocean.
- ➢ A by-product was oxygen released into the water and atmosphere.
- ➢ Initially all the oxygen was taken up by dissolved iron in the water and iron compounds in rocks to form iron oxides.
- ➢ Gradually oxygen began to remain dissolved in the oceans.
- ➢ This allowed the evolution of the much more efficient aerobic respiration pathway and marine organisms flourished.
- ➢ Huge quantities of carbon dioxide were removed from the atmosphere via the oceans into calcium carbonate in the shells and skeletons of marine organisms and these eventually formed massive chalk deposits.
- ➢ As more oxygen accumulated in the upper atmosphere it reacted with sunlight to form ozone.
- ➢ Ozone protects the Earth's surface from damaging ultraviolet light. (UV light causes DNA mutations).
- ➢ This allowed organisms to move onto the land.

4.5 The White Cliffs of Dover. These huge cliffs are chalk formed from tiny marine animals called Foraminifera.

48. In which region of the chloroplast does the Calvin cycle take place?	49. In which region of the chloroplast does photophosphorylation take place?	50. Name the molecule that combines with carbon dioxide at the start of the Calvin cycle.
51. Name the enzyme that catalyses this reaction.	52. Glycerate 3-phosphate is converted to triose phosphate. What is required for this reaction?	53. How many carbon atoms in triose phosphate?
54. Where have these carbon atoms come from?		

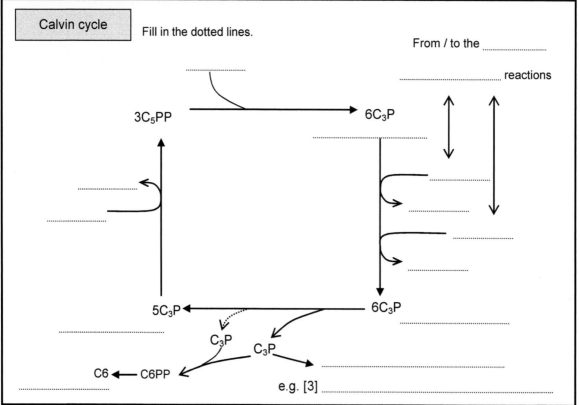

Calvin cycle   Fill in the dotted lines.

From / to the ....

.... reactions

$3C_5PP$ ⟶ $6C_3P$

$5C_3P$ ← $6C_3P$

C_3P C_3P

$C6$ ← $C6PP$

e.g. [3] ....

Respiration

- Cell respiration is the controlled release of energy from organic compounds to produce ATP.
- This ATP is immediately available as a source of energy in the cell.
- Two types:
  - anaerobic,
  - aerobic.
- Anaerobic respiration does not require oxygen; aerobic respiration requires oxygen.
- Glycolysis is the first stage for both the anaerobic and aerobic pathways.

Glycolysis
Key points
- Occurs in the cytoplasm.
- Anaerobic.
- End product is pyruvate.
- Net energy yield is 2ATP per glucose molecule.

> Remember the standard colour code.
>
> The basic carbon path is black.
> Hydrogen transfers are blue.
> Energy transfers are red.

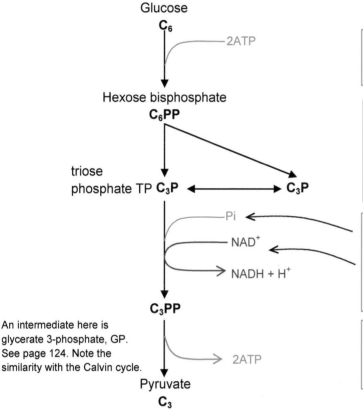

2 molecules of ATP are used to start the process.
This is called phosphorylation.

The hexose bisphosphate molecule is split in half.
This is called lysis.
The two C_3P molecules are chemically different but can easily be converted from one to the other.

This is a very significant reaction since phosphorylation occurs using a phosphate ion, not ATP.
The energy for this comes from oxidation by removing hydrogen onto the carrier NAD^+.

An intermediate here is glycerate 3-phosphate, GP. See page 124. Note the similarity with the Calvin cycle.

In this sequence of steps the two phosphate groups are removed to make two molecules of ATP. This is called ATP formation.

Energy balance
We put 2ATP in at the start and have gained 2ATP so the balance appears to be zero. However we have only used half the glucose molecule – there is still a C_3P from the lysis reaction unused. If this is converted to pyruvate down the same pathway another 2ATP are made creating a net yield of 2ATP.

Anaerobic respiration
Key points
- An anaerobic branch pathway is used when oxygen is not available.
- Muscle tissue and yeasts are both able to switch from an aerobic pathway to an anaerobic one.
- Anaerobic respiration is much less efficient producing only a small yield of ATP per glucose molecule.

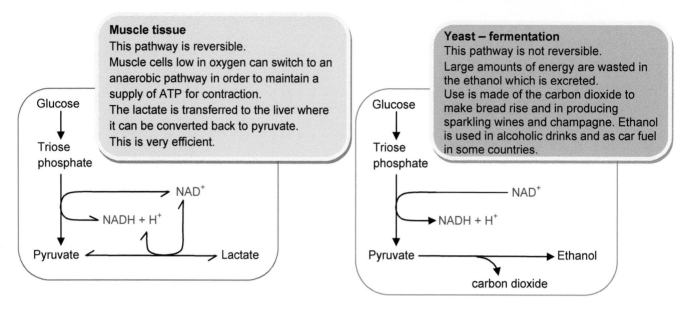

Muscle tissue
This pathway is reversible.
Muscle cells low in oxygen can switch to an anaerobic pathway in order to maintain a supply of ATP for contraction.
The lactate is transferred to the liver where it can be converted back to pyruvate.
This is very efficient.

Glucose
↓
Triose phosphate
↓
Pyruvate ⟷ Lactate

NAD⁺
NADH + H⁺

Yeast – fermentation
This pathway is not reversible.
Large amounts of energy are wasted in the ethanol which is excreted.
Use is made of the carbon dioxide to make bread rise and in producing sparkling wines and champagne. Ethanol is used in alcoholic drinks and as car fuel in some countries.

Glucose
↓
Triose phosphate
↓
Pyruvate → Ethanol
carbon dioxide

NAD⁺
NADH + H⁺

Aerobic respiration

Key points

➢ Occurs in the mitochondrion.
➢ Requires oxygen.
➢ Three stages:
  • link reaction,
  • Krebs cycle,
  • oxidative phosphorylation via chemiosmosis.
➢ Net energy yield is 36 ATP per glucose.

The mitochondrion

> Compare these annotations with those for the chloroplast on page 119. Note the similarities.

cristae
Form large surface area for oxidative phosphorylation.

outer membrane
Isolates mitochondrial contents from cytoplasm forming a compartment.

70S ribosomes
Synthesis of mitochondrial proteins.

Remember:
Mitochondrion
– Matrix

narrow inter-membrane space
Allows for rapid build-up of H⁺ concentration.

matrix
Contains enzymes for Krebs cycle.

Annotate

inner membrane

circular DNA
Contains mitochondrial genes.

1–2μm

inner membrane of mitochondrial envelope folded to form cristae

matrix

cluster of free ribosomes

4.6 TEM of the mitochondrion

The link reaction and Krebs cycle

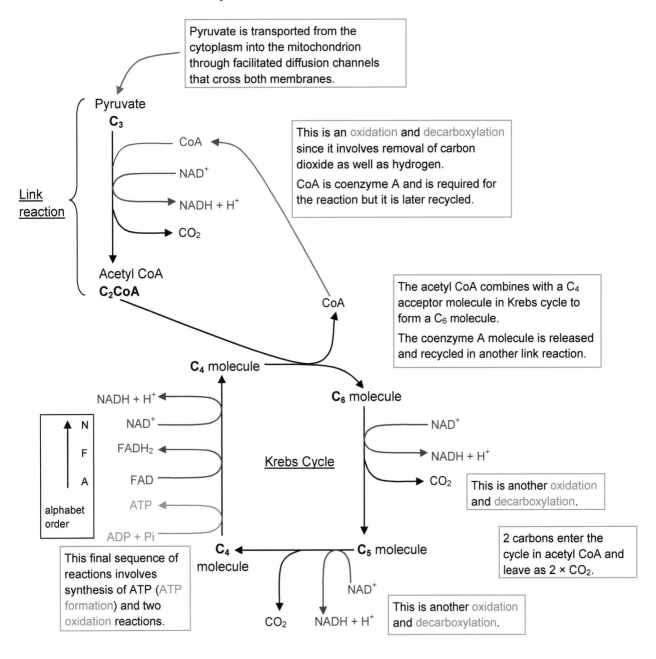

Pyruvate is transported from the cytoplasm into the mitochondrion through facilitated diffusion channels that cross both membranes.

Pyruvate
C_3

This is an oxidation and decarboxylation since it involves removal of carbon dioxide as well as hydrogen.

CoA is coenzyme A and is required for the reaction but it is later recycled.

Link reaction

CoA

NAD^+

$NADH + H^+$

CO_2

Acetyl CoA
C_2CoA

CoA

The acetyl CoA combines with a C_4 acceptor molecule in Krebs cycle to form a C_6 molecule.

The coenzyme A molecule is released and recycled in another link reaction.

C_4 molecule

C_6 molecule

$NADH + H^+$

NAD^+

FADH$_2$

FAD

ATP

ADP + Pi

N
F
A

alphabet order

Krebs Cycle

NAD^+

$NADH + H^+$

CO_2

This is another oxidation and decarboxylation.

This final sequence of reactions involves synthesis of ATP (ATP formation) and two oxidation reactions.

C_4 molecule

C_5 molecule

2 carbons enter the cycle in acetyl CoA and leave as 2 × CO_2.

NAD^+

CO_2

$NADH + H^+$

This is another oxidation and decarboxylation.

The mitochondrion and oxidative phosphorylation

This is the synthesis of ATP using the energy released from the glucose which has been stored as electron energy in reduced NAD. The principle is exactly the same as for photophosphorylation in the chloroplast on page 121.

In the five oxidation reactions above the products are at progressively lower energy levels. The difference in energy level is partly stored in the electron of the hydrogen atom, (Remember that a hydrogen atom = a proton, H^+,+ an electron), and the difference is lost as heat. This electron energy is then released via the electron transport pathway and used to form ATP.

Key points

➢ Electrons flow through a sequence of carriers, the electron transport pathway, that include proton pumps.
➢ There are three proton pumps.
➢ At the final pump, cytochrome oxidase, they are added to oxygen and, together with protons from the matrix, form water.
➢ The energy from the electron flow is used to pump protons from the matrix to the inter-membrane space.
➢ The inter-membrane space is narrow so that a high concentration of protons can be built up quickly.
➢ Protons diffuse from the high concentration in the inter-membrane space back into the matrix via a channel linked to the enzyme ATP synthase.
➢ The energy from this proton flow is used to synthesise ATP.
➢ NADH + H$^+$ releases its electrons at the first pump thus generating 3 ATP.
➢ FADH$_2$ releases its electrons at the second pump thus generating only 2 ATP.

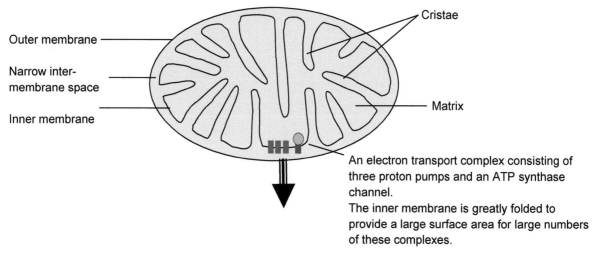

An electron transport complex consisting of three proton pumps and an ATP synthase channel.
The inner membrane is greatly folded to provide a large surface area for large numbers of these complexes.

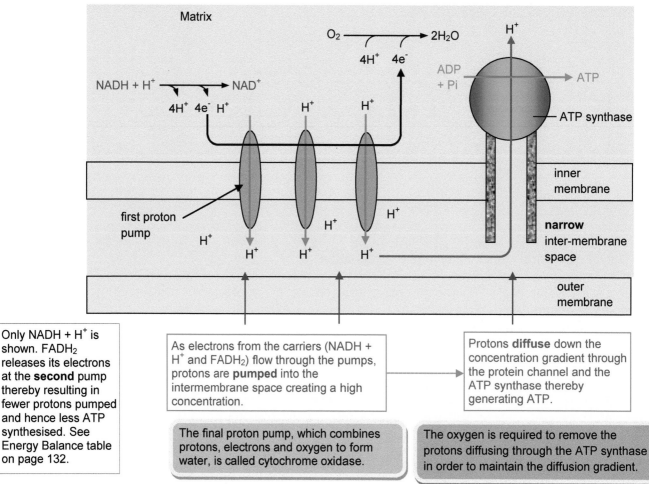

Only NADH + H$^+$ is shown. FADH$_2$ releases its electrons at the **second** pump thereby resulting in fewer protons pumped and hence less ATP synthesised. See Energy Balance table on page 132.

As electrons from the carriers (NADH + H$^+$ and FADH$_2$) flow through the pumps, protons are **pumped** into the intermembrane space creating a high concentration.

Protons **diffuse** down the concentration gradient through the protein channel and the ATP synthase thereby generating ATP.

The final proton pump, which combines protons, electrons and oxygen to form water, is called cytochrome oxidase.

The oxygen is required to remove the protons diffusing through the ATP synthase in order to maintain the diffusion gradient.

IBHL Biology 2016 © Ashby Merson-Davies

Comparing chemiosmosis in photosynthesis and respiration

1. Photosynthesis

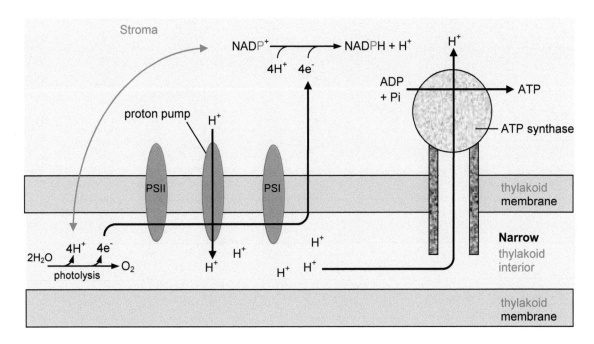

2. Respiration

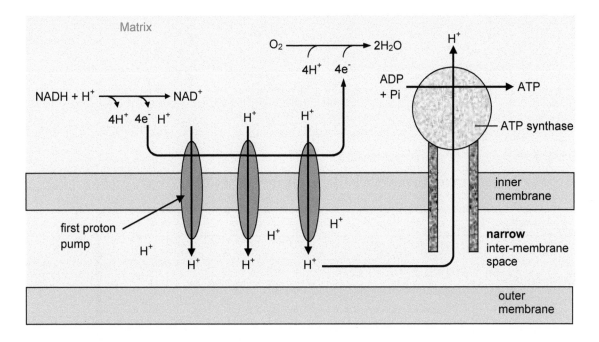

Notice that the two pathways are almost identical. This means that once you have learnt the pathway for photosynthesis there are only seven small differences to learn. These are marked in red on the photosynthesis diagram.

Differences:
1. Stroma instead of matrix.
2. $NADP^+$ instead of NAD^+.
3. Thylakoid membranes instead of cristae.
4. There is only one proton pump instead of three.
5. On either side of the single proton pump are photosystems II and I.
6. The two chemical equations have swapped ends of the electron transport chain.
7. The position of the start of the electron transport chain has moved slightly.

Summary of respiration

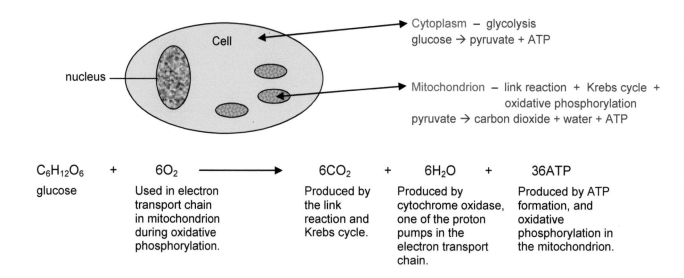

Cytoplasm – glycolysis
glucose → pyruvate + ATP

Mitochondrion – link reaction + Krebs cycle + oxidative phosphorylation
pyruvate → carbon dioxide + water + ATP

$C_6H_{12}O_6$ + $6O_2$ ⟶ $6CO_2$ + $6H_2O$ + 36ATP

| glucose | Used in electron transport chain in mitochondrion during oxidative phosphorylation. | Produced by the link reaction and Krebs cycle. | Produced by cytochrome oxidase, one of the proton pumps in the electron transport chain. | Produced by ATP formation, and oxidative phosphorylation in the mitochondrion. |

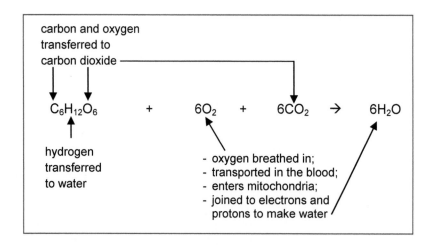

carbon and oxygen transferred to carbon dioxide

$C_6H_{12}O_6$ + $6O_2$ + $6CO_2$ → $6H_2O$

hydrogen transferred to water

- oxygen breathed in;
- transported in the blood;
- enters mitochondria;
- joined to electrons and protons to make water

Overall energy balance from respiration of one glucose molecule

Stage		
Glycolysis	2ATP used at start	-2 ATP
	2NADH + H$^+$ If oxygen is present its electrons are transferred across the envelope to form 2FADH$_2$ inside the mitochondrion.	4 ATP
	ATP formation	4 ATP
Link reaction	2NADH + H$^+$	6 ATP
Krebs cycle	ATP formation	2 ATP
	2FADH$_2$	4 ATP
	6NADH + H+	18 ATP
	Net Energy Yield	**36 ATP**

Electron tomography

➢ This process is similar to a scanning electron micrograph but can be done on very much smaller subjects such as cell organelles.

➢ In this situation much thicker slices are used and multiple images are taken as the specimen is rotated.

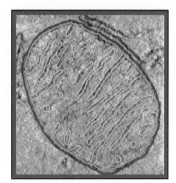

➢ For each image the membranes are carefully traced, as shown on the right, and then a computer programme is used to build up a three dimensional image.

➢ The image can then be artificially coloured.

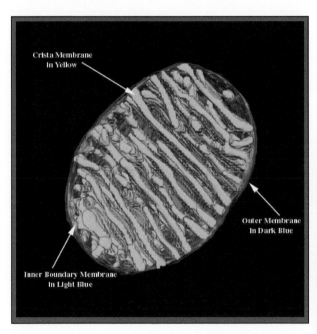

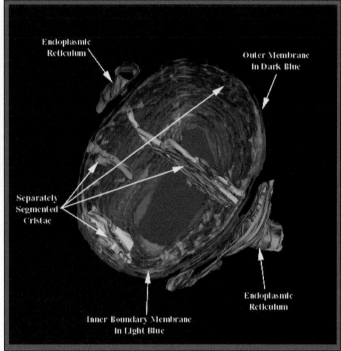

4.7 Electron tomography images of a mitochondrion

55. Name two 'chain' metabolic pathways.

56. Name two 'ring' metabolic pathways.

57. How many molecules of ATP are required to convert glucose to hexose bisphosphate?

58. Name (initials) the hydrogen carrier in the glycolysis pathway.

59. Name the end product of glycolysis.

60. What is the net energy yield from glycolysis for one glucose molecule?

61. In the anaerobic pathway in muscle what is pyruvate converted into?

62. In the anaerobic pathway in yeast what is pyruvate converted into?

63. Why is the muscle pathway more efficient than the yeast pathway?

64. Is glycolysis aerobic or anaerobic?

65. Is oxidation loss or gain of hydrogen?

66. In which part of the cell does glycolysis take place?

67. What is the reason for the inner mitochondrial membrane being folded?

68. What are these folds called?

69. In which part of the mitochondrion does Krebs cycle take place?

70. In which part of the mitochondrion does the link reaction take place?

71. Name (initials) two molecules that transfer electrons to the electron transport pathway.

72. How many proton pumps are used in oxidative phosphorylation?

73. Name the enzyme in the final step in the electron transport pathway.

74. Why is it important to have a narrow inter-membrane space?

75. Name the enzyme attached to the proton channel.

76. From 1 molecule of glucose how many molecules of reduced NAD are formed in glycolysis?

77. Name the type of reaction when a phosphate is added to a compound.

78. What is a lysis reaction?

79. Name the transport method used to transfer protons from the intermembrane space to the matrix.

80. Why does reduced FAD produce less ATP then reduced NAD?

81. List four differences between photophosphorylation and oxidative phosphorylation.

82. In Krebs cycle a C_6 molecule is converted to a C_5 molecule using two types of reaction. Name these two reactions.

83. Oxygen is used to remove protons from the matrix. Explain why.

IBHL Biology 2016 © Ashby Merson-Davies

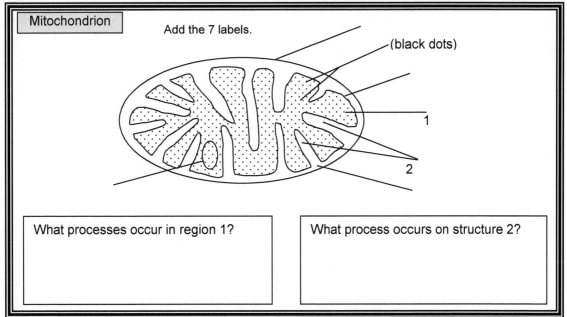

Mitochondrion   Add the 7 labels.

(black dots)

1

2

What processes occur in region 1?	What process occurs on structure 2?

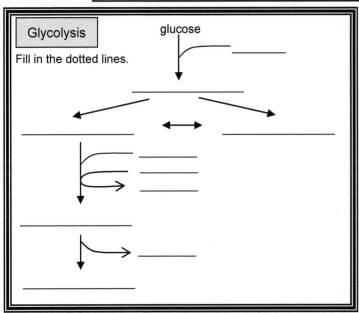

Glycolysis   glucose

Fill in the dotted lines.

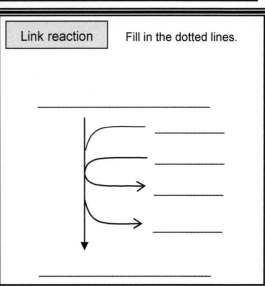

Link reaction   Fill in the dotted lines.

Krebs cycle

Fill in the dotted lines.

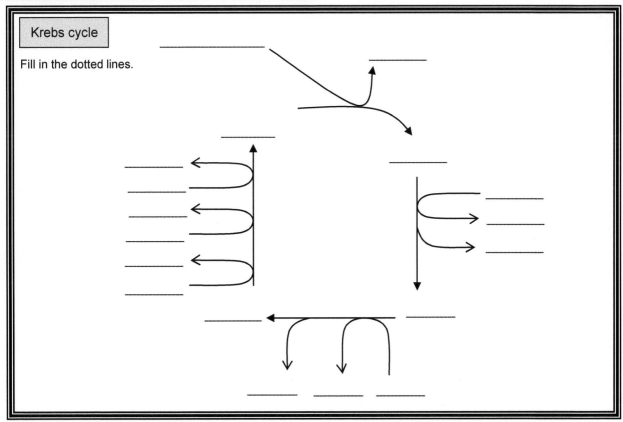

Glossary

ABSORPTION SPECTRUM	The pattern of absorption of light (by chloroplast pigments) at different wavelengths.
ACTION SPECTRUM	The pattern of a chemical action (e.g. photosynthesis – production of oxygen) at different wavelengths of light.
AEROBIC	A chemical reaction that requires oxygen.
ANAEROBIC	A chemical reaction that can proceed without oxygen.
CHEMIOSMOSIS	The passive facilitated diffusion of hydrogen ions / protons down a concentration gradient across a membrane.
CONFORMATIONAL CHANGE	A change in the shape of a protein.
EXPONENTIAL INCREASE	An increase where the rate of increase continues to increase.
pH	The measure of the acidity or alkalinity of a solution. Neutral is a pH of 7, acids have a pH of less than 7 and alkalis a pH of more than 7.
PHYSIOLOGICAL TEMPERATURES	The temperature range within which most organisms live. Approximately $0 – 45^0$C.
SUBSTRATE	The organic molecule on which an enzyme acts.

Answers to Grey Box Questions   Underlined words are required.

1. The breaking down of complex organic molecules into simpler ones.   2. Tertiary.
3. A bond between a negative and positive charge.
4. A decrease in pH is due to an increase in the number of H^+ ions. These bind to the COO^- group in the ionic bond forming COOH. This breaks the bond.
5. The breakdown of the normal stable form of a protein.   6. Lock and key.
7. Active site.   8. The same chemical properties as the substrate.

9.

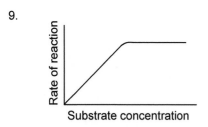

10. With more substrate the rate of reaction increases; eventually all the active sites are occupied at any one time an further addition of substrate has no effect.
11. Anabolism.   12. They are continually moving.   13. Reduce it.
14. Competitive inhibition – the substrate and inhibitor compete for the active site. Non-competitive inhibition – the inhibitor binds to a different site.
15. There are too few molecules of inhibiter and they are outnumbered by the substrate molecules.
16. Loss.   17. Gain.   18. Non-competitive.
19. Substrate – threonine; product – isoleucine; enzyme – threonine deaminase.
20. A change in the shape of a protein.
21. A. No inhibitor present. B. Competitive inhibitor present. C. Non-competitive inhibitor present.
22. An enzyme that has been attached to an inert/non-reactive base.
23. Production of lactose-free milk.
24. Some people are intolerant of lactose in milk; produces better quality ice-cream; yoghurt production is faster; glucose and galactose taste sweeter than lactose.
25. The enzyme does not contaminate the product/does not need to be removed from the product; enzyme is not lost so costs cheaper; production can be on a continuous basis.
26. Blue and red.   27. 400 – 700nm.
28. Temperature; light intensity.
29. Absorption spectrum – the range of wavelengths that are absorbed by the photosynthetic pigments; action spectrum – the amount of photosynthesis produced at different wavelengths.

IBHL Biology 2016 © Ashby Merson-Davies

30.

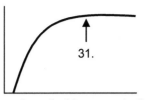

Rate of photosynthesis

31.

carbon dioxide concentration

32. Light intensity.
33. See page 117.   34.   Stroma.   35.   Thylakoid membranes.
36. A group of thylakoid membranes.   37.   An electron is promoted to a higher energy level.
38. Thylakoid membranes.   39. $2H_2O = O_2 + 4e- + 4H+$.
40. Activation of the photosystem by light energy.   41.   PSII the PSI.   42.   PSI.
43. To allow a rapid build-up in proton concentration.   44.   Between.   45.   NADP/NADP$^+$.
46. ADP + Pi → ATP.   47.   The non-cyclic pathway does not generate enough ATP.
48. Stroma.   49.   Thylakoid membranes.   50.   Ribulose bisphosphate.
51. Ribulose bisphosphate carboxylase / rubisco.
52. Reduced NADP / NADPH + H$^+$ and ATP. (The actual numbers of molecules are not required.)
53. Three.   54.   Carbon dioxide.   55.   Glycolysis; link reaction.
56. Krebs cycle; Calvin cycle.   57.   Two.   58.   NAD / NAD$^+$.
59. Pyruvate.   60.   2ATP.   61.   Lactate.
62. Ethanol and carbon dioxide.   63.   The lactate can be converted back to pyruvate and recycled.
64. Anaerobic.   65.   Loss.   66.   Cytoplasm.
67. To increase the surface area for the electron chain pathways.
68. Cristae.   69.   Matrix.   70.   Matrix.
71. Reduced NAD / reduced NAD$^+$ / NADH + H$^+$ and reduced FAD / FADH$_2$.
72. Three.   73.   Cytochrome oxidase.
74. To allow a rapid build-up in proton concentration. (Remember – the same reason as in the thylakoid membranes.)
75. ATP synthase. 76.   Two.   77.   Phosphorylation.
78. When a larger molecule is split into smaller ones.   79.   Diffusion.
80. It releases its electrons onto the second proton pump.
81. Photophosphorylation – only one proton pump; NADP is the hydrogen carrier not NAD; hydrogen is added to NADP but removed from reduced NAD; water is split; stroma instead of matrix; thylakoid membranes not cristae.
82. Oxidation; decarboxylation.
83. To maintain the high diffusion gradient between the intermembrane space and the matrix.

Self-test Quiz

1. Oxidation can be described as:
   a.   loss of oxygen and gain of hydrogen,
   b.   gain of oxygen and loss of electrons,
   c.   loss of electrons and gain of hydrogen,
   d.   gain of electrons and gain of oxygen.

2. In the glycolysis pathway starting with 1 molecule of glucose:
   a.   4 molecules of ATP are used,
   b.   lysis occurs twice,
   c.   2 molecules of carbon dioxide are produced,
   d.   2 molecules of NAD$^+$ are reduced.

3. Acetyl Co-A is produced from pyruvate by:
   a.   reduction and dehydrogenation,
   b.   oxidation and decarboxylation,
   c.   phosphorylation,
   d.   oxidation and condensation.

4. Acetyl Co-A joins Krebs cycle by combining with a:
   a. 2-carbon compound,
   b. 4-carbon compound,
   c. 5-carbon compound,
   d. 6-carbon compound.

5. In the process of oxidative phosphorylation in the mitochondrion:
   a. both active transport and diffusion of protons takes place,
   b. reduction of $NADH + H^+$ takes place,
   c. electrons are moved to higher energy levels,
   d. ADP + Pi is formed from ATP.

6. During the light dependent reactions of photosynthesis:
   a. ATP is used in the process of cyclic photophosphorylation,
   b. a condensation reaction occurs forming water,
   c. $NADP^+$ is oxidised,
   d. chlorophyll is both oxidised and reduced.

7. During the light independent reactions of photosynthesis:
   a. pyruvate combines with ribulose bisphosphate to form glycerate 3-phosphate,
   b. $NADPH + H^+$ is oxidised during the formation of triose phosphate,
   c. ribulose carboxylase catalyses the formation of ribulose bisphosphate using carbon dioxide,
   d. ATP is produced during the conversion of glycerate 3-phosphate to triose phosphate.

8. Which of the following statements is correct?
   a. Both light dependent and light independent reactions take place in the stroma.
   b. Photophosphorylation occurs in the stroma.
   c. Chemiosmosis occurs on the thylakoid membranes.
   d. The Calvin cycle occurs on the grana.

9. Which of the following statements is correct?
   a. Electrons flow through photosystem I and then photosystem II.
   b. Non-cyclic photophosphorylation involves only photosystem II.
   c. During photolysis water is split to release oxygen as a waste product.
   d. Cyclic photophosphorylation involves photosystems I and II.

10. Which of the following statements is correct?
    a. Photophosphorylation produces ATP.
    b. Photophosphorylation produces ATP and $NADPH + H^+$.
    c. Photolysis produces ATP.
    d. Six rotations of the Calvin cycle produces one molecule of triose phosphate.

11. Which of the following graphs represents the absorption spectrum for photosynthesis?

 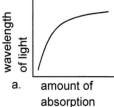
a. amount of absorption

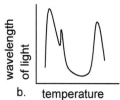
b. temperature

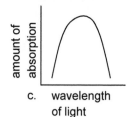
c. wavelength of light

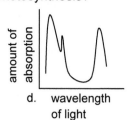
d. wavelength of light

12. Which of the following graphs correctly shows that light intensity is acting as a limiting factor for photosynthesis?

a.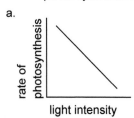
light intensity

b.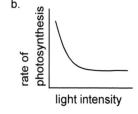
light intensity

c.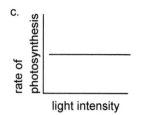
light intensity

d.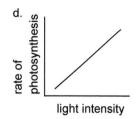
light intensity

13. Which of the following statements correctly describes a limiting factor?
    a. The optimum temperature at which an enzyme works.
    b. A variable factor that controls the rate of a process and is nearest to its minimum value.
    c. A variable factor in a sequence that functions at the slowest rate.
    d. A factor in a chemical chain that varies in concentration.

14. Which two colours of light does chlorophyll absorb most?
    a. yellow and red,
    b. blue and green,
    c. blue and red,
    d. red and green.

15. During ATP synthesis in mitochondria, which way do the protons flow?
    a. From the matrix to the intermembrane space,
    b. From the intermembrane space to the matrix,
    c. From the intermembrane space to the cytoplasm,
    d. From the cytoplasm to the intermembrane space.

16. During the conversion of glucose into pyruvate in glycolysis what is the sequence of stages?
    a. Lysis → phosphorylation of sugar → oxidation,
    b. Phosphorylation of sugar → lysis → oxidation,
    c. Lysis → oxidation → phosphorylation of sugar,
    d. Phosphorylation of sugar → oxidation → lysis.

17. How is the proton gradient generated in chloroplasts during photosynthesis?
    a. Electrons passing from carrier to carrier in the thylakoid membrane cause protons to be pumped across the thylakoid membrane.
    b. Light energy excites protons to flow through channels in the thylakoid membrane.
    c. Light energy splits water molecules in the stroma producing protons.
    d. Protons are pumped across the thylakoid membrane using energy from ATP.

18. Why is the action spectrum for photosynthesis similar to the absorption spectrum of chlorophyll?
    a. The light energy is used by chlorophyll instead of enzymes to lower the activation energy.
    b. Photosynthetic pigments such as chlorophyll function at the same optimum temperature as the enzymes used in photosynthesis.
    c. Only the energy in the wavelengths of light absorbed by photosynthetic pigments such as chlorophyll can be used in photosynthesis.
    d. All plants use the same photosynthetic pigments for photosynthesis.

19. During which process are oxygen molecules directly involved during cellular respiration?
    a. Oxidation reaction during glycolysis,
    b. Oxidation reactions during Krebs cycle,
    c. Oxidation of pyruvate to acetyl CoA,
    d. Accepting electrons at the end of the electron transport chain.

20. Which of the following is the first product in the Calvin cycle?
    a. Ribulose bisphosphate (RuBP),
    b. Glycerate 3-phosphate (GP),
    c. Triose phosphate (TP),
    d. Acetyl CoA.

21. What accumulates in the inter-membrane space of the mitochondrion during electron transport?
    a. ATP,
    b. electrons,
    c. protons,
    d. oxygen.

22. Anabolism can best be described as:
    a. the breakdown of macromolecules into their constituent monomers,
    b. the formation of peptide bonds during the synthesis of polypeptides,
    c. the formation of organic macromolecules from simpler molecules,
    d. building larger molecules using enzymes and ribosomes.

23. Which of the following represents activation energy?

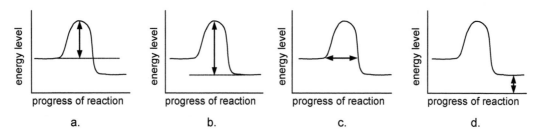

| a. | b. | c. | d. |

24. Which of the following statements about end-product inhibition is correct?
    a. The end-product of a metabolic pathway can act as competitive inhibitor on an enzyme earlier in the pathway.
    b. The end-product of a metabolic pathway can act as non-competitive inhibitor on an enzyme earlier in the pathway.
    c. The enzyme that catalyses the final reaction in a metabolic pathway is inhibited by the substrate at the start of the pathway.
    d. The end-product of a metabolic pathway can inhibit any of the enzymes controlling that pathway.

25. Which of the dotted lines represents the effect of a competitive inhibitor? The solid line is the rate of the reaction with no inhibitor. The amount of enzyme is the same for each one.

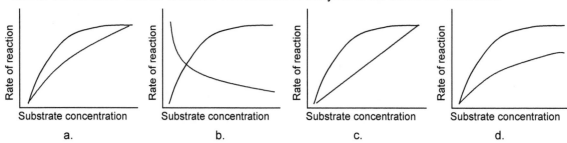

| a. | b. | c. | d. |

26. An immobilised enzyme is one which:
    a. does not affect the rate of reaction,
    b. is not altered by the reaction,
    c. is attached to an inert substance,
    d. is fixed in the plasma membrane.

27. Which of the graphs represents the effect of temperature on the rate of an enzyme controlled reaction?

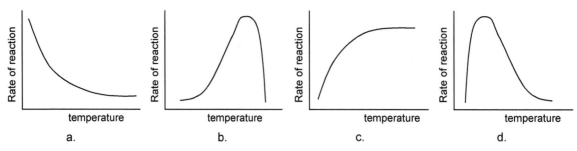

| a. | b. | c. | d. |

28. The effect of pH on the rate of an enzyme controlled reaction is because:
    a. changing the pH affects the ionic bonding holding the molecule in its 3-D shape,
    b. metabolic reactions can only work at a neutral pH,
    c. changing the pH affects the primary structure of the protein,
    d. changing the pH alters the shape of the substrate.

29. A photosynthesis investigation was carried out to measure oxygen output under two different wavelengths of light. The difference in the rates of reaction was:
    a. 0.075 cm^3 min^{-1},
    b. 0.082 cm^3 min^{-1},
    c. 0.092 cm^3 min^{-1},
    d. 0.1 cm^3 min^{-1}.

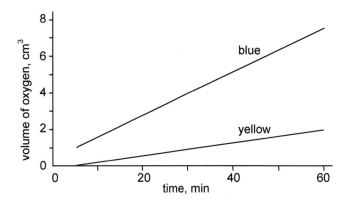

30. In oxidative phosphorylation protons move from the intermembrane space to the matrix by:
    a. active transport,
    b. osmosis,
    c. simple diffusion,
    d. facilitated diffusion.

Chapter Five

Animal Physiology

This chapter looks at the main aspects of animal anatomy and physiology, mainly human. There are a seemingly endless number of adaptations of form and function which allow animals to adapt to their environment.

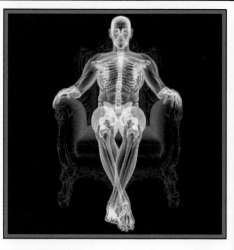

The human gut

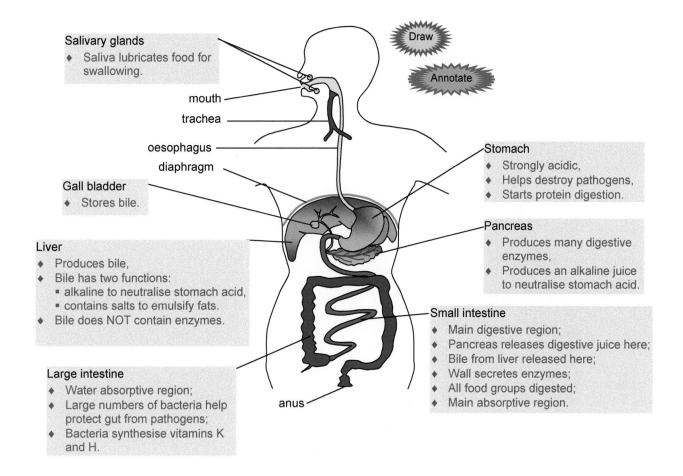

Salivary glands
- ♦ Saliva lubricates food for swallowing.

Draw

Annotate

mouth

trachea

oesophagus

diaphragm

Stomach
- ♦ Strongly acidic,
- ♦ Helps destroy pathogens,
- ♦ Starts protein digestion.

Gall bladder
- ♦ Stores bile.

Pancreas
- ♦ Produces many digestive enzymes,
- ♦ Produces an alkaline juice to neutralise stomach acid.

Liver
- ♦ Produces bile,
- ♦ Bile has two functions:
  - ▪ alkaline to neutralise stomach acid,
  - ▪ contains salts to emulsify fats.
- ♦ Bile does NOT contain enzymes.

Small intestine
- ♦ Main digestive region;
- ♦ Pancreas releases digestive juice here;
- ♦ Bile from liver released here;
- ♦ Wall secretes enzymes;
- ♦ All food groups digested;
- ♦ Main absorptive region.

Large intestine
- ♦ Water absorptive region;
- ♦ Large numbers of bacteria help protect gut from pathogens;
- ♦ Bacteria synthesise vitamins K and H.

anus

Digestion
Key facts
- ➤ Large molecules cannot pass through the wall of the villus.
- ➤ Large molecules need to be broken down into their constituent units in order to be reassembled in the way the body wants.
- ➤ Macromolecules – starch, glycogen, lipids and nucleic acids – are digested into monomers.
- ➤ Cellulose is undigested.
- ➤ Without enzymes the reactions are too slow at body temperature.

Pancreatic enzymes
Key facts
- ➤ The pancreatic duct carries pancreatic juices to the duodenum.
- ➤ Pancreatic juice contains:
  - • alkaline salts to help neutralise the acidic stomach juices,
  - • many enzymes.

Enzyme	Substrate
Amylase	Starch
Endopeptidase	Proteins
Lipase	Lipid

Digestion of starch
- • Amylase breaks starch down to maltose.
- • Maltase breaks maltose into glucose.
- • The glucose is actively transported into the villus cells.
- • Maltase is attached to the outer plasma membrane of the villus cells.

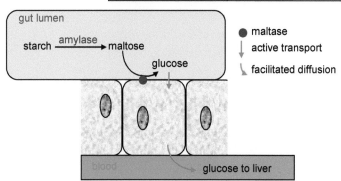

The gut wall

The small intestine is divided into two regions.
1. Duodenum leads from the stomach and is where the bile and pancreatic ducts join.
2. Ileum, which is much longer, and is the main absorptive region.

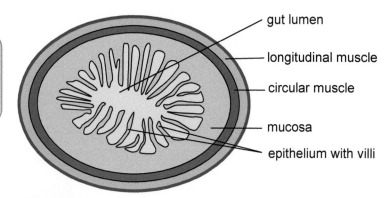

gut lumen

longitudinal muscle

circular muscle

mucosa

epithelium with villi

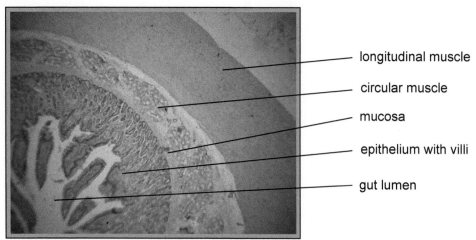

longitudinal muscle

circular muscle

mucosa

epithelium with villi

gut lumen

5.1 Cross section of the small intestine

Dialysis tubing
➤ This is an artificial partially permeable membrane.
➤ It can be used for digestion investigations.
▪ Example:

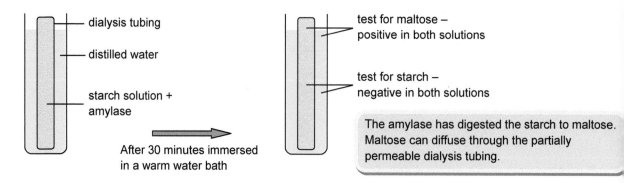

dialysis tubing

distilled water

starch solution + amylase

After 30 minutes immersed in a warm water bath

test for maltose – positive in both solutions

test for starch – negative in both solutions

The amylase has digested the starch to maltose. Maltose can diffuse through the partially permeable dialysis tubing.

Peristalsis
➤ This is the contraction of the circular and longitudinal muscles in a wave motion.
➤ This:
● mixes the food with the enzymes,
● moves the food along the gut.

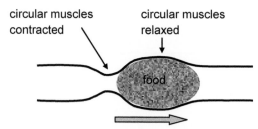

circular muscles contracted

circular muscles relaxed

food

circular muscles contract in a wave which pushes the food along the gut.

Absorption

This is done through the millions of villi lining the wall of the small intestine.

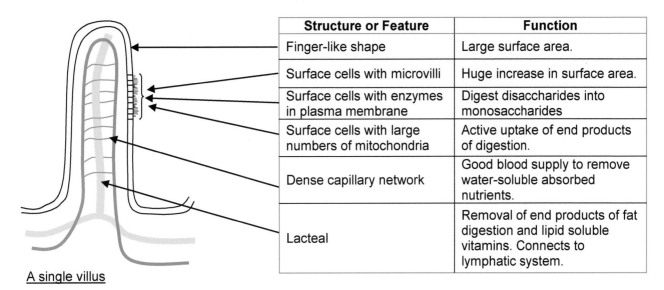

Structure or Feature	Function
Finger-like shape	Large surface area.
Surface cells with microvilli	Huge increase in surface area.
Surface cells with enzymes in plasma membrane	Digest disaccharides into monosaccharides
Surface cells with large numbers of mitochondria	Active uptake of end products of digestion.
Dense capillary network	Good blood supply to remove water-soluble absorbed nutrients.
Lacteal	Removal of end products of fat digestion and lipid soluble vitamins. Connects to lymphatic system.

A single villus

Key points

➢ Villi are tiny folds in the gut wall epithelium.
➢ Villus surface cells have microvilli.
➢ Together they bring about a huge increase in surface area.
➢ The monomer end products of digestion are absorbed over the villus surface.
➢ Mineral ions are absorbed over the villus surface.
➢ Methods of absorption over the villus surface are:
- simple diffusion,
- facilitated diffusion, see pages 85-7
- active transport,
- pinocytosis.
➢ Absorbed substances are transferred to the blood stream and lacteal for transport to the liver.

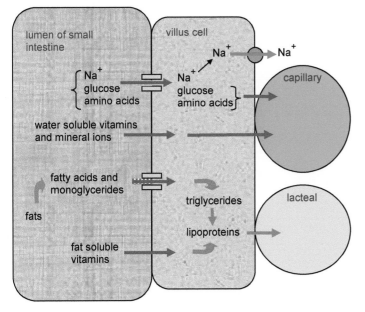

Absorption mechanisms

Capillary
- Sodium ions are actively transported out of the villus cell.
- This creates a diffusion gradient.
- Sodium ions combine with glucose or amino acid molecules to diffuse through a facilitated diffusion co-transporter channel.
- Glucose and amino acids diffuse into the capillary through facilitated diffusion channels.

Lacteal
- Fatty acids and monoglycerides diffuse through facilitated diffusion channels into the villus cell.
- They are recombined into triglycerides.
- These are combined with phospholipids, cholesterol and proteins to make lipoproteins.
- Fat soluble vitamins combine with the lipoproteins.
- These leave the villus cell by exocytosis and most enter the lacteal.
- Some lipoprotein enters the capillary.

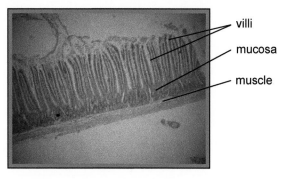

villi

mucosa

muscle

5.2a Low power view of villi

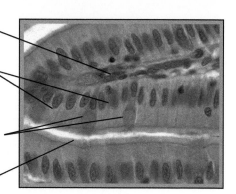

capillaries and lacteal

villus cells absorb end products of digestion

goblet cells produce mucus

microvilli

5.2b Tip of a villus

1. State the function of the gall bladder.	2. State two features about the stomach.	3. Is the pH of pancreatic juice alkaline or acidic?
4. State two functions of the small intestine.	5. State two functions of the large intestine.	6. State two functions of bile.
7. List two pancreatic enzymes other than endopeptidase.	8. State the function of endopeptidase.	9. Name the enzyme that breaks starch into maltose.
10. Name the enzyme that breaks maltose into glucose.	11. State precisely where the enzyme named in Q10 is found.	12. State the transport mechanism to transfer glucose into villus cells.
13. Where is the glucose transported to after it enters the blood stream?	14. Give two reasons why digestion is necessary.	15. Why are digestive enzymes necessary?
16. Name the two regions of the small intestine.		17. Name the process which moves food along the gut.
18. Name the two muscles that bring about the movement state in Q17.	19. List 5 features of a villus related to its role in absorption.	20. Name the region of the gut into which pancreatic juices are released.
		21. Name a dietary component that is not digested.

Gas exchange

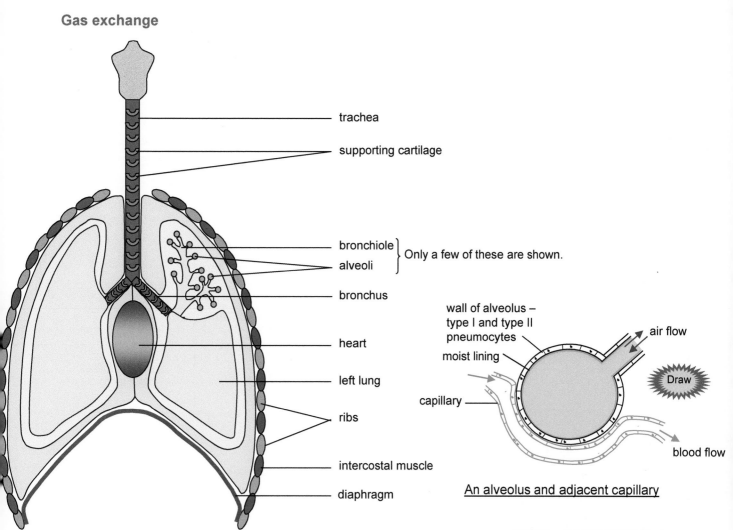

trachea

supporting cartilage

bronchiole } Only a few of these are shown.
alveoli

bronchus

heart

left lung

ribs

intercostal muscle

diaphragm

wall of alveolus –
type I and type II
pneumocytes

moist lining

capillary

air flow

Draw

blood flow

An alveolus and adjacent capillary

Alveoli
Key points
- Very small so large surface area to volume ratio.
- Wall of single layer of flattened cells called pneumocytes.
- Type I pneumocytes are extremely thin to allow efficient gas exchange.
- Type II pneumocytes secrete a solution containing a surfactant.
- This surfactant creates:
  - a moist surface to assist gas exchange,
  - prevents the walls of the alveoli adhering to each other.
- Covered in dense capillary network.

Ventilation
Key points
- As oxygen diffuses into blood, carbon dioxide diffuses out of blood, concentration gradients decrease.
- Ventilation brings in fresh oxygen and removes carbon dioxide, which maintains concentration gradients.
- Steep diffusion gradients of oxygen and carbon dioxide between alveolar air and alveolar blood capillaries results in rapid diffusion of gases.

Tip: Type I pneumocytes are thin and I is thinner than II.

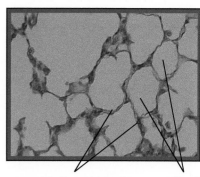

Note the very thin walls containing both the alveolus wall and the capillaries.

alveoli

5.3a Healthy lung tissue

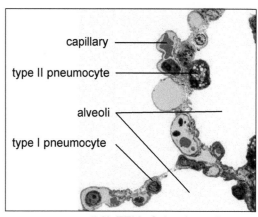

capillary

type II pneumocyte

alveoli

type I pneumocyte

5.3b TEM of alveolar walls.

Mechanism of ventilation

➢ The thoracic cavity is a sealed box.
➢ Atmospheric pressure is effectively constant.
➢ If the volume of the thoracic cavity increases the pressure decreases.
➢ Atmospheric pressure forces air into the lungs.
➢ If the volume of the thoracic cavity decreases the pressure increases.
➢ Air is forced out of the lungs.
➢ Two sets of antagonistic muscles work to carry out ventilation.

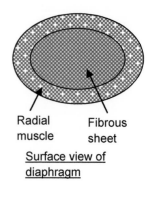

External intercostal muscles	Attached to the rib cage. When contract rib cage moves up **and** out. Volume increases; pressure decreases → breathe in. Internal intercostal muscles relaxed.
Internal intercostal muscles	Attached to the rib cage. When contract rib cage moves down **and** in. Volume decreases; pressure increases → breathe out. External intercostal muscles relaxed.
Diaphragm	Dome shaped structure separating thoracic cavity from abdominal cavity. When radial muscle contracts dome flattens. Volume increases; pressure decreases → breathe in.
Abdominal muscles	Abdominal muscles contract and push diaphragm back to dome shape. Volume decreases; pressure increases → breathe out. Diaphragm muscle relaxed.

Radial muscle   Fibrous sheet

Surface view of diaphragm

Measuring ventilation
➢ Instruments such as a spirometer can measure various lung volumes.
➢ Breathing normally in and out produces the **tidal volume**.

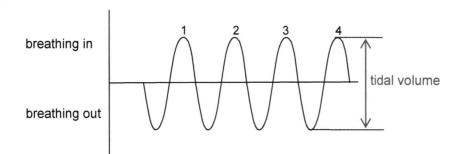

Ventilation rate is the number of breaths per minute.

The graph shows 4 breaths.

Lung cancer

- The vast majority of cases are caused by smoking, especially cigarettes.
- The rest are due to carcinogenic particles such as coal or asbestos dust breathed in.

- If detected early enough the tumour, or entire lung can be removed.
- Death.

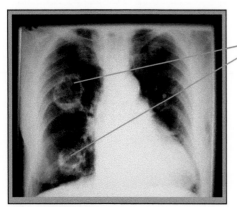

tumours

normal lung tissue that is being compressed by growth of the tumour.

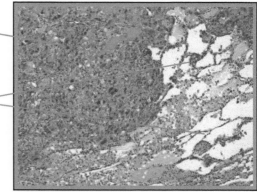

5.4a X-ray of lung tumours

5.4b Stained section of lung tumour

Emphysema

Key point

➤ Alveolar walls are broken down resulting in the reduction of surface area for gas exchange.

Causes

• The vast majority of cases are caused by smoking

Consequences

• Difficulty in breathing.
• Gradual loss of ability to carry out any exercise and eventually even slow walking becomes nearly impossible.
• Breathing oxygen through a face mask or nasal tubes may be necessary in order to get enough oxygen into the blood.

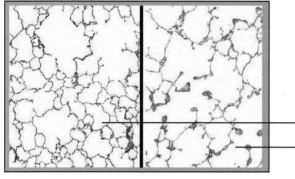

—— normal healthy lung

—— lung with emphysema

5.5 Healthy and damaged lung tissue

1. Name the two cell types in the alveolus wall.	2. State the function of each cell type.	3. What is the purpose of ventilation?
4. What happens to thoracic pressure when the volume increases?	5. List two muscles which cause the thoracic volume to increase.	6. List two muscles which cause the thoracic volume to decrease.
7. Muscle work in pairs. What is the name given to this pair?	8. What is the name given to the volume of air breathed in and out in a normal breath?	9. What is ventilation rate?

10. Draw an alveolus and attached capillary.

11. State the major cause of lung cancer.

12. What is cancer?

13. State a possible consequence of lung cancer.

14. What is emphysema?

15. State a major cause of emphysema.

16. State a possible consequence of emphysema.

The blood system

The circulatory system

Key facts

➢ The heart is a double pump.
➢ The right side is the pulmonary circuit.
➢ The left side is the systemic circuit.
➢ Arteries carry blood away from the heart at high pressure. (**A**rteries – **A**way)
➢ Veins carry blood to the heart at low pressure.
➢ Pressure in the pulmonary artery is lower than pressure in the aorta.
➢ Valves in the veins and heart ensure a one-way flow in the circulatory system.
➢ The blood leaving the gut goes directly to the liver via the hepatic portal vein.

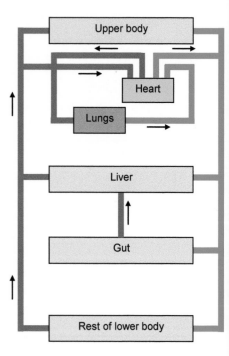

The mammalian double circulation

Blood is composed of:

◆ Plasma.
◆ Erythrocytes (red cells).
◆ Leucocytes (white cells) –
  ▪ Phagocytes,
  ▪ Lymphocytes.
◆ Platelets.

Transported by the blood:

◆ Nutrients.
◆ Oxygen.
◆ Carbon dioxide.
◆ Hormones.
◆ Antibodies.
◆ Urea.
◆ Heat.

Transport by the blood

Key points

➢ Blood is mostly water which is a polar solvent – see pages 20–1.
➢ Polar molecules such as glucose, amino acids and sodium chloride dissolve.
➢ Oxygen also dissolves.
➢ Fats are non-polar and do not dissolve.
➢ Cholesterol is only very slightly soluble.
➢ Fats and cholesterol are transported as lipoproteins – see page 25.

The heart

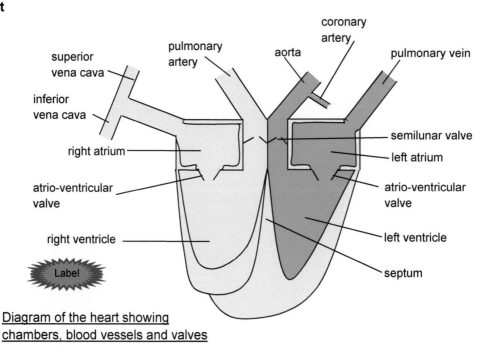

Diagram of the heart showing chambers, blood vessels and valves

IBHL Biology 2016 © Ashby Merson-Davies

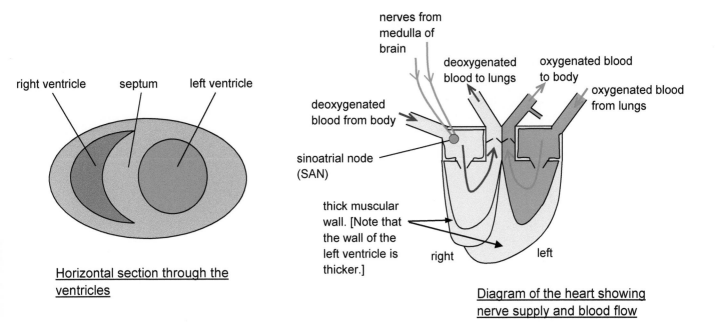

right ventricle   septum   left ventricle

Horizontal section through the ventricles

nerves from medulla of brain

deoxygenated blood to lungs

oxygenated blood to body

deoxygenated blood from body

oxygenated blood from lungs

sinoatrial node (SAN)

thick muscular wall. [Note that the wall of the left ventricle is thicker.]

right   left

Diagram of the heart showing nerve supply and blood flow

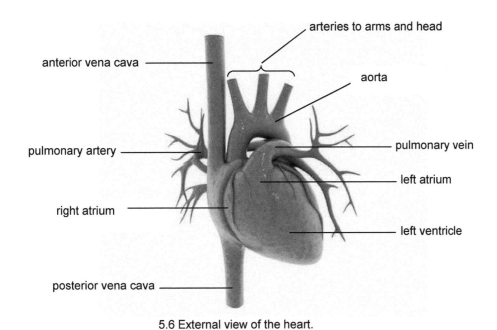

arteries to arms and head

anterior vena cava

aorta

pulmonary artery

pulmonary vein

left atrium

right atrium

left ventricle

posterior vena cava

5.6 External view of the heart.

Control of the heartbeat

Key points
- The sinoatrial node, SAN, is a small patch of special muscle tissue on the wall of the right atrium near the point where the vena cava enters.
- The SAN acts as a pacemaker.
- It releases an electrical impulse approximately 70 times per minute.
- The electrical impulse is propagated (transmitted) through the heart muscle.
- This causes the atrial heart muscle to contract, followed by the ventricular muscle.
- Involuntary nerves from the cardiac control centre in the medulla of the brain are attached to the pacemaker.
- Impulses down the cardiac depressor nerve cause the heart rate to slow down, e.g. during sleep.
- Impulses down the cardiac accelerator nerve cause the heart rate to speed up, e.g. during exercise.
- The hormone epinephrine (adrenalin) from the adrenal gland stimulates the pacemaker causing the heart rate to speed up in preparation for vigorous physical activity.

Pressure changes in the left side of the heart and the aorta

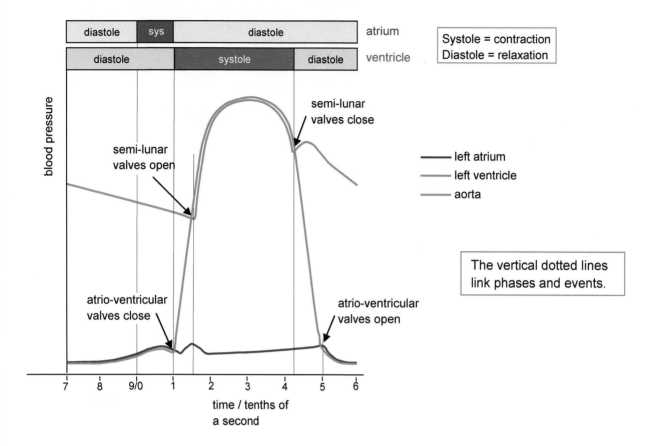

Systole = contraction
Diastole = relaxation

The vertical dotted lines link phases and events.

Legend:
— left atrium
— left ventricle
— aorta

The cardiac cycle

Key stages
Relate these events to the graphs above. Times are in tenths of a second.

Time 0 – 1
Atrial systole
➤ SAN (see page 151) fires when the ventricles are about 70% full.
➤ Atria contract filling ventricles further. Note the volume rises sharply.

Time 1 – 4.2
Ventricular systole
➤ Ventricles contract.
➤ Increase in pressure immediately closes atrio-ventricular valves.
➤ The flaps of the valves striking together as they close create the first of the two heart sounds.
➤ The pressure increases further until the semi-lunar valve is opened allowing blood to flow into the aorta.
➤ At this time the volume decreases.

Time 4.2 – 9
Ventricular diastole
➤ Ventricles relax.
➤ Back pressure of blood in arteries causes semi-lunar valves to snap shut.
➤ The flaps striking together cause the second of the two heart sounds.
➤ Blood pressure in the vena cava pushes blood into the atria.
➤ Elastic recoil of the ventricular muscle lowers ventricular pressure.
➤ As soon as ventricular pressure is below the atrial pressure the atrio-ventricular valves open and the ventricles start to fill rapidly at first but then more slowly.

 IBHL Biology 2016 © Ashby Merson-Davies

Occlusion (blockage) of the coronary arteries

Causes
- A high LDL: HDL ratio in the blood stream – see page 25.
- Results in a fatty deposit, a plaque or atheroma, forming in the walls of the coronary arteries.
- This is called atherosclerosis.
- This restricts blood flow.
- This results in coronary heart disease or CHD.
- The plaque can stimulate the formation of a blood clot.
- The clot could break free and lodge in a smaller artery.

Consequences
- Reduction in oxygenated blood flow to the heart muscle reduces respiration.
- Reduction in respiration lowers availability of ATP.
- Reduced ATP means the ventricular muscles work less efficiently.
- This causes pain in the heart called angina.
- If the blood flow is completely blocked this can produce a heart attack.

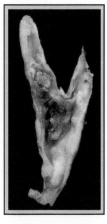

5.7 An atheroma in a carotid artery

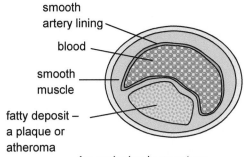

smooth artery lining

blood

smooth muscle

fatty deposit – a plaque or atheroma

An occlusion in an artery

The blood vessels

	Structure	Function
Arteries	Thick muscular wall	Withstand high pressure. Contracts to increase blood pressure.
	Elastic fibres	Stretched by pulse and when contract help to maintain steady blood flow.
	Collagen fibres	Tough inelastic fibres protect and prevent the wall from being over stretched.
	Endothelium	Smooth lining.
Capillaries	Wall of single layer of flattened cells	Reduced distance for diffusion between blood and tissues.
	Narrow lumen	Increased surface area.
	No muscle, elastic or fibrous tissue	Facilitate diffusion as substances only have to pass through the single layer of cells. Some capillaries have gaps between the cells – see page 174.
Veins	Endothelium	Smooth lining.
	Large lumen	Reduces resistance to flow.
	Some collagen, muscle and elastic fibres	Mainly protection.
	Valves	Prevent backflow when pressure very low.
	Thin walls	Allows vein to be squashed between muscle blocks which pumps the blood.

Transverse section of artery

basement membrane

flow

Longitudinal section of vein

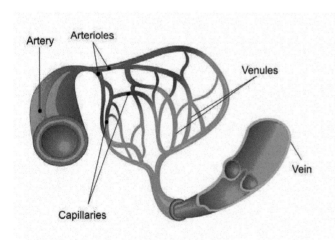

5.9a The relationship between artery, capillaries and vein

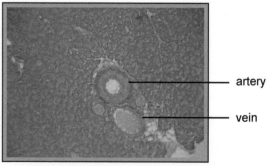

5.8 Cross sections of an artery and a vein. Note the distinct difference in wall thickness.

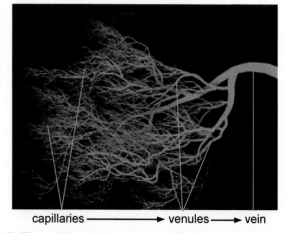

capillaries ⟶ venules ⟶ vein

5.9b The relationship between capillaries and veins

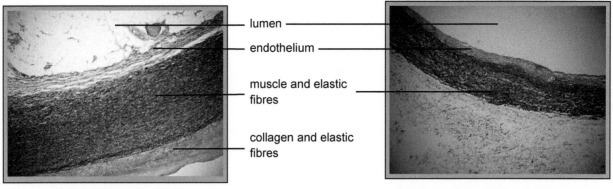

5.10a Wall of an artery	5.10b Wall of a vein

lumen
endothelium
muscle and elastic fibres
collagen and elastic fibres

William Harvey's discovery of circulation
Born Folkestone, UK 1578.

➢ Earlier views on blood were that when it was pumped out from the heart it was 'used up' in the body or turned to 'vapour' in the lungs and fresh blood 'made' in the liver.

➢ Harvey disproved this by measuring the volume of the heart and multiplying this by the number of heart beats in a day.

    Volume of left and right ventricles = 140cm^3

    Number of beats per 24 hours = 75 beats per minute × 60 × 24 = 108,000 beats

    Volume of blood pumped per 24 hours = 108000 × 140 = 15,120 litres

➢ Harvey stated that it would be impossible for the liver to generate this volume of blood.

➢ Therefore the blood must circulate around the body, pumped out from the heart and then returning to it.

➢ He was aware of arteries and veins and that these vessels repeatedly branched, but had to propose that there must be tiny connecting vessels that could not be seen. (The microscope had been invented in Harvey's time but it was not widely known about and Harvey did not have one).

➢ He showed that blood in veins can only flow one way due to valves.

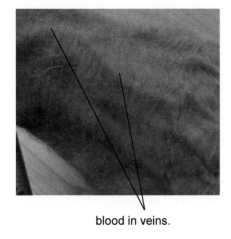

blood in veins.

valve here prevents backflow of blood.

blood squeezed out of vein by sliding finger away from the heart.

5.11a, b. A valve in action

1. What is meant by the term double circulation?	2. Which side of the heart is the pulmonary circuit?	3. What is the name of the other circuit?
4. Name the blood vessel supplying blood to the heart muscle.	5. Where does blood from the gut go to?	6. Is blood pressure highest in arteries or veins?.
7. Name the blood vessel attached to the right atrium.	8. Name the blood vessel attached to the left ventricle.	9. Name the valve between the atrium and ventricle.
10. Name the valve in the base of the pulmonary artery.	11. Which wall of the heart is thickest?	12. To which chamber of the heart is the pulmonary vein attached?
13a. Name the structure in the heart which acts as a pacemaker.	13b. Where in the heart is this structure found?	13c. What is the function of this structure?
13d. Two nerves are attached to this structure. Where do they come from?	13e. What is the function of these two nerves?	14. Name the hormone that affects heart rate.
15. Which gland produces this hormone?	16. What is the function of the valves in the heart?	17. Is contraction of the heart systole or diastole?
18a. What causes the left atrio-ventricular valve to close?	18b. What causes the aortic semilunar valves to open?	18c. What causes the aortic semilunar valves to close?
19. What can cause an occlusion of the coronary artery?	20. What is the consequence of a coronary occlusion?	21. Which type of blood vessel has valves?
22. What is the function of the elastic fibres in the arteries?	23. Name the molecule in arterial walls which prevents overstretching.	24. What is the function of the muscle in arterial walls?

25. List two features of capillary walls which promote transport through them.

Defence against infectious disease

Key points
- A pathogen is an organism or virus that can cause infectious disease.
- Most pathogens are species specific.
- Some pathogens can cross the species barrier.
- Specificity is due to the ability to recognise unique molecules on the surface of its host cells.

> Viruses are not organisms because they are not living.

Pathogenic organisms
Include bacteria, fungi, protozoans, flatworms and tapeworms.
They can infect the skin, gut, liver, blood stream, brain and nervous system.

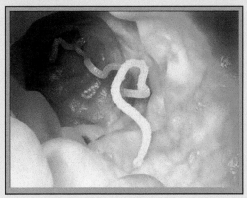

5.12 Tapeworm in the small intestine

5.13 *Entomophthora muscae*
A fungal infection of a fly

> Both HIV and the Ebola virus appear to have crossed the species barrier from wild animals to humans.

Antibiotics

Key points
- Act against specific chemicals or chemical pathways in prokaryotes.
- Hence do not affect eukaryotic cells.
- Some strains of bacteria have evolved genes that confer resistance to specific antibiotics.
- Some strains of bacteria have evolved multiple antibiotic resistance – see page 287.
- Viruses are intra-cellular parasites and lack metabolism.
- They use the host cell chemical pathways.
- Hence any drugs used against viruses would damage the host cell.

Florey and Chain
- Alexander Fleming accidentally discovered the penicillin fungus in 1928 but he was not aware of what use could be made of it.
- Ten years later Florey and Chain, along with a team of biochemists, produced enough penicillin to test in mice.
- They first injected healthy mice with penicillin to test its toxicity and found it had no effect.
- A group of mice were injected with haemolytic streptococci bacteria.
- Half of the group was then injected with penicillin.
- Several hours later the mice that received the penicillin were alive but those that had not were all dead.
- On the basis of this single success a toxicity test case in humans was proposed.
- A patient with terminal cancer agreed to the toxicity test but started shaking and developed a high fever.
- It was shown that these symptoms were due to impurities in the sample.
- The first human patient (trialled in 1941) was suffering from a bacterial infection of a wound.
- He was injected with a purified penicillin preparation and showed immediate signs of recovery.
- Insufficient penicillin was available to continue treatment and the patient later died.
- Further trials proved its effectiveness and production on a large scale was started in America.

Primary defence
1. Surface barriers

Key points – skin
➢ Dead waterproof surface layer.
➢ Tough, elastic.
➢ Oily secretion (sebum) from sebaceous gland in hair follicle controls fungal and bacterial growth and stops skin cracking. Sebum contains fatty acids.
➢ Dry – discourages growth of pathogens.
➢ Surface layer continually shed which removes pathogens.
➢ Cuts in the skin can be sealed by blood clotting.

Key points – mucous membranes
➢ In air passages sticky mucus traps pathogens, swept up to throat by ciliated cells and swallowed.
➢ In vagina, acidic (due to bacterial activity) to prevent growth of pathogens.
➢ Enzyme lysozyme in mucus kills bacteria.

2. Blood clotting cascade

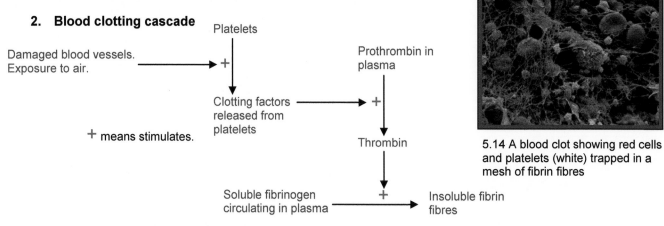

5.14 A blood clot showing red cells and platelets (white) trapped in a mesh of fibrin fibres

Fibrin is an insoluble fibrous protein. The fibres become entangled and create a mesh in which red blood cells become trapped, blocking blood flow.

Secondary defence
1. Non-specific

Phagocytes
➢ These white blood cells ingest pathogens such as bacteria and viruses by endocytosis.
➢ They contain many lysosomes which contain digestive enzymes – see page 76.
➢ These enzymes destroy the pathogens.
➢ They can leave capillaries and enter tissues.
➢ They are able to identify pathogens by detecting foreign proteins on the pathogen surface.
➢ They are assisted by antibodies attached to pathogens.
➢ They concentrate at sites of infection.

2. Specific – antibody production
Antigens and antibodies
➢ An antigen is a molecule, usually a protein, which is foreign to the body and stimulates the production of a specific antibody.
➢ Every organism has unique molecules on the surface of its cells.
➢ These molecules can act as antigens.
➢ An antibody is a specific protein produced by the body in response to a specific antigen.
➢ Antibodies act in several different ways:
  • opsonisation – makes a pathogen more recognisable to phagocytes,
  • neutralisation of viruses – binding to a virus to prevent it locking on to a host cell,
  • neutralisation of toxins – bind to pathogen toxins preventing them from damaging cells,
  • agglutination – linking pathogens into clumps preventing them from entering cells.

Key components

- ➤ B lymphocytes.
- ➤ Helper T lymphocytes or T_H lymphocytes.
- ➤ Memory cells.
- ➤ Plasma cells.

Key points

- ➤ Both helper T lymphocytes and B lymphocytes are specific for a particular antigen.
- ➤ Helper T lymphocytes activate B lymphocytes.
- ➤ Activated B lymphocytes are called plasma cells.
- ➤ Plasma cells secrete large quantities of antibody.
- ➤ Antibodies aid the destruction of pathogens.
- ➤ Both B lymphocytes and T lymphocytes produce clones of memory cells.
- ➤ Plasma cells only remain active for a short period of time.
- ➤ Memory cells remain dormant for many years and are reactivated when stimulated by the same pathogen.
- ➤ This is the basis of immunity.

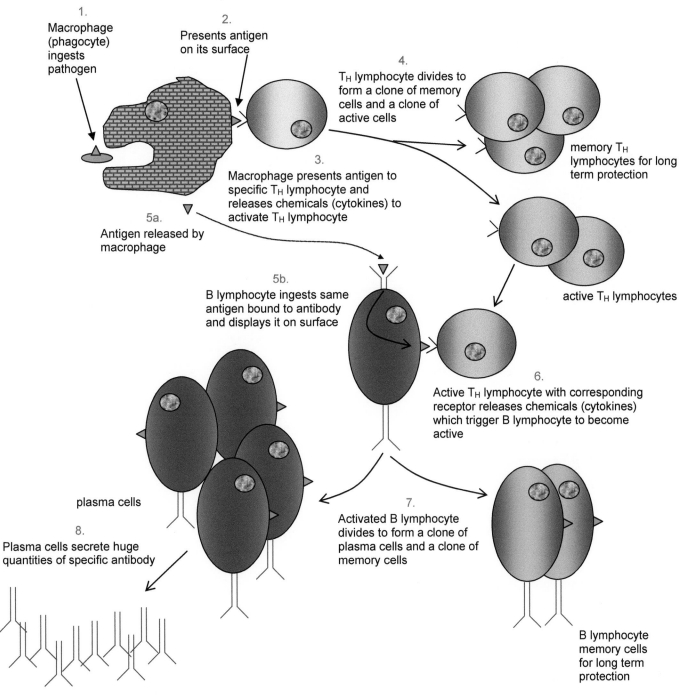

1. Macrophage (phagocyte) ingests pathogen

2. Presents antigen on its surface

3. Macrophage presents antigen to specific T_H lymphocyte and releases chemicals (cytokines) to activate T_H lymphocyte

4. T_H lymphocyte divides to form a clone of memory cells and a clone of active cells

memory T_H lymphocytes for long term protection

active T_H lymphocytes

5a. Antigen released by macrophage

5b. B lymphocyte ingests same antigen bound to antibody and displays it on surface

6. Active T_H lymphocyte with corresponding receptor releases chemicals (cytokines) which trigger B lymphocyte to become active

7. Activated B lymphocyte divides to form a clone of plasma cells and a clone of memory cells

plasma cells

8. Plasma cells secrete huge quantities of specific antibody

B lymphocyte memory cells for long term protection

Vaccination
Principles
➢ Stimulation of B lymphocytes and helper T lymphocytes produces memory cells.
➢ Memory cells bring about a rapid secondary response.

A vaccine contains a form of the pathogen or toxin that has been modified (attenuated) such that it is unable to harm the body. However it still triggers the immune response leading to clones of memory cells. This **immunological memory** means that if the real pathogen invades the body it is rapidly destroyed before it causes harm.

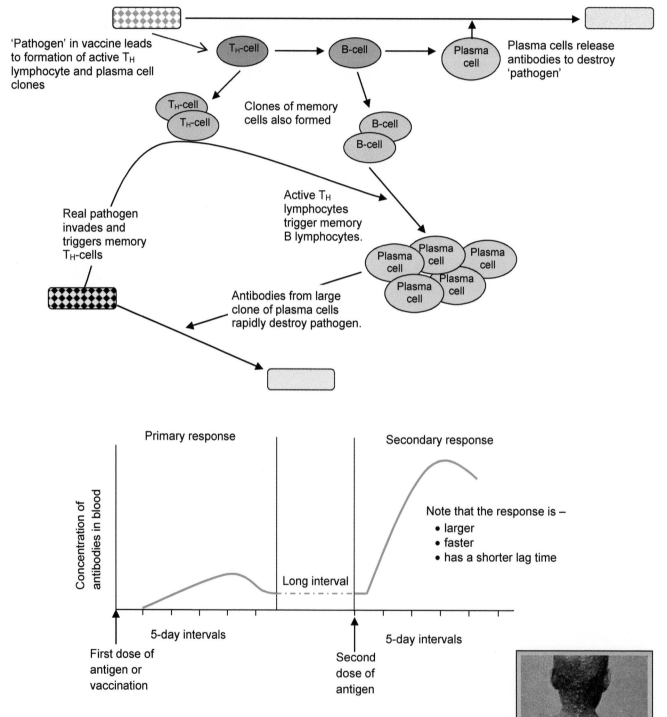

'Pathogen' in vaccine leads to formation of active T_H lymphocyte and plasma cell clones

T_H-cell → B-cell → Plasma cell

Plasma cells release antibodies to destroy 'pathogen'

Clones of memory cells also formed

T_H-cell
T_H-cell

B-cell
B-cell

Real pathogen invades and triggers memory T_H-cells

Active T_H lymphocytes trigger memory B lymphocytes.

Plasma cell, Plasma cell, Plasma cell, Plasma cell, Plasma cell

Antibodies from large clone of plasma cells rapidly destroy pathogen.

Primary response   Secondary response

Concentration of antibodies in blood

Note that the response is –
• larger
• faster
• has a shorter lag time

Long interval

5-day intervals

5-day intervals

First dose of antigen or vaccination

Second dose of antigen

Smallpox
➢ This was the first, and so far only, infectious disease of humans to have been eradicated by vaccination.
(Polio is close to becoming the second. See
http://www.polioeradication.org)

5.15a An African child infected with smallpox

Monoclonal antibodies

Key points 1

➢ A pathogen will usually have several antigens.
➢ Each antigen will result in a clone of plasma cells (active B lymphocytes) since a plasma cell only produces a single type of antibody.
➢ This results in a polyclonal response.
➢ Monoclonal antibodies are the antibodies from a single clone of plasma cells.

Key points 2

➢ A myeloma cell is a cancerous tumour of a plasma cell.
➢ Myeloma cells divide repeatedly in culture but do not produce antibody.
➢ Plasma cells have a short life span.
➢ Plasma cells only produce a specific antigen.

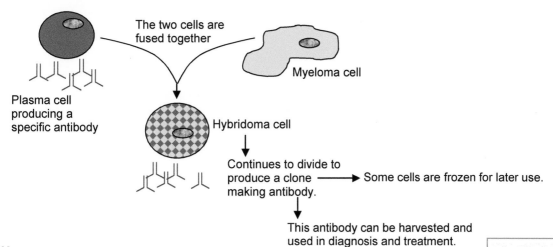

The two cells are fused together

Myeloma cell

Plasma cell producing a specific antibody

Hybridoma cell

Continues to divide to produce a clone making antibody. → Some cells are frozen for later use.

This antibody can be harvested and used in diagnosis and treatment.

Use

Diagnosis – Pregnancy testing.

▪ Detect hCG present in the urine – see page 194.

5.15b Pregnancy test

Blood groups

Key points

➢ Red blood cells contain specific protein molecules on their surface.
➢ These create:
  • the four ABO blood groups – Group A, Group B, Group AB and Group O,
  • the two Rhesus groups – Rhesus positive and Rhesus negative.
➢ These molecules can act as antigens.
➢ These can stimulate the production of antibodies.

Blood transfusions

Normally a blood transfusion is done using the same blood group. Using the wrong group can result in the recipient's antibodies causing the donor's blood to form clumps which can block vessels. In the table below + means clumping occurs. Group O is known as the universal donor and group AB as the universal recipient.

		Recipient			
		O	A	B	AB
Donor	O	-	-	-	-
	A	+	-	+	-
	B	+	+	-	-
	AB	+	+	+	-

Babies

If a Rhesus negative mother has a Rhesus positive baby then during labour some fetal red cells may get into the mother's blood. She responds by producing anti-Rhesus antibodies and memory cells. The first baby will not be affected but if there is a second Rhesus positive baby a small amount of fetal blood can get into the mother stimulating the memory cells and causing her to produce large amounts of antibody. This crosses the placenta into the fetal blood and destroys the red blood cells resulting in anaemia which can be fatal for the baby.

Histamines

➢ Histamines are chemicals released by two types of white blood cell, one found in the blood and the other, mast cells, found in tissues.
➢ Histamines have important roles in the body including acting as a neurotransmitter and in defence.
➢ Sometimes certain mast cells, e.g. those in the nose, can become sensitised by binding of a particular antibody called IgE. (Remember, Ig stands for immunoglobulin.)
➢ Specific environmental chemicals called **allergens** cause these sensitised mast cells to release large amounts of histamine.
➢ Histamines cause allergic symptoms, e.g. the runny nose and itchy eyes associated with hay fever caused by pollen grains.
➢ The allergic response may be very serious, e.g. nut allergy, insect sting or asthma.

HIV and the immune system

➢ HIV – Human Immunodeficiency Virus.
➢ The virus destroys helper T lymphocytes.
➢ B lymphocytes therefore cannot be activated to form plasma cells.
➢ Antibodies are not produced and the pathogen survives to cause an infection.
➢ This leads to the development of AIDS – Acquired Immuno-Deficiency Syndrome.
➢ Infections begin to accumulate in the body – the lungs are especially vulnerable.

Transmission of HIV

♦ Unprotected sexual intercourse, vaginal or anal.
♦ Oral sex.
♦ During birth.
♦ Breast feeding.
♦ Blood transfusion.
♦ Contaminated needles.
♦ Across placenta (but this is rare).

1. What is a pathogen?

2. Why do antibiotics not work against viruses?

3. What did Florey and Chain discover using mice?

4. What are the two surface barriers that provide primary defence?

5a. In the blood clotting cascade what starts the process?

5b. Name the blood component that releases clotting factors.

5c. Name the molecule that causes fibrinogen fibres to form fibrin.

6. Name the blood component that forms the non-specific secondary defence.

7. Distinguish between an antibody and an antigen.

8. Name the blood cell type that activates a B lymphocyte.

9. What is the name of an activated B lymphocyte?

10. What is the principle behind vaccinating?

11. State two significant features about the secondary response.

12. Name the first infectious disease of humans to have been eradicated by vaccination.

13. Why does a pathogen usually result in a polyclonal response?

14. Name the two cell types required to make a hybridoma cell.

15. Name one use for monoclonal antibodies.

16. Which cells produce histamines?

17. State a normal function of histamines in the body?

18. What is an allergen and what does it do?

19a. Which type of blood cell is destroyed by HIV?

19b. How does this result in reduced immunity?

20. List three ways HIV can be transmitted.

The nervous system

The nervous system
The nervous system is one of two systems that control the body, the endocrine system being the other one – see page 168.

It consists of:

➤ a central nervous system (CNS)
  • brain and spinal cord,
➤ a peripheral nervous system (PNS).
  • two types of nerve cell or neuron –
  • sensory neurons and motor neurons.

Sensory and motor neurons connect with other neurons in the CNS and these connections are called synapses.

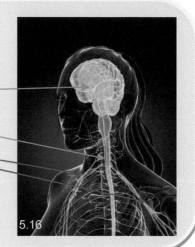
5.16

Neurons
Key points

➤ Sensory neurons carry electrical impulses from receptors towards the central nervous system.
➤ Motor neurons carry electrical impulses away from the central nervous system to effectors.
➤ Neurons are covered by special cells which act as insulation.
➤ This insulating layer is called a myelin sheath.
➤ There are small gaps between these cells called nodes of Ranvier.

A motor neuron with myelin sheath

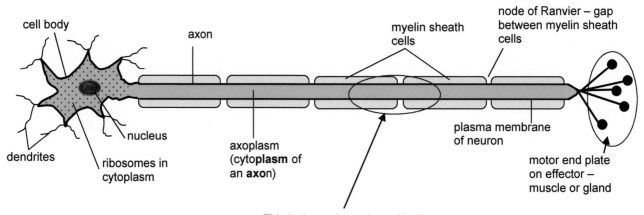

cell body

axon

myelin sheath cells

node of Ranvier – gap between myelin sheath cells

nucleus

dendrites

ribosomes in cytoplasm

axoplasm (cyto**plasm** of an **axon**)

plasma membrane of neuron

motor end plate on effector – muscle or gland

This is the region enlarged in the following sequence of diagrams but without myelin sheath cells.

Neuron potentials
Key vocabulary

• Sodium-potassium ion linked pump,
• Open facilitated potassium ion channel,
• Voltage gated sodium ion channel,
• Voltage gated potassium ion channel,
• Axoplasm,
• Threshold value,
• Potential difference,
• Resting potential,
• Action potential,
• Depolarisation,
• Repolarisation.

Potential difference
This is the electrical difference between the positive and negative regions. It is the same as a battery – a 1.5 volt AA battery has a potential difference of 1.5 volts between the positive and negative ends.

Voltage gated channels
These facilitated channels have gates which control the flow of ions through them. The gate is normally in the closed position, but a change in voltage causes a conformational change which opens the gate.

1. Resting potential

➢ This is the potential difference when the neuron is not transmitting an impulse.
➢ Sodium ions are actively pumped out of the neuron.
➢ Potassium ions are actively pumped into the neuron.
➢ Potassium ions diffuse out of the axoplasm through an open facilitated diffusion channel.
➢ Negative ions remain in the axoplasm.
➢ This generates the resting potential.

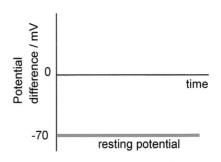

For every 3 Na^+ pumped out 2 K^+ are pumped in and one molecule of ATP is used.

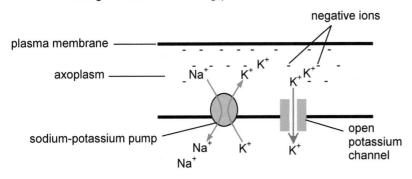

2. Action potential

Key points

➢ The action potential has two parts:
  • Depolarisation,
  • Repolarisation.
➢ Nerve impulses are action potentials propagated (passed) along the axons of neurons.

Note on the diagram that the minimum number of ions is shown to indicate concentration gradients. A red arrow indicates active transport and a green arrow diffusion.

Depolarisation

Key points

➢ A stimulus causes the sodium gated facilitated diffusion channel to open briefly.
➢ This allows a few sodium ions to diffuse into the axoplasm.
➢ The axoplasm starts to become less negative.
➢ If insufficient sodium ions diffuse in it fails to reach the threshold potential and it returns to the resting potential. ━━━━━
➢ If it reaches the threshold potential it continues and changes from a negative potential to a positive potential. ━━━━━
➢ This is depolarisation.

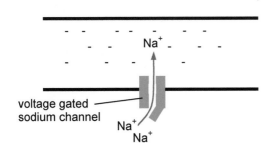

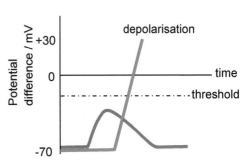

Repolarisation

➢ The potassium gated facilitated diffusion channel opens briefly.
➢ More potassium ions can now diffuse out of the axoplasm making the axoplasm less positive.
➢ The sodium ions that diffused in are now pumped out.
➢ The axoplasm returns to the resting potential.

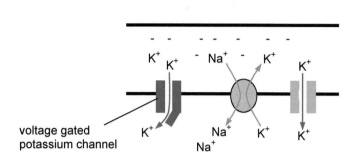

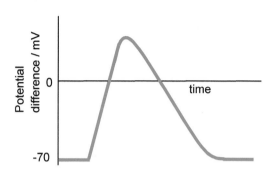

voltage gated
potassium channel

Transmission of an impulse

Key facts

➢ When depolarisation occurs at a node of Ranvier local currents stimulate the next node to become depolarised.
➢ This is done by causing the voltage gated sodium channel to open.
➢ Thus the impulse jumps from node to node.
➢ This is called **saltatory conduction**.

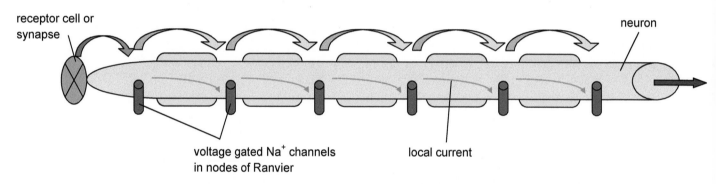

voltage gated Na⁺ channels
in nodes of Ranvier

local current

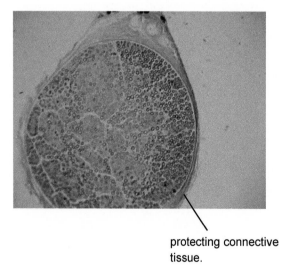

protecting connective
tissue.

5.17a Section through a
nerve – low magnification

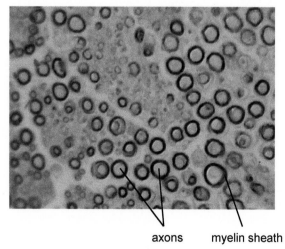

axons   myelin sheath

5.17b Section through a
nerve – high magnification

Synapses

➢ A synapse is a junction where a neuron connects with another neuron.
➢ The signal is carried across the gap by a chemical called a neurotransmitter.
➢ An example of a neurotransmitter is acetyl choline.

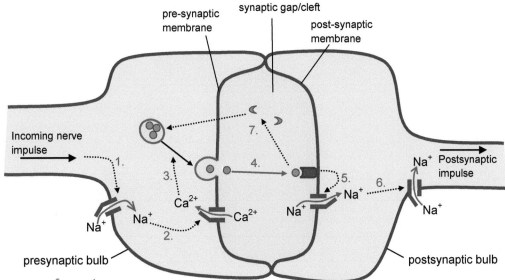

1. An incoming impulse opens a gated sodium channel causing depolarisation of the presynaptic membrane.
2. This opens a gated calcium channel allowing calcium ions to diffuse into the presynaptic bulb.
3. The calcium ions cause vesicles of neurotransmitter to attach to the presynaptic membrane.
4. The neurotransmitter is released by exocytosis, diffuses across the gap and binds to specific receptors on the postsynaptic membrane.
5. This causes a gated sodium channel to open which causes depolarisation of the postsynaptic bulb.
6. This opens a gated sodium channel which initiates the postsynaptic impulse.
7. The acetyl choline is hydrolysed by an enzyme (acetyl cholinesterase) into acetate and choline, transported into the presynaptic bulb and re-synthesised into new vesicles.

Blocking synaptic transmission

➢ Some natural and synthetic chemicals can mimic neurotransmitters.
➢ This will stimulate the synapse even in the absence of the normal neurotransmitter.
➢ Other types of chemical act as inhibitors.
➢ An inhibitor molecule will bind to the postsynaptic receptor but not cause depolarisation.
➢ The normal neurotransmitter cannot bind so no postsynaptic impulse occurs.
➢ Example – neonicotinoid pesticide binds to acetyl choline receptors.

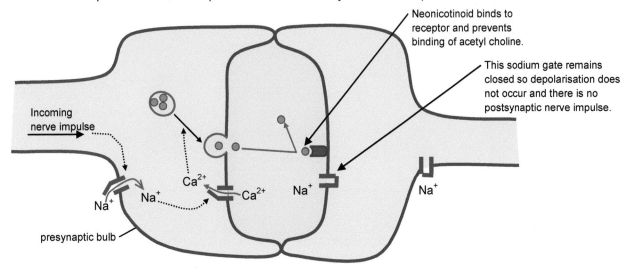

1. What is the name given to the layer of cells covering the neuron?	2. What is the name of the gaps between these cells?	3. Does the sodium-potassium pump transport sodium ions into or out of the axoplasm?
4. What is the approximate potential difference at the resting potential?	5. What is the name given to the potential difference that has to be reached before an action potential occurs?	6a. Name the two phases of an action potential?
6b. What causes the first of these two phases to occur?	6c. What causes the second of these two phases to occur?	7. How is the diffusion of sodium ions controlled?
8. In a myelinated neuron the impulse jumps from gap to gap. What is the name for this type of conduction?	9. Are vesicles of neurotransmitter released from the pre- or post-synaptic membrane?	10. What causes neurotransmitter to be released?
11a. What does the neurotransmitter do when it reaches the other side of the synaptic gap?	11b. What does this cause?	12. State two consequences of a chemical mimicking a neurotransmitter.

The endocrine system

The endocrine system

This is the second of the two systems that control the body. It consists of many glands distributed around the body. These glands secrete chemicals called hormones directly into the blood stream and the hormones circulate in the blood and stimulate specific cells. Only certain cells will respond to the circulating hormone. These cells have receptors – glycoproteins – for the particular hormone on their plasma membrane – see page 83.

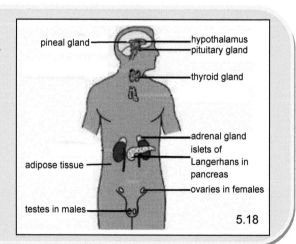

pineal gland
hypothalamus
pituitary gland
thyroid gland
adrenal gland
islets of Langerhans in pancreas
adipose tissue
ovaries in females
testes in males

5.18

Homeostasis

Key point

Homeostasis is maintaining the internal environment between narrow limits:

- blood pH,
- carbon dioxide concentration,
- blood glucose concentration,
- body temperature,
- water balance.

Principles

➤ Receptor or sensor monitors level of variable.
➤ Co-ordinating centre regulates level of variable.
➤ Effectors bring about the changes directed by the co-ordinating centre.
➤ The process is called **negative feedback**.
➤ The endocrine and nervous systems are both involved in homeostasis.

Negative feedback

Principle

➤ When a variable deviates from the norm the result of the effector mechanisms is to return the variable back to the norm.

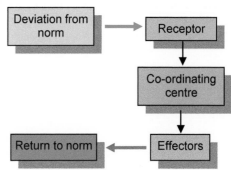

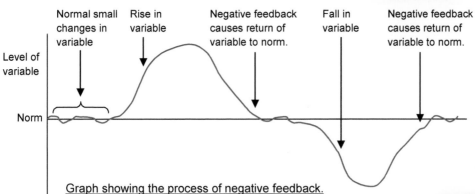

Graph showing the process of negative feedback.

Control of blood glucose

Change in blood sugar level detected by islet cells in pancreas

Increase

Decrease

Beta cells in pancreas secrete insulin

Alpha cells in pancreas secrete glucagon

Blood glucose lowered by –

1. Increased uptake into cells.
2. Increased conversion to glycogen in muscles and liver.
3. Increased conversion to fat in adipose tissue.
4. Increased rate of respiration.

Blood glucose raised by –

1. Increased breakdown of liver glycogen, (not muscle glycogen).
2. Synthesis of glucose from fats and amino acids (gluconeogenesis)

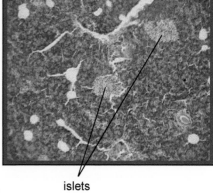

islets

5.19 Section through a pancreas

Tip – You are studying the IB course – Insulin – Beta cells.	Warning – take care not to confuse glycogen and glucagon. Glucagon is the hormone.

Diabetes
Key facts
➢ Diabetes is failure to control blood glucose level leading to abnormally high levels of glucose in the blood (hyperglycaemia).
➢ The kidney threshold* is exceeded and glucose is excreted.
➢ Urine volume increases causing thirst.
➢ Muscle tissue is broken down leading to weight loss.
➢ Vision can be seriously damaged (retinopathy).
➢ Kidney failure may occur.

> * When the kidney first filters the blood glucose is found in this filtrate. However it is normally all reabsorbed back into the blood. The threshold is the maximum level of glucose in the filtrate that can all be reabsorbed.

Type I (early onset or juvenile) diabetes

• Usually starts early in life, often very suddenly.
• Due to loss of insulin secreting cells in the pancreas.
• Controlled by testing level of blood sugar and then injecting an appropriate quantity of insulin.
• Control has to continue throughout life.
• Potential for stem cell therapy – see blue box.

> In October 2014 stem cell researchers at Harvard University announced a breakthrough in the production of human beta cells from embryonic stem cells – see page 73. Trials in animal models, including non-human primates, are being conducted along with methods of protecting the cells from attack by the immune system.

Type II (late onset) diabetes

• Comes on gradually, usually in late middle age.
• Commonly associated with being overweight for a long time.
• Persistent over-eating of sugary foods causes high levels of plasma insulin.
• This reduces the sensitivity of the insulin target cells so they fail to take up sufficient glucose from the blood.
• Often controlled by reducing carbohydrate intake which allows the target cells to recover.
• Controlled by eating a healthy diet high in fibre and complex carbohydrates – beans, lentils, pulses and wholegrain cereals and low in saturated fats and salt. Sugary and fatty snack foods and sugary drinks should be avoided.

Control of metabolic rate and temperature
Key points
➢ Thyroxin is secreted by the thyroid gland – see page 168.
➢ Its release is regulated by a hormonal pathway controlled by the hypothalamus in the brain.
➢ Thyroxin controls the metabolic rate and is essential for proper growth and development, both physical and mental.
➢ Prolonged exposure to cold will stimulate the hypothalamus to release more thyroxin to increase the metabolic rate.
➢ A side product of metabolism is heat.

Control of appetite
Key points
➢ Leptin is one of several hormones involved in energy homeostasis.
➢ It regulates the amount of fat stored in the body.
➢ It is secreted by cells in adipose (fat) tissue.
➢ It is secreted when the adipose tissue reaches a particular level and acts on the hypothalamus to inhibit appetite and increase metabolism.

Clinical obesity

- Clinical obesity is when a person has been diagnosed as obese by a doctor.
- They have a BMI of over 30kg m^{-2}.
- Obese patients generally have a higher level of plasma leptin than a non-obese person.
- This is contrary to expectation.
- One hypothesis is that there is a fault with the leptin signalling system in the cells of the hypothalamus.
- Hence injections of leptin to try and reduce hunger feelings are unsuccessful.

Control of circadian rhythms

Key points

- Several aspects of the body have circadian rhythms, e.g. hormone release, temperature.
- The most obvious one is the sleep-wake cycle.
- The 'master' clock for the body is a group of cells (called the SCN) in the hypothalamus.
- The sleep-wake cycle is controlled by the hormone melatonin.
- Melatonin is secreted by the pineal gland in the brain.
- Secretion follows a regular pattern of high during the night and low during the day.
- It is broken down rapidly by the liver so blood concentrations rise and fall sharply.
- The pattern is maintained by the natural light – dark cycle.
- A special type of ganglion cell in the retina detects light at wavelength around 470nm (blue light) and sends signals to the SCN to maintain the rhythm.
- Melatonin stimulates the sleep part of the cycle.
- In teenagers melatonin secretion follows a cycle to the right of the adult pattern, making them wakeful during the evening and sleepy in the morning.

Circadian rhythm

This is a daily physical, mental or behavioural rhythm based on the 24 hour light/dark cycle and is shown by a very wide variety of organisms – animals, plants and fungi. The clock is a cellular mechanism and is largely independent from the light /dark cycle, the organism continues to show the circadian rhythm even when the light/dark pattern is changed. Repeated behaviour contrary to the natural circadian rhythm, e.g. night-time shift work, can lead to ill health.

Jet lag

- This is caused by rapid travel across time zones.
- Moving to a different time zone disrupts the natural circadian rhythm.
- Over a period of time the brain resets to the new rhythm.
- The greater the number of time zones crossed the longer it takes for the brain to reset.
- Melatonin tablets can be used to alleviate it – see blue box.

Use of melatonin

Melatonin tablets can be bought over the counter in many countries or online, but in some countries they are not approved for sale. Like all drugs, they are open to misuse and their efficacy is not proven since dosage and timing are highly variable.

1. What is the name given to the process of maintaining a constant internal environment?	2. What is the name given to the regulatory pathway for this process?	3. State two examples excluding control of blood sugar.
4. Which pancreatic cells produce glucagon?	5. What is the most common cause of type II diabetes?	6. Name the hormone used to control metabolic rate.
7a. Name the hormone used to control appetite.	7b. What does this hormone measure in order to do this?	8. What is the minimum BMI for a person to be classed as obese?
9. What is the name given to daily rhythms such as the sleep-wake cycle?	10. Name the hormone used to regulate the sleep-wake cycle?	11. Is this hormone secreted in the dark or light?

Osmoregulation and excretion

> - Osmoregulation is maintaining the correct fluid balance in the body.
> - It is carried out by:
>   - the malpighian tubule system in insects,
>   - the kidney in mammals.

> - Metabolic pathways produce waste products that could be toxic or damage molecular structures if allowed to accumulate, eg urea breaks weak non-covalent bonds in proteins leading to denaturing.
> - Excretion is the removal of these substances.
> - It is carried out by:
>   - the malpighian tubule system in insects,
>   - the kidney in mammals.

Osmoconformers and osmoregulators

Osmotic potential
This is the potential of water molecules to move by osmosis from a solution with a higher water potential to a solution with a lower water potential.

Osmoconformers
Key facts
> - These organisms allow their body fluid osmotic potential to mirror the environmental osmotic potential.
> - They do this by using active transport mechanisms to maintain specific ions in their tissue fluid at concentrations different from those in the environment.

Osmoregulators
Key facts
> - Osmoregulators maintain an osmotic potential of their body fluids that is different from that of their environment.
> - Organisms living in fresh water have to eliminate the excess water that flows in by osmosis.
> - Organisms living in salt water have to conserve water and eliminate salts.
> - Organisms living on land have to conserve water.
> - It is controlled by a homeostatic mechanism – see page 169.

The malpighian tubule system in insects
Key facts
> - The malpighian tubules are blind ending outgrowths from the gut and are surrounded by the insect's blood in the body cavity or haemocoel.
> - They carry out both osmoregulation and excretion.
> - Uric acid is synthesized by the insect's tissues and released in soluble form into the blood.
> - This is actively transported into the tubules.
> - The low pH in the tubule lumen causes uric acid to precipitate out as dry matter.
> - Active transport of solutes creates an osmotic gradient.

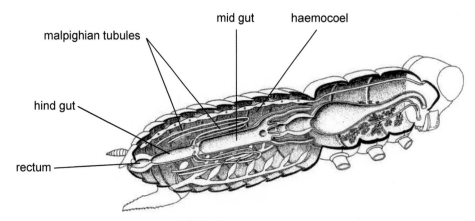

5.20 Vertical section through an insect gut.

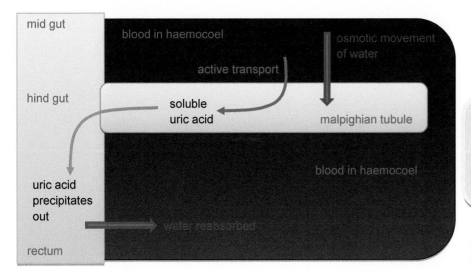

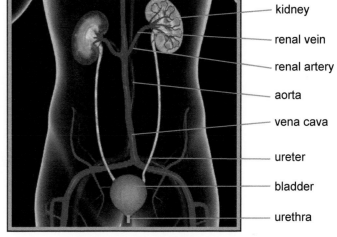

The osmotic movement of water into the malpighian tubule decreases the water potential of the haemocoel.
This causes water to be reabsorbed from the rectum into the haemocoel to maintain the concentration.

<u>Osmoregulation and excretion in insects.</u>

The kidney
Key points

➢ The blood flow is through the renal artery and vein.

➢ The **ureter** carries urine from the kidneys to the bladder.

➢ The **urethra** carries the urine from the bladder to the outside.

➢ There are three regions in the kidney:
  - cortex,
  - medulla,
  - pelvis.

➢ The renal tubules in the kidney carry out the processes of osmoregulation and excretion.

➢ The tubules are in the cortex and medulla and empty into the hollow pelvis.

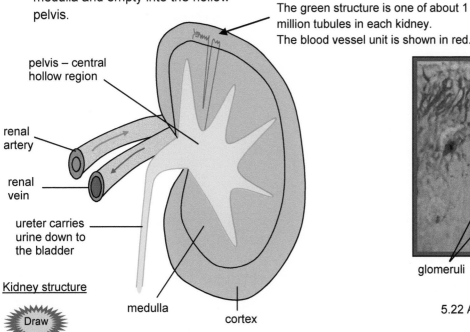

5.21 The urinary system

Kidney structure

Draw

The green structure is one of about 1 million tubules in each kidney.
The blood vessel unit is shown in red.

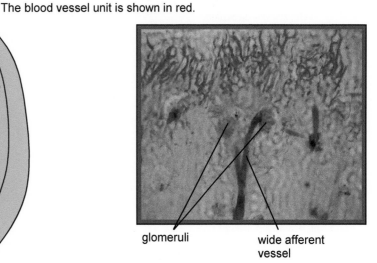

5.22 A section through the cortex

The kidney tubule

Annotate

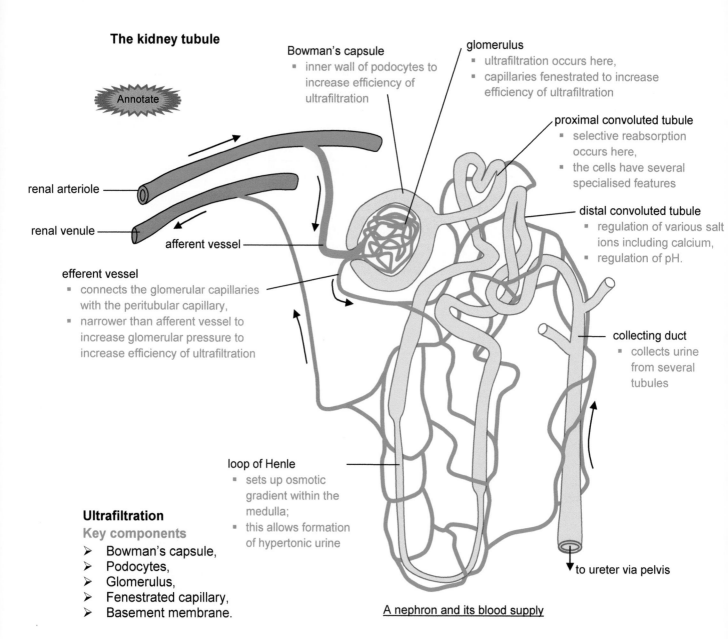

renal arteriole

renal venule

afferent vessel

Bowman's capsule
- inner wall of podocytes to increase efficiency of ultrafiltration

glomerulus
- ultrafiltration occurs here,
- capillaries fenestrated to increase efficiency of ultrafiltration

proximal convoluted tubule
- selective reabsorption occurs here,
- the cells have several specialised features

distal convoluted tubule
- regulation of various salt ions including calcium,
- regulation of pH.

efferent vessel
- connects the glomerular capillaries with the peritubular capillary,
- narrower than afferent vessel to increase glomerular pressure to increase efficiency of ultrafiltration

collecting duct
- collects urine from several tubules

loop of Henle
- sets up osmotic gradient within the medulla;
- this allows formation of hypertonic urine

to ureter via pelvis

A nephron and its blood supply

Ultrafiltration

Key components
➢ Bowman's capsule,
➢ Podocytes,
➢ Glomerulus,
➢ Fenestrated capillary,
➢ Basement membrane.

Definition
➢ Ultrafiltration is filtration at the molecular level.

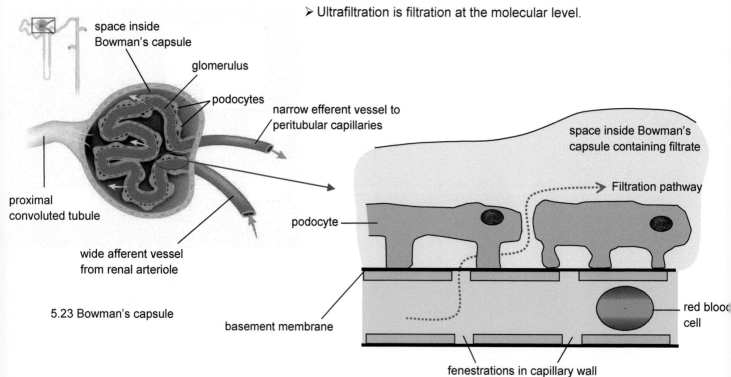

space inside Bowman's capsule

glomerulus

podocytes

narrow efferent vessel to peritubular capillaries

proximal convoluted tubule

wide afferent vessel from renal arteriole

5.23 Bowman's capsule

space inside Bowman's capsule containing filtrate

Filtration pathway

podocyte

basement membrane

fenestrations in capillary wall

red blood cell

IBHL Biology 2016 © Ashby Merson-Davies

- Glomerulus has a large surface area.
- Large molecules in the blood can enter the **fenestrations** (gaps) between the capillary cells but are unable to pass through the **basement membrane.**
- Thus the basement membrane acts as the 'ultra-filter' and is the only barrier between the filtrate and the blood, allowing small solute molecules such as glucose and urea through but not larger ones such as large proteins.
- Smaller proteins such as the glycoprotein hCG can pass through and is used in the pregnancy test – see page 161.
- The **podocytes** (cells with feet) allow the filtrate to pass rapidly and easily into the space of Bowman's capsule as there are gaps between the cells.

Bowman's capsule   glomerulus covered in podocytes   proximal tubules

5.24 High power section through the kidney cortex

Reabsorption

The kidney tubule can be divided into three reabsorption regions:
1. proximal convoluted tubule,
2. loop of Henle,
3. collecting duct.

1. Proximal convoluted tubule
Key points
- Desirable substances taken back into blood by **selective reabsorption**.
- Glucose and salts reabsorbed by active transport.
- Water reabsorbed by osmosis.
- Other solutes reabsorbed by diffusion.
- All glucose (under normal conditions) is reabsorbed.
- About 80% of the filtrate is reabsorbed here.

Key features
- Long, to increase surface area.
- Surrounded by peritubular capillaries.
- Cells lining tubule have adaptations shown on the diagram.

Tubule lumen

Microvilli increase absorptive area

selective reabsorption

Mitochondria provide ATP for active transport

Intercellular and subcellular spaces increase surface area for export

Capillary lumen

Active transport channels in plasma membrane

Structural features of a proximal convoluted tubule cell

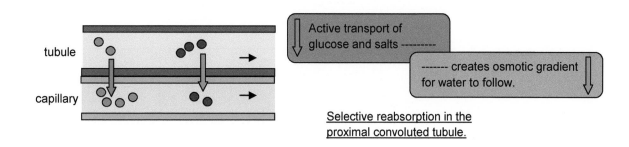

tubule

capillary

Active transport of glucose and salts --------

------- creates osmotic gradient for water to follow.

Selective reabsorption in the proximal convoluted tubule.

2. Loop of Henle

Principles

➢ The primary function of the loop of Henle is to create and maintain hypertonic conditions within the medullary region of the kidney.

➢ Some water and salt reabsorption occurs.

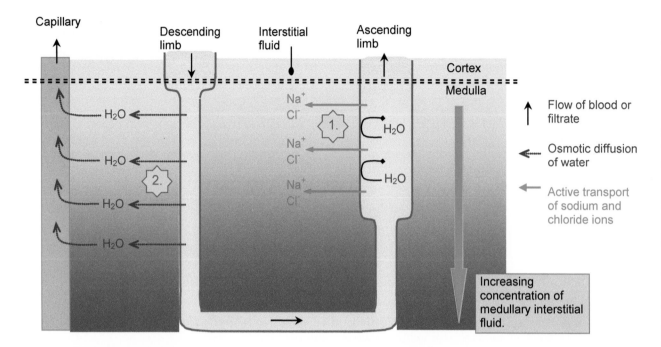

 The cells of the ascending limb actively transport sodium and chloride ions out into the interstitial fluid – see page 87.

In theory water should follow because an osmotic gradient has been created, but the walls of the ascending limb are impermeable to water.

 The walls of the descending limb <u>are</u> permeable to water. As a result of the salt ions being pumped into the interstitial fluid the resulting osmotic gradient causes water to leave the descending limb.

This water is removed by the blood in an ascending capillary.

Salt continues to enter the loop in the filtrate in the descending limb but less leaves the loop in the filtrate in the ascending limb and so it accumulates in the interstitial fluid of the medulla. This is called a counter-current multiplier. (Counter-current because the flows are opposite in the descending and ascending limbs).

1. What is the name given to maintaining the correct fluid balance in the body?	2. What is the name given to organisms that maintain an osmotic potential of their body fluids that is different from that of their environment?	3. What is the name given to organisms that allow their body fluid osmotic potential to mirror the environmental osmotic potential?
4. What is the name given to removal of the waste products of metabolism?		
5. Name the structures in insects that carry out Q4.	6. What is the name of the waste product made by insects in these structures?	7. Name the artery that supplies blood to the kidney.

3. Collecting duct

➢ The walls have a variable permeability to water.
➢ The hormone ADH from the pituitary gland increases the permeability.
➢ Water flows down the osmotic gradient created by the loop of Henle.

1.
As filtrate flows down the collecting duct the surrounding interstitial fluid is increasingly more concentrated (hypertonic). Thus there is an osmotic gradient between the filtrate and the interstitial fluid.

In the absence of ADH there are few water channels and the duct wall is impermeable to water. This results in isotonic or hypotonic (dilute) urine.

2.
If the blood concentration rises osmoreceptors in the hypothalamus stimulate neurosecretory cells to release ADH from the posterior pituitary gland which travels in the blood stream to the collecting duct.

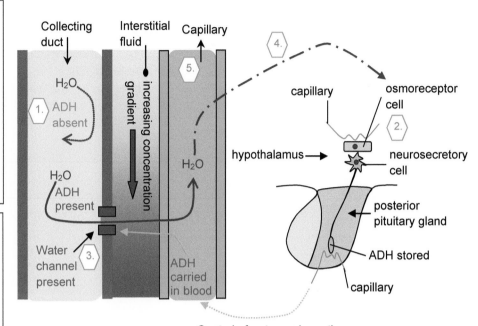

Control of water reabsorption

3.
Water channels called aquaporins are inserted in the duct wall by the presence of ADH so water leaves the filtrate by osmosis and is removed by the blood.
This results in hypertonic (concentrated) urine.

4.
As blood concentration returns to normal a negative feedback circuit operates and ADH secretion stops.

The half-life of ADH is only 15–20 minutes so this allows water balance to be tightly controlled.

5.
Note that the blood flow is opposite to the filtrate flow. This is so that there is always an osmotic gradient between the filtrate and the blood.

Composition of blood in the renal vessels

Substance	Renal artery plasma	Renal vein plasma	Reason
Proteins	Normal concentration	Normal concentration	Only a few small proteins such as hCG are able to pass through the basement membrane.
Glucose	Normal concentration	Lower concentration	Some will have been used in respiration by kidney cells.
Urea	Normal concentration	Lower concentration	During ultrafiltration not all the urea passes into the filtrate since the process is passive. Some urea in the filtrate is reabsorbed back into the blood.

Habitat and the loop of Henle

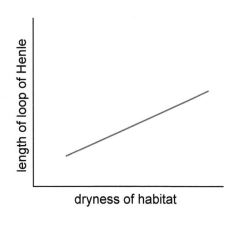

Key points

➤ Recall that the loop of Henle creates an increasing osmotic gradient within the medulla.
➤ This is used to reabsorb water from the filtrate in the collecting duct under the control of ADH.
➤ Thus the longer the loop the greater:
  • the concentration gradient,
  • the length of peritubular capillary in contact with interstitial fluid.
➤ The drier the habitat the greater the need to conserve water.
➤ A longer loop of Henle combined with a long collecting duct increases the volume of water reabsorbed from the filtrate.

Animal	Habitat	Maximum urine concentration mOsmol l^{-1}
Beaver	Aquatic	520
Human	Land with available water	1300
Camel	Land with intermittent water availability	2800
Kangaroo rat	Desert	5500

Evolution and excretion of nitrogenous waste

Key points

➤ The metabolism of proteins and nucleic acids produces ammonia as a waste.
➤ Ammonia is highly toxic.
➤ If it cannot be excreted continuously then it has to be converted to less toxic compounds.
➤ These conversions require energy.
➤ Early animals in evolution were aquatic and used ammonia as the most energy efficient excretory molecule.
➤ As they moved onto land and further away from a constant supply of water there was the need to evolve a molecule that could be retained in the body for longer without toxic effects.

Nitrogen compound	Organisms	Reasons
Ammonia	aquatic invertebrates, bony fish, crocodiles, amphibian tadpoles.	Ammonia is used if plenty of water is available as this is the most energy efficient nitrogenous excretory compound. It is very soluble and diffuses easily.
Urea	mammals, most amphibian adults, cartilaginous fish.	Urea is used if there is a reasonably good supply of water. It has good solubility and low toxicity. It can be excreted in solution. Mammals can reabsorb water to create hypertonic urine.
Uric acid	insects, reptiles, birds.	Uric acid has low solubility and can be excreted as a solid. This conserves water in dry habitats. It reduces weight e.g. for flight.

Dehydration

Key points

➢ If more water is lost from the body than consumed the blood becomes hypertonic.
➢ Water is drawn out of cells by osmosis.
➢ This impairs cell function.
➢ Brain cells are particularly vulnerable.
➢ Symptoms include:
  • dizziness or light-headedness,
  • headache,
  • tiredness,
  • dry mouth, lips and eyes,
  • dark coloured urine.

Overhydration

Key points

➢ If more water is consumed than is lost the blood becomes hypotonic.
➢ Cells absorb water by osmosis.
➢ The cells swell and may burst.
➢ Red blood cells and brain cells are particularly vulnerable.
➢ Symptoms include:
  • headache,
  • personality and behaviour changes,
  • confusion,
  • irritability,
  • drowsiness.

Kidney failure

➢ This is when the kidney tubules fail to filter enough blood and hence fail to clear toxins from the blood.
➢ It can be treated by:
  • haemodialysis,
  • transplant.

❖ **Haemodialysis**

Key points

➢ A catheter is placed in a large vein in the arm, the blood circulates through the dialysis machine and is returned to the arm vein.
➢ In the machine the blood passes along one side of a partially permeable membrane and dialysis fluid passes in the opposite direction on the other side .
➢ The dialysis fluid is a solution where the solutes are balanced to either cause or prevent diffusion:
  ▪ urea concentration is zero so urea diffuses out of the blood,
  ▪ glucose concentration is equal to that of blood so no glucose leaves the blood.
➢ Haemodialysis takes several hours and has to be done two or three times a week.

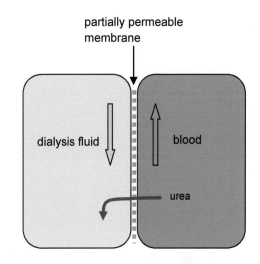

partially permeable membrane

dialysis fluid

blood

urea

❖ **Transplant**

Key points

➢ A kidney transplant would allow the patient to lead a near normal life.
➢ A close tissue match has to be found.
➢ The patient has to take anti-rejection drugs for the rest of their life.

Many tissues or organs can easily be transplanted with modern surgery but there is a shortage of suitable material. People can carry donor cards to say any of their tissues or organs can be used after their death, but too few people carry these cards to meet demand.

Urinary tests

Key points

Looked for	Reason
Protein	Could indicate kidney damage or disease.
Red blood cells White blood cells	Could indicate, for example, kidney damage or disease, cystitis, kidney stones.
Glucose	Could indicate diabetes.
Drugs	Testing for use of banned drugs in sports persons.

8. List the three regions of the kidney.	9. Name the tube that carries urine from the bladder to the outside.	10. Name the tube that carries urine from the kidneys to the bladder.
11. List the regions of a nephron.	12. Name the knot of capillaries where ultrafiltration occurs.	13. Name the blood vessel supplying these capillaries.
14. What is the name of the specialised cells lining Bowman's capsule?	15. What is the special feature of the glomerular capillaries?	16. What structure acts as the filter between the blood and the filtrate?
17. In the proximal tubule only certain substances are reabsorbed into the blood. What is the name for this process?	18. State the role of the loop of Henle.	19a. What is the important difference between the afferent and efferent vessels?
19b. What is the reason for this?	20. What significant process occurs in the collecting duct?	21. List three features of proximal tubule cells that aid reabsorption.
22. What mechanism creates the osmotic gradient in the proximal tubules?	23. Which substance is normally not found in the filtrate entering the loop of Henle, excluding protein?	
24. From which limb of the loop of Henle is water lost?	25a. What mechanism is used to transport sodium and chloride ions out of the loop of Henle?	25b. In which limb does this occur?
26. In which region of the kidney is the loop of Henle found?	27. State the hormone that controls the water permeability of the collecting duct.	28. From which gland is this hormone released?
29. Is the stimulus to release this hormone when the blood is hypertonic or hypotonic?	30. Why is the concentration of glucose in the renal vein lower than in the renal artery?	31. What is the relationship between length of loop of Henle and habitat dryness?
32. Which nitrogenous excretory compound is used by birds?	33. Which nitrogenous excretory compound is used by animals living in fresh water?	34. Is dark coloured urine due to overhydration or dehydration?
35. Name the process by which a machine is used to treat kidney failure.	36. List three things looked for in urinary tests apart from glucose.	37. What could the presence of glucose in the urine indicate?

Movement

Bones and the exoskeleton of arthropods:
- provide anchorage for muscles,
- act as levers.

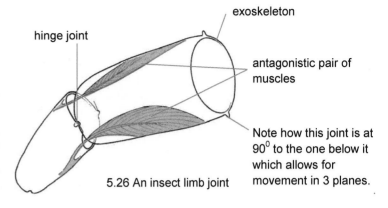

5.25 The shed exoskeleton of a cicada

hinge joint

exoskeleton

antagonistic pair of muscles

Note how this joint is at 90^0 to the one below it which allows for movement in 3 planes.

5.26 An insect limb joint

Synovial joints

Key points

➤ The joints in mammals are called synovial joints because they are lubricated by synovial fluid secreted by synovial membranes.

➤ They allow certain movements but not others.

➤ Two joint types are:
- hinge – elbow and knee – movement in one plane only,
- ball and socket – shoulder and hip – movement in three planes.

Muscles

Key points

➤ Muscles can only contract.

➤ Therefore movement at a joint is carried out by a pair of muscles attached on each side of the joint.

➤ This is called an **antagonistic pair**.

The human elbow joint

Annotate

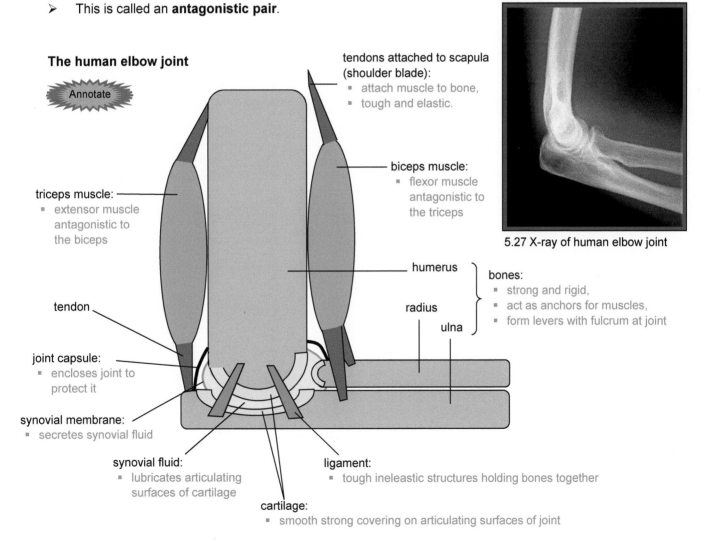

tendons attached to scapula (shoulder blade):
- attach muscle to bone,
- tough and elastic.

biceps muscle:
- flexor muscle antagonistic to the triceps

5.27 X-ray of human elbow joint

triceps muscle:
- extensor muscle antagonistic to the biceps

humerus

radius

ulna

bones:
- strong and rigid,
- act as anchors for muscles,
- form levers with fulcrum at joint

tendon

joint capsule:
- encloses joint to protect it

synovial membrane:
- secretes synovial fluid

synovial fluid:
- lubricates articulating surfaces of cartilage

ligament:
- tough ineleastic structures holding bones together

cartilage:
- smooth strong covering on articulating surfaces of joint

Muscle structure

Key components

➢ Tendon,
➢ Fibres,
➢ Myofibrils.

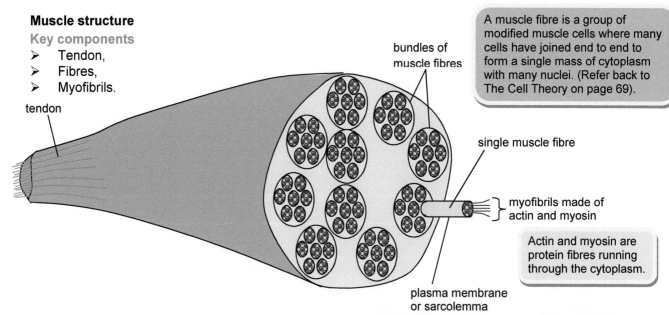

tendon

bundles of muscle fibres

A muscle fibre is a group of modified muscle cells where many cells have joined end to end to form a single mass of cytoplasm with many nuclei. (Refer back to The Cell Theory on page 69).

single muscle fibre

myofibrils made of actin and myosin

Actin and myosin are protein fibres running through the cytoplasm.

plasma membrane or sarcolemma

If we remove a single muscle fibre and look at it under the microscope we can see a distinct banding pattern (hence the name striated muscle). This banding is due to the arrangement of actin and myosin filaments which are of different thicknesses.

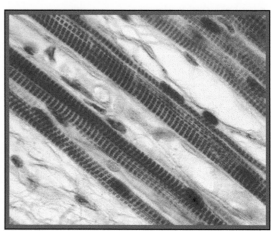

5.28 Skeletal muscle showing the banding pattern

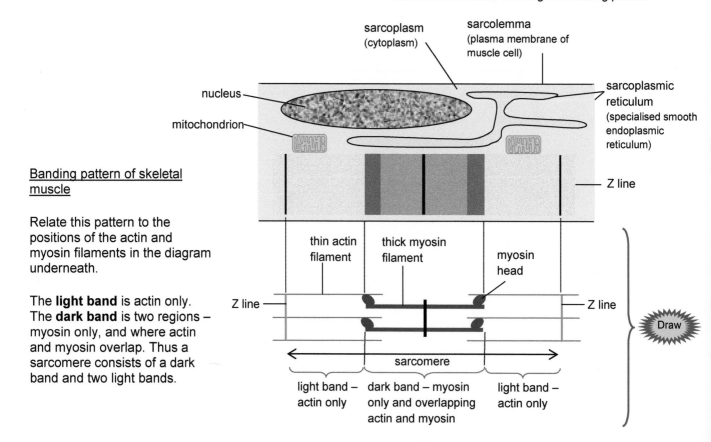

sarcoplasm (cytoplasm)

sarcolemma (plasma membrane of muscle cell)

nucleus

mitochondrion

sarcoplasmic reticulum (specialised smooth endoplasmic reticulum)

Z line

Banding pattern of skeletal muscle

Relate this pattern to the positions of the actin and myosin filaments in the diagram underneath.

The **light band** is actin only. The **dark band** is two regions – myosin only, and where actin and myosin overlap. Thus a sarcomere consists of a dark band and two light bands.

thin actin filament

thick myosin filament

myosin head

Z line

Z line

Draw

sarcomere

light band – actin only

dark band – myosin only and overlapping actin and myosin

light band – actin only

Cross-bridge formation during muscle contraction

Key components

➢ Actin (thin) filament,
➢ Myosin (thick) filament,
➢ Myosin head,
➢ Sarcoplasmic reticulum,
➢ Calcium ions,
➢ Troponin,
➢ Tropomyosin.

Key points

➢ Arranged along the myosin filaments are projecting heads.
➢ The actin filament has special binding sites for the myosin heads.
➢ Binding of the myosin head to the actin binding site forms a cross-bridge.
➢ The actin binding sites are covered by a spiral filament of the protein tropomyosin.
➢ Troponin is attached to the tropomyosin.
➢ Calcium ions bind to troponin, pulling the tropomyosin off the myosin binding sites.
➢ Calcium ions are stored by active transport in the sarcoplasmic reticulum.
➢ Depolarisation of the sarcoplasmic reticulum membrane opens voltage gated calcium channels allowing calcium ions to diffuse out and to bind to troponin.

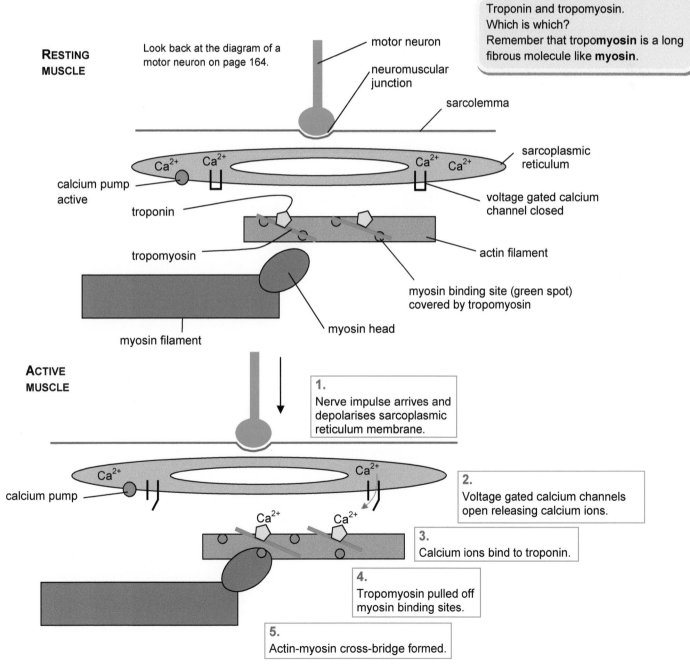

Troponin and tropomyosin.
Which is which?
Remember that tropo**myosin** is a long fibrous molecule like **myosin**.

RESTING MUSCLE

Look back at the diagram of a motor neuron on page 164.

motor neuron

neuromuscular junction

sarcolemma

sarcoplasmic reticulum

calcium pump active

troponin

voltage gated calcium channel closed

tropomyosin

actin filament

myosin binding site (green spot) covered by tropomyosin

myosin head

myosin filament

ACTIVE MUSCLE

1. Nerve impulse arrives and depolarises sarcoplasmic reticulum membrane.

calcium pump

2. Voltage gated calcium channels open releasing calcium ions.

3. Calcium ions bind to troponin.

4. Tropomyosin pulled off myosin binding sites.

5. Actin-myosin cross-bridge formed.

The sliding filament mechanism

➤ When a cross-bridge forms it can bend pulling the actin filament.
➤ When ATP binds to myosin it breaks the cross-bridge.
➤ The myosin head contains the enzyme ATPase which hydrolyses ATP.
➤ When the cross-bridge breaks the myosin head resets to its original position.
➤ The cross-bridge reforms further along the actin and the process repeats.
➤ The Z lines move closer together, ie the sarcomere shortens – see changes to banding pattern below.

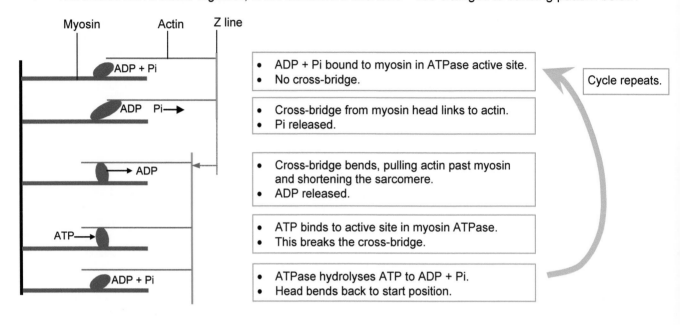

Changes to the banding pattern during muscle contraction

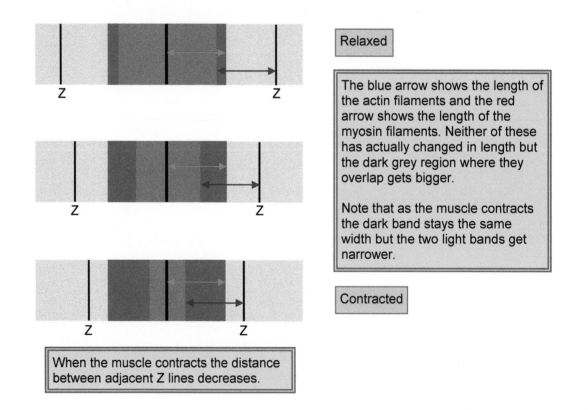

Relaxed

The blue arrow shows the length of the actin filaments and the red arrow shows the length of the myosin filaments. Neither of these has actually changed in length but the dark grey region where they overlap gets bigger.

Note that as the muscle contracts the dark band stays the same width but the two light bands get narrower.

Contracted

When the muscle contracts the distance between adjacent Z lines decreases.

1. What is the name given to the pair of muscles that oppose each other?	2. Why do muscles have to work in opposing pairs?	3. Name these two muscles in the arm which move the elbow joint.
4. What type of skeleton do insects have?	5. Name the fluid that lubricates the joints in mammals.	6. What type of joint is the elbow joint?
7. What type of joint is the hip joint?	8. What structure joins a muscle to a bone?	9. What structure encloses a joint to protect it?
10. Name the three bones in the elbow joint.	11. Name the smooth material covering the ends of bones at a joint.	12. What is the unusual feature of muscle cells?
13. What are the components of a myofibril?	14. Name the structure that stores calcium ions in a muscle cell.	15. Which muscle protein is only found in the light bands?
16. What is a sarcomere?	17. Name the protein that binds calcium ions during muscle contraction.	18. Name the protein that covers the binding sites on actin when the muscle is relaxed.
19. What process causes the actin-myosin cross-bridge to break?	20. Where precisely is the ATPase enzyme found?	21. When a muscle contracts what happens to the width of the dark band?
22. When a muscle contracts what happens to the length of the sarcomere?	23. What causes the voltage gated channels on the sarcoplasmic reticulum to open?	24. List the labels you would put on the diagram of a sarcomere (7).

Reproduction

oviduct
- picks up secondary oocyte at ovulation,
- site of fertilisation,
- transports blastocyst to uterus.

ovary
- releases one (usually) secondary oocyte once a month,
- releases progesterone and oestrogen during pregnancy.

uterus
- place where the fetus grows

endometrium
- lining which breaks down and is replaced each month. When the blastocyst reaches the uterus it sinks into the endometrium.

pubic bone

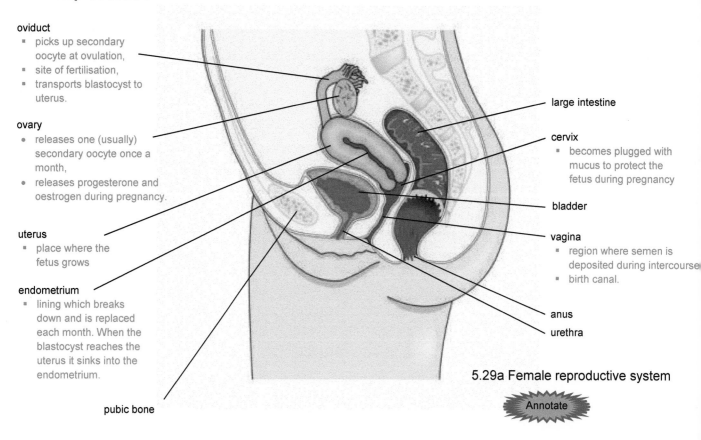

large intestine

cervix
- becomes plugged with mucus to protect the fetus during pregnancy

bladder

vagina
- region where semen is deposited during intercourse
- birth canal.

anus

urethra

5.29a Female reproductive system

Annotate

erectile tissue
- fills with blood to produce an erection

penis
- enters vagina to release semen near cervix during ejaculation

Urethra
Transports
- urine,
- semen during an ejaculation.

vas deferens / sperm duct
- transfers sperm during ejaculation

testis – produces
- sperm,
- testosterone.

scrotal sac / scrotum
- keeps testes at a lower temperature

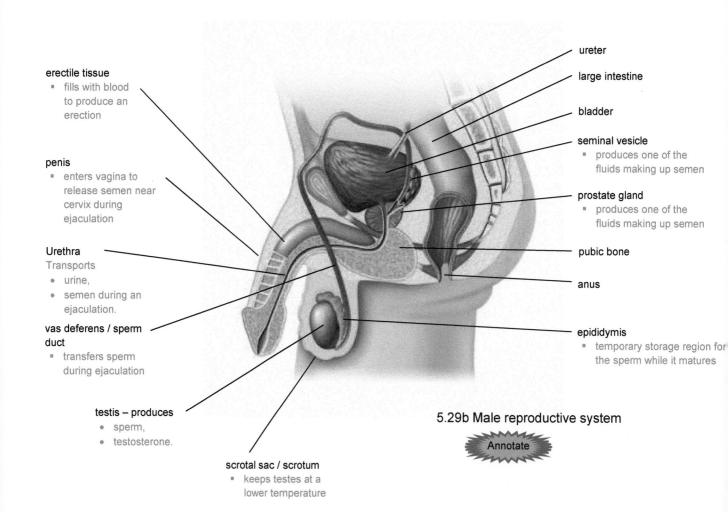

ureter

large intestine

bladder

seminal vesicle
- produces one of the fluids making up semen

prostate gland
- produces one of the fluids making up semen

pubic bone

anus

epididymis
- temporary storage region for the sperm while it matures

5.29b Male reproductive system

Annotate

Reproductive hormones

- During early fetal development both male and female gonads develop close to the kidney and the male external genitalia look like that of a female.
- A gene on the Y chromosome causes the gonads in the male embryo to develop as testes and to move down through the abdominal cavity into the scrotal sac.
- The testes start to produce testosterone and this causes the external genitalia to develop into the male structures.

Hormone	Function	
	Boys	**Girls**
Testosterone	• Pre-natal development of genitalia. • Development of secondary sexual characteristics. • Stimulates final stages of spermatogenesis. • Maintains the sex drive.	
Oestrogen		• Pre-natal development of genitalia. • Development of secondary sexual characteristics.
Follicle stimulating hormone (FSH)		• Causes one or more follicles in the ovaries to mature. • Stimulates secretion of oestrogen.
Luteinising hormone (LH)		• Stimulates ovulation. • Stimulates conversion of empty follicle into corpus luteum. • Stimulates secretion of progesterone.
Oestrogen		• Initiates repair of uterus lining. • Positive feedback on LH to trigger ovulation.
Progesterone		• Completes repair of uterus lining. • Negative feedback on pituitary to block release of FSH. • Maintains uterus lining in early part of pregnancy – see page194.

The menstrual cycle

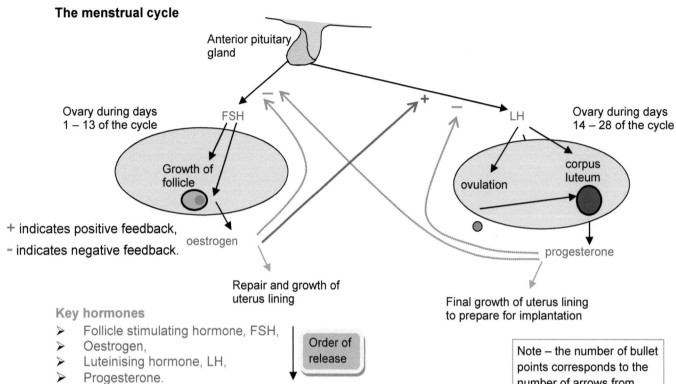

Anterior pituitary gland

Ovary during days 1 – 13 of the cycle

FSH

Growth of follicle

oestrogen

+ indicates positive feedback,

- indicates negative feedback.

Repair and growth of uterus lining

LH

ovulation

corpus luteum

Ovary during days 14 – 28 of the cycle

progesterone

Final growth of uterus lining to prepare for implantation

Key hormones

➢ Follicle stimulating hormone, FSH,
➢ Oestrogen,
➢ Luteinising hormone, LH,
➢ Progesterone.

Order of release

Note – the number of bullet points corresponds to the number of arrows from each hormone on the diagram above.

Link these steps to both the diagram above and to the levels of hormones on the graphs below.

Key steps

➢ FSH released from anterior pituitary:
  • stimulates growth of follicle,
  • stimulates secretion of oestrogen.
➢ Oestrogen released from follicle cells:
  • initiates repair and growth of endometrium (uterus lining),
  • negative feedback on pituitary to block FSH release,
  • nearing middle of cycle it reaches a critical level which causes a positive feedback on pituitary to release LH.
➢ LH released from anterior pituitary:
  • stimulates ovulation through a positive feedback mechanism – hence the sharp peak,
  • stimulates conversion of empty follicle to corpus luteum,
  • stimulates secretion of oestrogen and progesterone by corpus luteum.
➢ Progesterone released from corpus luteum:
  • completes growth of endometrium,
  • negative feedback on pituitary blocking FSH,
  • negative feedback on pituitary blocking LH.

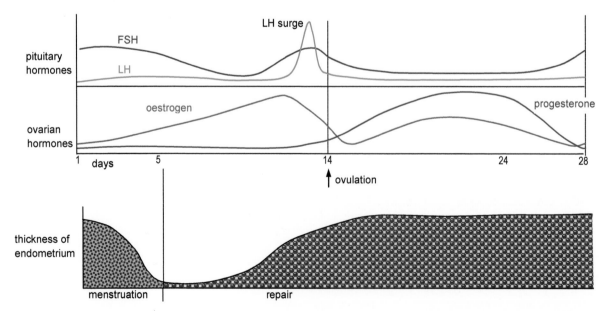

pituitary hormones — FSH, LH, LH surge

ovarian hormones — oestrogen, progesterone

days 1, 5, 14, 24, 28

↑ ovulation

thickness of endometrium — menstruation, repair

Gametogenesis

Spermatogenesis and oogenesis

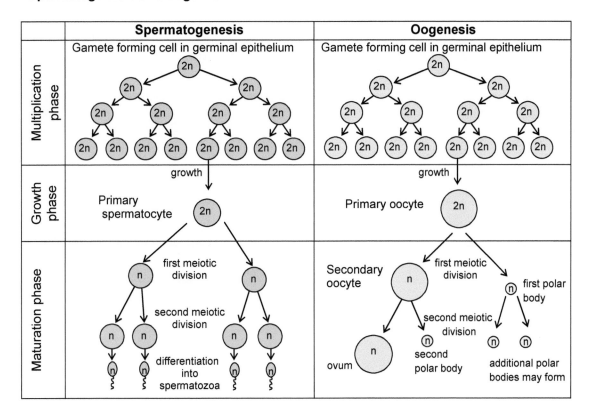

Stages of spermatogenesis and oogenesis

Spermatogenesis				Oogenesis
Male germ cell	2n	mitosis	2n	Female germ cell
Spermatogonium	2n	mitosis	2n	Oogonium
Primary spermatocyte	2n	mitosis	2n	Primary oocyte
Secondary spermatocyte	n	meiosis	n	Secondary oocyte + first polar body
Spermatid	n		n	[Ootid + second polar body/bodies]
Sperm cells	n		n	Ovum

Comparing spermatogenesis and oogenesis
Key points

Similarities
- Mitosis at the start.
- Cell growth.
- Two divisions of meiosis.
- Differentiation - sperm: acrosome, midpiece, tail.
               - egg: cortical granules.

Differences
- Polar bodies are structures that remove the excess genetic material during oogenesis and do not develop further into gametes.
- Polar bodies are not formed during spermatogenesis.
- The secondary oocyte contains more cytoplasm than sperms.
- Each gamete forming cell in a male produces four gametes, whereas that in a female only produces one gamete plus 2 or 3 polar bodies.
- Spermatogenesis is a continuous process whereas oogenesis pauses after prophase II.

Testis structure

seminiferous tubules

lumen of seminiferous tubule

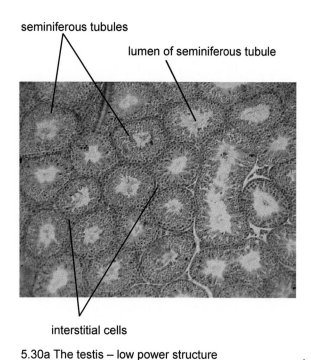

interstitial cells

5.30a The testis – low power structure

Sertoli cell
These cells surround and feed the sperm-forming cells and provide them with the right environment for meiosis.

The dark spots are the sperm heads with the tails projecting into the lumen

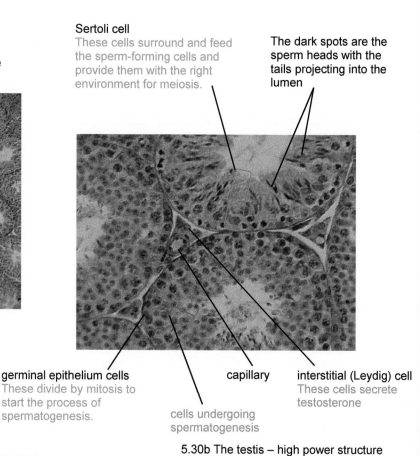

germinal epithelium cells
These divide by mitosis to start the process of spermatogenesis.

capillary

interstitial (Leydig) cell
These cells secrete testosterone

cells undergoing spermatogenesis

5.30b The testis – high power structure

germinal epithelium – cells undergoing mitosis

spermatogonium – diploid, grows

spermatocytes – undergo meiosis to become haploid

spermatid – haploid, starting to differentiate

spermatozoon (sperm)

Annotate

5.31 Section through part of a seminiferous tubule to show stages of spermatogenesis

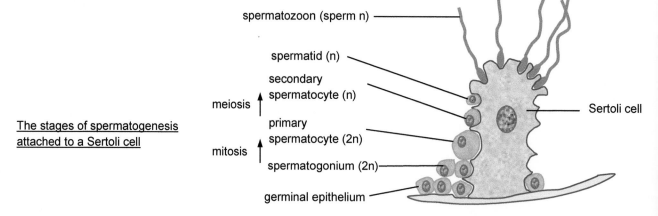

spermatozoon (sperm n)

spermatid (n)

secondary spermatocyte (n)

meiosis

The stages of spermatogenesis attached to a Sertoli cell

primary spermatocyte (2n)

mitosis

spermatogonium (2n)

germinal epithelium

Sertoli cell

Ovary structure

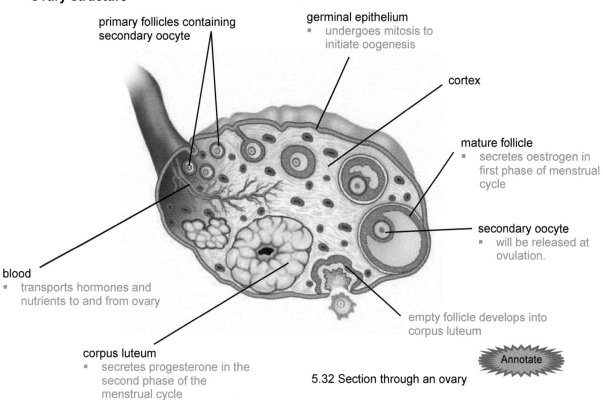

primary follicles containing
secondary oocyte

germinal epithelium
- undergoes mitosis to
  initiate oogenesis

cortex

mature follicle
- secretes oestrogen in
  first phase of menstrual
  cycle

secondary oocyte
- will be released at
  ovulation.

blood
- transports hormones and
  nutrients to and from ovary

empty follicle develops into
corpus luteum

Annotate

corpus luteum
- secretes progesterone in the
  second phase of the
  menstrual cycle

5.32 Section through an ovary

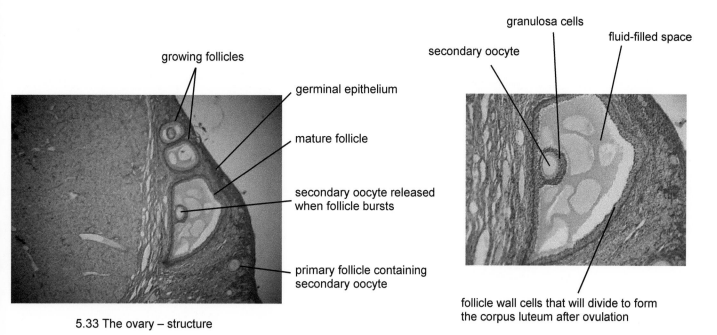

growing follicles

germinal epithelium

mature follicle

secondary oocyte released
when follicle bursts

primary follicle containing
secondary oocyte

5.33 The ovary – structure

granulosa cells

fluid-filled space

secondary oocyte

follicle wall cells that will divide to form
the corpus luteum after ovulation

5.34 Structure of a mature follicle

Structure of the secondary oocyte (egg)

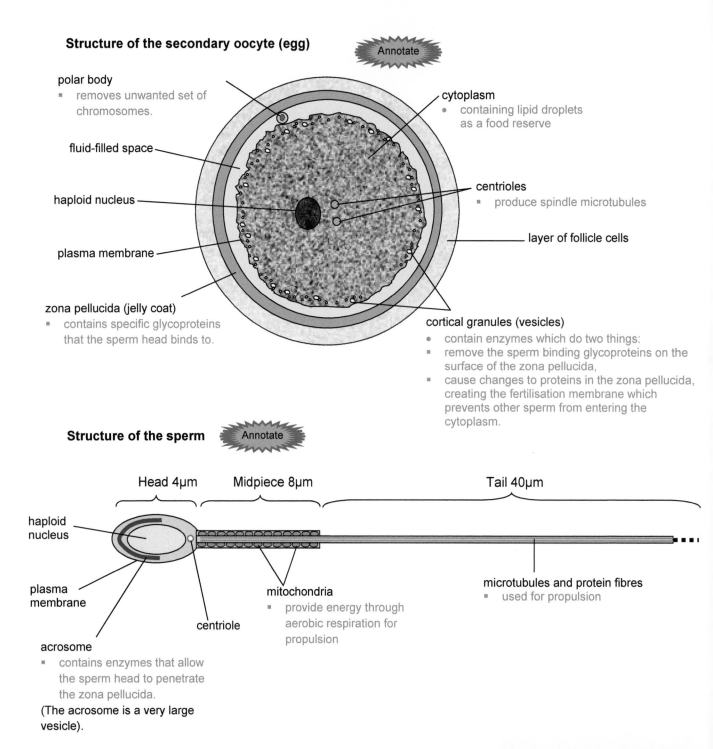

Annotate

polar body
- removes unwanted set of chromosomes.

fluid-filled space

haploid nucleus

plasma membrane

zona pellucida (jelly coat)
- contains specific glycoproteins that the sperm head binds to.

cytoplasm
- containing lipid droplets as a food reserve

centrioles
- produce spindle microtubules

layer of follicle cells

cortical granules (vesicles)
- contain enzymes which do two things:
- remove the sperm binding glycoproteins on the surface of the zona pellucida,
- cause changes to proteins in the zona pellucida, creating the fertilisation membrane which prevents other sperm from entering the cytoplasm.

Structure of the sperm

Annotate

Head 4μm   Midpiece 8μm   Tail 40μm

haploid nucleus

plasma membrane

acrosome
- contains enzymes that allow the sperm head to penetrate the zona pellucida.
(The acrosome is a very large vesicle).

centriole

mitochondria
- provide energy through aerobic respiration for propulsion

microtubules and protein fibres
- used for propulsion

Fertilisation

Fertilisation can be internal, as in most animals, or external as in corals, fish and amphibians. With these animals the female releases her eggs into the water and the male releases sperm over them.

The oocyte releases chemicals that can be detected by sperm allowing them to locate the oocyte. This is called positive chemotaxis.

5.35 A female frog surrounded by frogspawn

Fertilisation and the acrosome and cortical reactions

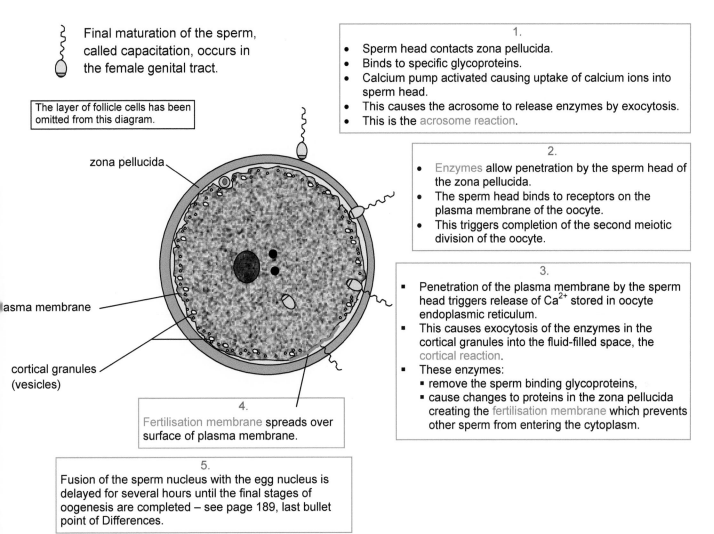

Final maturation of the sperm, called capacitation, occurs in the female genital tract.

The layer of follicle cells has been omitted from this diagram.

zona pellucida

plasma membrane

cortical granules (vesicles)

1.
- Sperm head contacts zona pellucida.
- Binds to specific glycoproteins.
- Calcium pump activated causing uptake of calcium ions into sperm head.
- This causes the acrosome to release enzymes by exocytosis.
- This is the acrosome reaction.

2.
- Enzymes allow penetration by the sperm head of the zona pellucida.
- The sperm head binds to receptors on the plasma membrane of the oocyte.
- This triggers completion of the second meiotic division of the oocyte.

3.
- Penetration of the plasma membrane by the sperm head triggers release of Ca^{2+} stored in oocyte endoplasmic reticulum.
- This causes exocytosis of the enzymes in the cortical granules into the fluid-filled space, the cortical reaction.
- These enzymes:
  - remove the sperm binding glycoproteins,
  - cause changes to proteins in the zona pellucida creating the fertilisation membrane which prevents other sperm from entering the cytoplasm.

4.
Fertilisation membrane spreads over surface of plasma membrane.

5.
Fusion of the sperm nucleus with the egg nucleus is delayed for several hours until the final stages of oogenesis are completed – see page 189, last bullet point of Differences.

Prevention of polyspermy
Key points

- Polyspermy is when more than one sperm fertilises the egg.
- The excess genetic information would be fatal so mechanisms to prevent it have evolved.
- There are two mechanisms   – fast block.
                              – slow block.
- Fast block:
  - The oocyte plasma membrane is polarised at -70mV. (This is exactly the same as in neurons.)
  - This potential difference allows the sperm plasma membrane to bind to the oocyte membrane.
  - Binding of the sperm plasma membrane opens many sodium ion channels in the oocyte membrane.
  - This influx of sodium ions depolarises the oocyte membrane.
  - This prevents any further sperms binding.
  - The oocyte membrane will gradually repolarise so a second block is required.
- Slow block:
  - Substances released from the cortical granules have several functions:
    - Enzymes remove proteins that link the zona pellucida to the oocyte membrane.
    - Water absorption occurs which lifts the zona pellucida away from the plasma membrane forming the fertilisation membrane.
    - Enzymes remove the sperm binding receptors on the oocyte membrane and also harden the zona pellucida.

Early embryo development

zygote ──────────────→ blastocyst

Single diploid cell　　Several mitotic divisions　　Hollow ball of cells

Implants into endometrium. This is essential for the continuation of pregnancy.

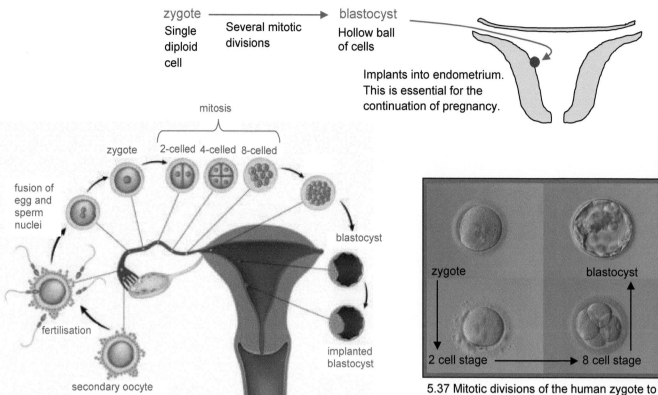

5.36 Early stages of embryo development

5.37 Mitotic divisions of the human zygote to produce a blastocyst ready to implant

Human Chorionic Gonadotrophin (hCG)

Key facts
➤ Produced by the developing placenta.
➤ Production starts soon after implantation.
➤ Maintains corpus luteum so production of progesterone continues.
➤ High levels of progesterone and oestrogen prevent the endometrium from breaking down.
➤ hCG is small enough to pass through the basement membrane of the glomerulus and it can be detected in the urine with the use of monoclonal antibodies as a pregnancy test – see page 161.

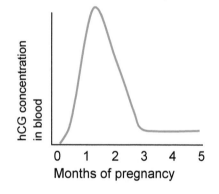

The placenta
Key points
➤ Barrier between maternal blood and fetal blood.
➤ Nutrients and waste materials are exchanged between fetal blood and maternal blood through the placenta.
➤ The exchange is by diffusion.
➤ Is an endocrine organ – hCG, oestrogen, progesterone, human placental lactogen (stimulates mammary development).
➤ Has complete hormonal control of pregnancy by week 12. (Note in graph above that the level of hCG has dropped to a very low level by week 12 as it is no longer required to maintain the corpus luteum).

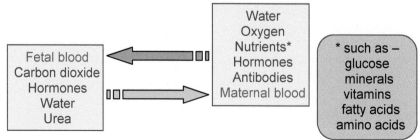

　　IBHL Biology 2016 © Ashby Merson-Davies

Birth and its hormonal control

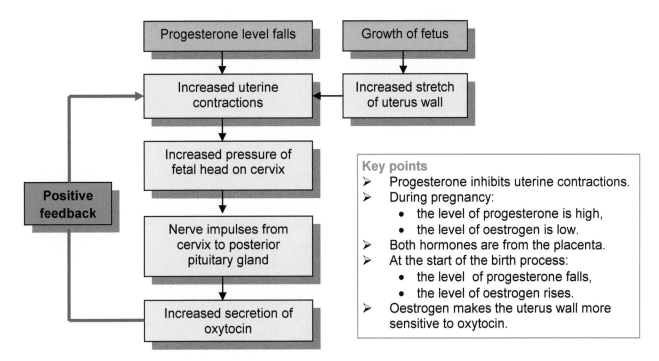

Progesterone level falls → Increased uterine contractions ← Increased stretch of uterus wall ← Growth of fetus

Increased uterine contractions → Increased pressure of fetal head on cervix → Nerve impulses from cervix to posterior pituitary gland → Increased secretion of oxytocin

Positive feedback

Key points
➢ Progesterone inhibits uterine contractions.
➢ During pregnancy:
   • the level of progesterone is high,
   • the level of oestrogen is low.
➢ Both hormones are from the placenta.
➢ At the start of the birth process:
   • the level of progesterone falls,
   • the level of oestrogen rises.
➢ Oestrogen makes the uterus wall more sensitive to oxytocin.

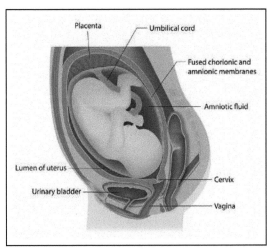

5.38 Just before birth the baby moves into a head down position

IVF – *in vitro* fertilisation

Key steps
➢ A drug is injected daily for about 2–3 weeks to stop the normal menstrual cycle.
➢ FSH is then injected daily for about 12 days in order to induce development of several follicles in the ovaries.
➢ hCG is then injected to cause the follicles to mature.
➢ About 35 hours later eggs from the mature follicles in both ovaries are collected by a tube inserted via the vagina.
➢ The eggs are transferred to a dish of warmed physiological saline and the sperms from the man added.
➢ After about 20 hours incubation the eggs are checked to see if fertilisation has occurred.
➢ After 1–5 days the embryos are examined for any signs of abnormalities.
➢ If necessary a more detailed genetic check can be carried out by karyotyping and/or gene probes.
➢ Hormonal treatment, progesterone or hCG, prepares the mother's uterus.
➢ A selected embryo is then inserted into the mother's uterus. Usually this is a single embryo but under certain circumstances two may be inserted.

William Harvey and sexual reproduction in deer
(1578–1657)

5.39 Roe deer

➢ Harvey investigated human circulation.
➢ He also investigated sexual reproduction.
➢ The prevailing idea at the time was that an embryo was a fully formed organism but in miniature form and it simply grew.
➢ Harvey first observed growth in fertilised hens' eggs as these were large and easy to obtain and observe.
➢ He saw that a simple drop of blood on the surface of the yolk would grow into the new chick and this led him to disagree with the preformed idea.
➢ He repeated his observations many times to provide sufficient evidence.
➢ Observing deer he noticed that offspring appeared only after mating.
➢ He examined the uteruses of female deer during the mating season but only found a developing embryo two or more months after mating.
➢ Since he did not have a microscope he was unable to observe the early stages of development and therefore wrongly concluded that the male 'seed' was of no importance.
➢ Microscopes had been invented in the 1590s but were not widely known about.
➢ In 1677 Anton van Leeuwenhoek, a Dutch draper and amateur scientist, used powerful lenses and a simple microscope that he had made to observe sperm in semen.

Gestation period and development

Mammals differ in the strategy that they use for development and growth, and in general they fall into one of two groups.

➢ **Altricial** species give birth to young that are incompletely developed and relatively helpless.
➢ **Precocial** species give birth to young that are relatively well developed, have hair, open eyes, and are mobile.

Mammals with a large body size are likely to be precocial since this is correlated with a long gestation period.

5.40a The mouse is an altricial species

5.40b The horse is a precocial species

The graph below shows the relationship between the body mass and the gestation period for a range of mammals. The blue dots are precocial species; the brown dots are altricial species.

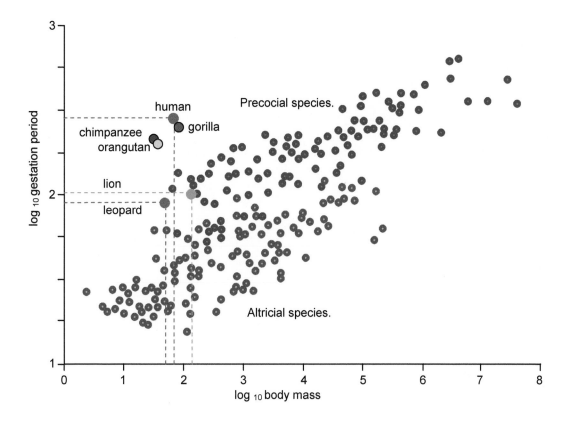

Note the positive correlation and also the considerable overlap. New-born cats, for example lion and leopard, are fairly well developed and have fur, but their eyes are closed and they are not mobile.

Humans appear to be outliers. The mean human female body mass is around 60kg ($\log_{10} 60 = 1.8$) and the mean gestation period is about 270 days ($\log_{10} 270 = 2.43$). The gestation period appears to be abnormally long but the baby is still partially altricial. (It has open and functional eyes but it cannot control its body temperature and is completely helpless). One reason could be that our much enlarged brain requires a long period of growth in the safety of the uterus. Mothers can safely give birth to twins, and even triplets, due to the size of the uterus and structure of the placenta. However the norm is for a single fetus which allows it to grow for a longer time period before birth. Twins and triplets tend to have lower average birth weights.

Note also on the graph that the other three higher primates are also outliers but humans have the longest gestation period.

1. What is the name of the lining of the uterus?	2. List two structures that produce the semen fluid.	3. Name the hormone that results in development of the secondary sexual characteristics in girls.
4. Name the hormone that stimulates the secretion of oestrogen in the menstrual cycle.	5. Which part of the ovary produces oestrogen?	6. Name the main hormone that causes ovulation.
7a. Name the hormone that maintains the uterus lining for the first few weeks of pregnancy.	7b. Name the structure in the ovary that secretes this hormone.	8. Name the placental hormone that maintains the uterus lining after the 12th week of pregnancy.
9. Name the hormone that results in development of the secondary sexual characteristics in boys.	10. What type of feedback does oestrogen have on the release of FSH?	11. List the three phases in gametogenesis.
12. Is a primary spermatocyte haploid or diploid?	13. Is a secondary oocyte haploid or diploid?	14. What type of nuclear division do germinal epithelial cells undergo?
15. What is the name of the structure that removes unwanted genetic material during oogenesis?	16. Name the structures in the testes that produce sperm.	17. Name the cell type in the testes that produces testosterone.
18. Name the structure in the ovary that the corpus luteum develops from.	19. Name the placental hormone that maintains the secretion of progesterone at the start of pregnancy.	20. Which region of the sperm contains mitochondria?
21. Name the structure in the sperm that releases enzymes.	22. Name the ball of cells that burrows into the endometrium.	23. Name the layer surrounding the egg that the sperm head binds to.
24. What structures in the secondary oocyte release enzymes which result in the formation of the fertilisation membrane?	25. What is the function of the fertilisation membrane?	26. Name the gland that releases oxytocin.
27. List three substances that pass from maternal blood to fetal blood in the placenta.	28. Name the hormone that causes uterine contractions.	29. During pregnancy is the level of plasma progesterone high or low?
30. What structure produces oestrogen and progesterone during the last six months of pregnancy?	31. What is the feedback relationship between the uterus wall and oxytocin?	32. Name the structure that secretes hCG.

Glossary

BASEMENT MEMBRANE	A meshwork of fine collagen fibres embedded in a jelly-like substance.
CANCER	Uncontrolled mitosis resulting in a tumour.
CATHETER	A tubular instrument that can be inserted into the body to transfer fluids in or out of the body.
EFFECTOR	A gland or muscle which responds to a stimulus.
EMULSIFY	Breaking large fat droplets into much smaller droplets to increase surface area for digestion.
EPITHELIUM	A layer of cells covering the body and lining the digestive tract.
GONADS	Ovaries and testes.
HYPERTONIC	A solution with a higher osmotic potential than the solution on the other side of the partially permeable membrane.
HYPOTHALAMUS	A region of the brain just above the pituitary gland.
HYPOTONIC	A solution with a lower osmotic potential than the solution on the other side of the partially permeable membrane.
ISOTONIC	A solution with an equal osmotic potential to the solution on the other side of the partially permeable membrane.
NEUROSECRETORY CELL	A modified nerve cell that secretes a chemical into the blood stream.
OCCLUSION	Partial or complete blockage of a blood vessel.
OSMORECEPTOR	A receptor that monitors the water potential of the blood.
OSMOTIC POTENTIAL	The ability of a solution to lose water.
PESTICIDE	A chemical that kills pests.
PODOCYTE	A specialised cell, literally a 'cell with feet'.
POSITIVE FEEDBACK	A response where the output feeds back in to further increase the output.
PULMONARY	To do with the lungs.
SELECTIVE REABSORPTION	A process which selects particular substances to be reabsorbed.
SURFACTANT	A chemical which lowers surface tension.
SYSTEMIC	To do with the body.
VARIABLE	A factor which changes.
VENTILATION	Moving air or water over the gas exchange surfaces.

Answers to Grey Box Questions   Underlined words are required.

The human gut
1. Store bile.
2. Very acidic; destroys pathogens; starts protein digestion.
3. Alkaline.
4. Main digestive region; main absorptive region.
5. Absorb water; large numbers of bacteria.
6. Neutralise stomach acid; emulsify fats.
7. Amylase; lipase.
8. Break down / hydrolyse proteins.
9. Amylase.
10. Maltase.
11. On the (outer) plasma membrane of the villus cells.
12. Active transport.
13. Liver.
14. Large molecules cannot be absorbed; so that the body can build its own large molecules from the monomers.
15. Because the digestion reactions are too slow at body temperature.
16. Duodenum; ileum.
17. Peristalsis.
18. longitudinal and circular.
19. Finger-like shape to give large surface area; surface cells with microvilli to increase surface area; surface cells with large numbers of mitochondria for active transport; capillary network; lacteal.
20. Duodenum.
21. Cellulose.

Gas exchange
1. Type I and type II pneumocytes.
2. Type I very thin for gas exchange; Type II produce a surfactant.
3. To maintain a high concentration gradient between the alveolar air and the blood.
4. Decreases.
5. Diaphragm; external intercostal muscles.
6. Abdominal muscles; internal intercostal muscles.
7. Antagonistic.
8. Tidal volume.
9. Number of breaths per minute.
10. See page 147.
11. Smoking.
12. Uncontrolled cell division.
13. Removal of a lung; death.
14. Breakdown of the alveolar walls.
15. Smoking.
16. Difficulty in breathing; requiring an oxygen mask.

The blood system

1. Blood passes through the heart twice for each circuit.   2. Right.
3. Systemic.   4. Coronary <u>artery</u>.   5. Liver.   6. Arteries.
7. Vena cava.   8. Aorta.   9. Atrioventricular valve.
10. Semi lunar.   11. Left ventricle.   12. Left atrium.
13a. Sinoatrial node.   13b. Wall of the right atrium.
13c. It releases electrical pulses to control the basic heart rate.
13d. Medulla / cardiac control centre of the brain.
13e. To speed up and slow down the basic heart rate.
14. Epinephrine.   15. Adrenal.   16. Maintain a one-way flow.
17. Systole.   18.a.Contraction of the <u>left</u> ventricle.
18b. Contraction of the <u>left</u> ventricle.   18c. Relaxation of the <u>left</u> ventricle.
19. Plaque / fatty deposit in the artery wall.   20. Angina / heart attack.
21. Vein.   22. To maintain blood flow when the ventricles relax.
23. Collagen.   24. When they contract blood pressure and hence flow rate increase.
25. Single celled wall; cells are flattened.

Defence against infectious disease

1. An organism or virus that causes disease.
2. Antibiotics work on specific prokaryotic metabolic pathways; viruses use the eukaryotic host metabolic pathway so an antibiotic would damage the cell.
3. Penicillin could be used to destroy pathogenic bacteria with harming the patient.
4. Skin; mucus membranes.
5a. Damaged blood vessels; exposure to air.   5b. Platelets.   5c. Thrombin.
6. Phagocyte.
7. Antigen – a molecule foreign to the body that stimulates an immune response.
    Antibody – a specific protein made by lymphocytes in response to a specific antigen and helps to destroy the antigen.
8. <u>Active</u> helper T lymphocyte.   9. Plasma cell.
10. Production of memory helper T lymphocytes and memory B lymphocytes which can respond rapidly to the pathogen.
11. Faster and larger.   12. Smallpox.
13. It has many antigenic molecules on its surface.   14. Plasma cell + myeloma cell.
15. Pregnancy test / testing for hCG in pregnancy.
16. White blood cell in blood; white blood cell in tissues / mast cell.
17. Neurotransmitter / defence.
18. A molecule in the environment. Stimulates an allergic response by stimulating excess histamine release.
19a. Helper T lymphocyte.
19b. Plasma cells cannot be made and these are the antibody producing cells.
19c. <u>Unprotected</u> vaginal or anal intercourse; oral sex; across the placenta; breast feeding; during birth; contaminated needles; blood transfusion.

The nervous system

1. Myelin sheath cells (Schwann cells).   2. Nodes of Ranvier.
3. Out of.   4. -70mv (Must state units).   5. Threshold.
6a. Depolarisation; repolarisation.   6b. <u>Diffusion</u> of sodium ions <u>into</u> the axoplasm.
6c. <u>Diffusion</u> of potassium ions <u>out of</u> the axoplasm <u>and</u> <u>active transport</u> of sodium ions <u>out of</u> the axoplasm.
7. By voltage gated channels.   8. Saltatory.   9. Presysnaptic membrane.
10. Calcium ions.   11a. Binds to a receptor.
11b. Diffusion of sodium ions into the post-synaptic neuron / depolarisation of the post-synaptic neuron.
12. i. It can block the binding of the normal neurotransmitter.
    ii. It can stimulate a post-synaptic potential.

The endocrine system
1.   Homeostasis.   2.   Negative feedback.
3.   Blood pH; body temperature; blood concentration.   4.   Alpha.
5.   Over-weight / eating too many sugary foods.
6.   Thyroxin.   7a.   Leptin.   7b.   Amount of stored fat.
8.   30kg m^{-2} (must state units)   9.   Circadian rhythms.
10.   Melatonin.   11.   Dark.

Osmoregulation and excretion
1.   Homeostasis.   2.   Osmoregulators.   3.   Osmoconformers.
4.   Excretion.   5.   Malpighian tubules.   6.   Uric acid.   7.   Renal.
8.   Cortex; medulla; pelvis.   9.   Urethra.   10.   Ureter.
11.   Bowman's capsule; proximal convoluted tubule; loop of Henle; distal convoluted tubule; collecting
duct.   12.   Glomerulus.   13.   Afferent vessel / afferent arteriole.
14.   Podocyte cells.   15.   Fenestrated.   16.   Basement membrane.
17.   Selective reabsorption.   18.   Create an osmotic gradient within the medulla.
19a. The efferent vessel is narrower.   19b. Increase the filtration pressure in the glomerulus.
20.   Reabsorption of water.   21.   Microvilli; sub-cellular spaces; intercellular spaces.
22.   Active transport (of salts and glucose).   23.   Glucose.   24.   Descending.
25a. Active transport.   25b. Ascending.   26.   Medulla.   27.   ADH.
28.   (Posterior) pituitary.   29.   Hypertonic.   30.   Some has been used in respiration by the kidney cells.
31.   A positive correlation / the dryer the habitat the longer the loop.
32.   Uric acid.   33.   Ammonia.   34.   Dehydration.
35.   Dialysis.   36.   Blood; protein; drugs.   37.   Diabetes.

Movement
1.   Antagonistic.   2.   They can only contract.   3.   Biceps; triceps.
4.   Exoskeleton.   5.   Synovial.   6.   Hinge.
7.   Ball and socket.   8.   Tendon.   9.   Joint capsule.
10.   Humerus; ulna; radius.   11.   Cartilage.   12.   Multicellular.
13.   Actin and myosin.   14.   Sarcoplasmic reticulum.   15.   Actin.
16.   The distance between two Z lines.   17.   Troponin.
18.   Tropomyosin.   19.   Binding of ATP.   20.   Myosin head.
21.   It stays the same.   22.   It decreases.
23.   Depolarisation of the sarcolemma.
24.   Thin actin filament; thick myosin filament; myosin head; Z line; sarcomere; light band; dark band.

Reproduction
1.   Endometrium.   2.   Prostate gland; seminal vesicles.   3.   Oestrogen.
4.   Follicle stimulating hormone.   5.   Follicle cells.   6.   Luteinising hormone.
7a.   Progesterone.   7b.   Corpus luteum.   8.   Placental progesterone.
9.   Testosterone.   10.   Negative.   11.   Multiplication; growth; maturation.
12.   Diploid.   13.   Haploid.   14.   Mitosis.   15.   Polar body.
16.   Seminiferous tubules.   17.   Interstitial / Leydig cell.   18.   (Empty) follicle.
19.   hCG/human chorionic gonadotrophin.   20.   Midpiece.   21.   Acrosome cap.
22.   Blastocyst.   23.   Jelly layer / zona pellucida.   24.   Cortical granules.
25.   Prevents polyspermy.   26.   (Posterior) pituitary gland.
27.   Nutrients; hormones; oxygen; antibodies.   28.   Oxytocin.   29.   Low.
30.   Placenta.   31.   Positive.   32.   Placenta

Self-test Quizzes

Digestion and Absorption

1. Which of the following is the correct sequence for the gut structures?
    a. Mouth, stomach, oesophagus, small intestine, large intestine,
    b. Mouth, oesophagus, stomach, large intestine, small intestine,
    c. Mouth, oesophagus, stomach, small intestine, large intestine,
    d. Mouth, stomach, small intestine, large intestine, oesophagus.

2. Digestion is necessary because:
    a. large food molecules cannot be absorbed through the intestine wall,
    b. this makes the food more nutritious,
    c. it changes the pH so the food molecules can be absorbed,
    d. only large food molecules can be taken up by phagocytosis.

3. The finger-like shape of a villus is so that:
    a. the surface area is increased for absorption,
    b. it is able to move food along the intestine,
    c. it protects the absorptive surface of the intestine,
    d. it helps to break up the large pieces of food.

4. Assimilation is:
    a. absorption of digested food,
    b. use of absorbed food by the body,
    c. removal of undigested food from the body,
    d. absorption of gases through the alveoli.

5. Which of the following statements about bile is correct?
    a. It contains enzymes that digest all three food groups.
    b. It has a low pH to kill microbes.
    c. It has a high pH to emulsify fats.
    d. It is alkaline to neutralise stomach acid.

6. Which types of enzyme are found in the human digestive system?
    i. Amylases   ii.   Proteases   iii.   Nucleases
    a. i and ii only,
    b. i and iii only,
    c. ii and iii only,
    d. i, ii and iii.

7. Assimilation and absorption both occur in the body. What is required for assimilation but is not required for absorption?
    a. Enzymes to synthesize new molecules,
    b. Active transport mechanisms,
    c. Dissolved nutrients,
    d. Diffusion gradient.

8. Where in the body is the gall bladder located?
    a. in the neck,
    b. in the liver,
    c. beside the pancreas,
    d. above the small intestine.

9. What does the digestion of starch by pancreatic amylase produce?
    a. glucose,
    b. maltose,
    c. amylose,
    d. amylopectin.

    IBHL Biology 2016 © Ashby Merson-Davies

Gas exchange

1. Which of the following is the correct sequence as air flows into the lungs?
    a. Trachea – bronchus – bronchioles – alveoli,
    b. Trachea – bronchioles – bronchi – alveoli,
    c. Bronchi – bronchioles – trachea – alveoli,
    d. Trachea – alveoli – bronchi – bronchioles.

2. Which of the following is **not** part of the process of ventilation?
    a. The volume of the thoracic cavity changes.
    b. The pressure in the thoracic cavity changes.
    c. Gas exchange occurs between alveolar air and blood.
    d. The diaphragm muscle contracts.

3. How many plasma membranes are between alveolar air and haemoglobin in a red blood cell?
    a. Two,
    b. Three,
    c. Four,
    d. Five.

4. Which of the following is the function of type I pneumocytes?
    a. Production of surfactant,
    b. Form the capillary wall,
    c. Very thin to promote gas exchange,
    d. Contain contractile fibres to squeeze air out of the alveoli.

5. Which of the following statements about breathing in is correct?
    a. External intercostal muscles and diaphragm muscles contract.
    b. Internal intercostal and abdominal muscles contract.
    c. External intercostal muscles and abdominal muscles contract.
    d. Internal intercostal muscles contract and abdominal muscles relax.

6. Tidal volume is:
    a. the volume of air breathed in during one minute,
    b. the difference in the volume of air breathed in when at rest and when exercising,
    c. the volume of air breathed in and out during one minute,
    d. the volume of air breathed in and out during a single breath.

7. Which of the following statements about emphysema is correct?
    a. It is caused by strenuous exercise.
    b. It is a reduction in the surface area of the alveoli.
    c. It is due to the loss of the surfactant-producing pneumocytes.
    d. The alveolar walls break down due to a loss of capillaries.

8. Ventilation is necessary because it:
    a. regulates water vapour loss from the body,
    b. increases the loss of oxygen from the red blood cells,
    c. strengthens the abdominal muscles,
    d. maintains concentration gradients of gases between alveoli and blood.

The blood system

1. Which line in the table below shows correctly the type of blood in the vessel?

	Coronary artery	Pulmonary artery	Vena cava	Pulmonary vein
a.	oxygenated	oxygenated	deoxygenated	deoxygenated
b.	oxygenated	deoxygenated	oxygenated	deoxygenated
c.	deoxygenated	oxygenated	deoxygenated	deoxygenated
d.	oxygenated	deoxygenated	deoxygenated	oxygenated

2. Which line in the table below shows correctly the description for the blood vessels?

	Artery	Capillary	Vein
a.	Large lumen	Thin layer of muscle	Valves
b.	Thin layer of muscle	Valves	Large lumen
c.	Thick layer of muscle	Wall one cell thick	Valves
d.	Thick layer of muscle	Valves	Thin layer of muscle

3. Which of the following statements is correct?
    a. When the ventricles contract the semilunar valves are closed.
    b. When the atria contract the atrio-ventricular valves are closed.
    c. When the atria contract the semilunar valves are opened.
    d. When the ventricles contract the atrio-ventricular valves are closed.

4. The hormone that affects heart rate is:
    a. adrenalin,
    b. oxytocin,
    c. insulin,
    d. glucagon.

5. The right ventricle pumps blood into the:
    a. pulmonary vein,
    b. pulmonary artery,
    c. aorta,
    d. coronary artery.

6. Which of the following heart chambers contain oxygenated blood?
    a. right atrium and left atrium,
    b. left ventricle and right ventricle,
    c. left atrium and left ventricle,
    d. right ventricle and right atrium.

7. What is the cause of the semilunar valves closing?
    a. contraction of the ventricles,
    b. contraction of the atria,
    c. relaxation of the ventricles,
    d. relaxation of the atria.

8. In which heart chamber is the SAN found?
    a. right atrium,
    b. right ventricle,
    c. left atrium,
    d. left ventricle.

9. Two nerves are connected to the SAN. Which statement about these nerves is correct?
    a. They carry sensory impulses to the brain to monitor heart rate.
    b. They are connected to the medulla of the brain.
    c. One is a sensory nerve and the other is a motor nerve.
    d. Their nerve impulses maintain a steady heart rate during times of stress.

10. During systole of the left ventricle which of the following statements is correct?
    a. The semilunar valves are closed.
    b. The blood pressure in the aorta is falling.
    c. The atrioventricular valve is open.
    d. The blood pressure in the ventricle is rising.

11. Which of the following statements about the valves in the heart is correct?
    a. They ensure a one-way flow of blood through the heart.
    b. They prevent the oxygenated and deoxygenated blood from mixing.
    c. They help to pump the blood from the atria to the ventricles.
    d. They direct the flow of blood into the correct arteries.

12. Which of the following is a function of the collagen fibres in the artery wall?
    a. They prevent the wall from overstretching when the ventricles contract.
    b. They are elastic and so help maintain the blood flow between ventricular contractions.
    c. They can contract to assist in the pumping of the blood.
    d. They are very smooth which helps with the flow of blood through the artery.

13. Which of the following blood vessels have a large lumen relative to their diameter?
    a. arteries only,
    b. capillaries,
    c. both arteries and veins,
    d. veins only.

14. Which one of the following statements about the liver is correct?
    a. It receives blood only through an artery.
    b. It receives blood through an artery and a vein from the gut.
    c. Blood leaving the liver passes to the gut via a vein.
    d. The liver has a double arterial supply.

15. The pacemaker is:
    a. the region of the heart that regulates the rate of heart beat.
    b. the region of the brain that regulates the rate of heart beat.
    c. the region of the brain that regulates the rate of breathing.
    d. the nerves from the brain that affect the heart rate.

Defence against infectious diseases

1. Which of the following statements about macrophages is **not** true?
    a. Lysosomes play an important part in their function.
    b. They are found in both the blood stream and tissue fluid.
    c. They activate helper T lymphocytes.
    d. They produce antibodies.

2. Which of the following happens during the clotting process?
    a. Platelets in the plasma release fibrin when exposed to air.
    b. Fibrinogen in the plasma stimulates the release of clotting factors.
    c. Clotting factors from platelets convert prothrombin to thrombin.
    d. Macrophages release thrombin which results in the formation of fibrin fibres in the blood.

3. Which of the following statements is correct?
    a. An animal possesses large numbers of B lymphocytes, each producing a specific but different type of antibody.
    b. Each B lymphocyte produces many types of antibody.
    c. Antigens form clones when selected by the specific B lymphocyte.
    d. When a T lymphocyte is selected by an antigen it will produce a specific type of antibody.

4.   Which of the following does **not** have a role in antibody production?
     a.   helper T lymphocyte,
     b.   macrophages,
     c.   B lymphocytes,
     d.   erythrocytes.

5.   A pathogen may be defined as:
     a.   a form of vaccine that is used to stimulate a defensive response,
     b.   a type of white blood cell that fights infection,
     c.   an organism or virus that causes disease,
     d.   a bacterial population on or in the body.

6.   Antibodies are produced by:
     a.   helper T lymphocytes,
     b.   macrophages,
     c.   plasma cells,
     d.   erythrocytes.

7.   Memory cells are important in that:
     a.   they prevent the body from being invaded again by the same pathogen,
     b.   they permit the body to respond more rapidly to later invasions by the same pathogen,
     c.   they allow the body to reduce the number of different types of B lymphocyte,
     d.   a wider range of antibodies can be produced to destroy invading pathogens.

8.   Monoclonal antibodies are:
     a.   antibodies produced by T lymphocyte clones,
     b.   antibodies produced by a single clone of plasma cells,
     c.   antibodies that destroy only viruses,
     d.   antibodies that are produced by tumour cells.

9.   A vaccine is usually effective at preventing a serious disease because:
     a.   it increases the number of macrophages in the plasma,
     b.   it contains antibodies which remain in the plasma,
     c.   it stimulates the production of memory cells,
     d.   it maintains a high level of active plasma cells in the blood.

10. Monoclonal antibodies are manufactured by:
     a.   joining a plasma cell to a tumour cell,
     b.   joining a macrophage to a helper T lymphocyte,
     c.   culturing plasma cells collected from a blood sample,
     d.   joining a helper T lymphocyte to a tumour cell.

11. If a person has been vaccinated and then comes into contact with the disease, which of the following statements would apply?
     a.   The secondary response is the same size as the primary response.
     b.   The secondary response is larger and faster than the primary response.
     c.   The primary response is larger and faster than the secondary response.
     d.   The secondary response is larger but slower than the primary response.

12. Which of the following statements is correct?
     a.   Antibodies are proteins made by red blood cells.
     b.   Antigens are molecules made by white blood cells.
     c.   Antibodies are proteins that can destroy antigens.
     d.   Antigens are proteins that can destroy antibodies.

                                                      IBHL Biology 2016 © Ashby Merson-Davies

The nervous system

1. The nodes of Ranvier are found:
   a. at the ends of motor neurons,
   b. between myelin sheath cells,
   c. around the cell body of a motor neuron,
   d. between two neurons.

2. During the resting potential which of the following statements is true?
   a. Potassium ions are pumped out of the axoplasm.
   b. Potassium ions diffuse into the axoplasm.
   c. Sodium ions diffuse into the axoplasm.
   d. Potassium ions diffuse out of the axoplasm.

3. Which of the following ions initiates an action potential?
   a. potassium,
   b. calcium,
   c. sodium,
   d. phosphate.

4. During the recovery phase of an action potential:
   a. gated channels open to increase the flow of potassium ions out of the axoplasm,
   b. gated channels open to increase the flow of sodium ions out of the axoplasm,
   c. the sodium-potassium pump reverses direction,
   d. potassium ions are pumped out of the axoplasm.

5. During transmission of a nerve impulse along an axon which of the following events happens?
   a. Sodium ions diffuse into the axon and potassium ions diffuse out.
   b. Potassium ions diffuse into the axon and sodium ions diffuse out.
   c. Potassium ions are pumped into the axon and sodium ions diffuse out.
   d. Sodium ions are pumped into the axon and potassium ions diffuse out.

6. Which of the following occurs during transmission across a synapse?
   a. Vesicles of neurotransmitter bind to the post-synaptic membrane.
   b. The incoming nerve impulse opens gated sodium channels causing depolarisation.
   c. The incoming nerve impulse causes sodium ions to diffuse across the synaptic gap.
   d. Neurotransmitter diffuses through the post-synaptic membrane causing depolarisation.

7. Which of the following statements about synapses is correct?
   a. Diffusion of potassium ions through the post-synaptic membrane causes depolarisation.
   b. Acetyl choline acts as a synaptic inhibitor in insects.
   c. Acetic acid and choline are released from vesicles in the pre-synaptic membrane and form acetyl choline in the synaptic gap.
   d. Binding of neurotransmitter to a receptor on the post-synaptic membrane causes gated sodium channels to open.

8. Neonicotinoids pesticides are synaptic inhibitors. They work by:
   a. preventing the binding of neurotransmitter vesicles to the presynaptic membrane,
   b. binding to the acetylcholine receptor on the postsynaptic membrane,
   c. inhibiting the catalysis of acetylcholine by cholinesterase,
   d. preventing sodium ions diffusing through the postsynaptic membrane.

The endocrine system

1. Homeostasis can be described as:
    a. maintaining a constant internal environment,
    b. blood clotting,
    c. maintaining a steady breathing rate,
    d. maintaining a constant weight.

2. Negative feedback can be described as:
    a. ejection of the contents of the stomach through the mouth,
    b. changing the level of a variable to suit the demands of the body,
    c. a mechanism that corrects a change in the level of a variable,
    d. monitoring the level of a variable.

3. The diagram shows how the body regulates the level of glucose in the blood.

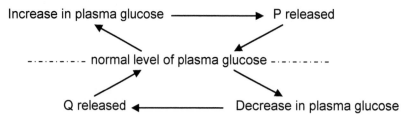

    What are P and Q?

	P	Q
a.	Glucagon	Insulin
b.	Insulin	Glycogen
c.	Glycogen	Thyroxin
d.	Insulin	Glucagon

4. Which cells secrete insulin?
    a. α cells of the pancreas,
    b. β cells of the pancreas,
    c. β cells of the liver,
    d. Epithelial cells of the small intestine.

5. Early onset or Type I diabetes is due to:
    a. loss of insulin secreting cells,
    b. persistent over-eating of sugary foods,
    c. failure of liver cells to remove glucose from the blood,
    d. over-production of insulin.

6. Which of the following lines in the table is correct?

	Thyroxin	Leptin	Melatonin
a.	Helps maintain body temperature.	Helps control appetite.	Causes pigmentation of the skin.
b.	Helps control appetite.	Helps maintain body temperature.	Controls the sleep-wake pattern.
c.	Helps maintain body temperature.	Helps control appetite.	Controls the sleep-wake pattern.
d.	Controls the sleep-wake pattern.	Helps control appetite.	Helps maintain body temperature.

7. Which of the following structures secretes melatonin?
    a. pituitary gland,
    b. hypothalamus,
    c. pineal gland,
    d. thyroid gland.

Osmoregulation and excretion

1. In which part of the kidney will glomeruli be found?
    a. proximal convoluted tubule,
    b. cortex,
    c. medulla,
    d. pelvis.

2. In the kidney the ureter is connected directly to the:
    a. urethra,
    b. cortex,
    c. medulla,
    d. pelvis.

3. The reason why some desert mammals have very long loops of Henle is because:
    a. it allows them to conserve water,
    b. it reduces the loss of nutrients,
    c. they can stay in their burrows during the heat of the day,
    d. they can increase the amount of urea lost.

4. Which of the following is **not** a characteristic feature of the cells of the proximal tubule?
    a. microvilli,
    b. cilia,
    c. large numbers of mitochondria,
    d. subcellular spaces.

5. Which of the following statements is correct?
    a. The collecting duct actively absorbs water.
    b. The active transport of glucose creates a gradient for salt to diffuse from the plasma to the proximal tubule,
    c. Glucose is returned to the blood stream by active transport from the descending limb of the loop of Henle.
    d. The osmotic gradient in the medulla created by the loop of Henle permits reabsorption of water from the collecting duct.

6. Which of the following statements is correct?
    a. There is relatively more urea in the renal vein than in the renal artery.
    b. The glomerular filtrate contains more glucose than the filtrate in the collecting duct.
    c. The filtrate pressure in Bowman's capsule is higher than the blood pressure in the glomerulus.
    d. There is the same amount of glucose in the renal vein as there is in the renal artery.

7. Glucose may be present in the urine of a diabetic because:
    a. the quantity of glucose in the filtrate exceeds the transport capacity of the proximal tubules,
    b. they produce more glucagon which raises plasma glucose,
    c. the glucose transport mechanism in the proximal tubules fails to function,
    d. there is insufficient insulin to activate the transport channels in the proximal tubules.

8. Ultrafiltration means:
    a. that only molecules below a certain size can pass through the filtration membrane,
    b. that filtration takes place under pressure in the glomerulus,
    c. the process of filtration is very efficient,
    d. active transport is involved in the process of transferring glucose and salts from the glomerulus to Bowman's capsule.

9. The hormone that controls water uptake in the collecting duct is:
    a. insulin,
    b. adrenalin,
    c. antidiuretic hormone,
    d. glucagon.

10. The hormone that controls water uptake in the collecting duct is released from the:
    a. hypothalamus,
    b. posterior pituitary gland,
    c. anterior pituitary gland,
    d. kidney.

11. Water is absorbed in the collecting duct when ADH is present. Which of the following is not a mechanism by which water moves from the filtrate to the blood?
    a. facilitated diffusion,
    b. active transport,
    c. osmosis,
    d. diffusion.

12. Glucose is not normally found in the urine because:
    a. it is unable to leave the glomerulus,
    b. it is actively removed from the filtrate in the loop of Henle,
    c. it diffuses out of the filtrate into the blood,
    d. it is actively transported into the blood from the proximal convoluted tubule.

13. Pressure in the glomerulus is maintained due to:
    a. the efferent vessel being narrower than the afferent vessel,
    b. some of the filtrate being removed in the proximal convoluted tubule,
    c. the afferent vessel being narrower than the efferent vessel,
    d. active transport of solutes into Bowman's capsule.

14. Proteins are not normally found in the urine because:
    a. proteins are not present in the plasma,
    b. proteins leaving the glomerulus are broken down into amino acids before being released into the filtrate,
    c. proteins in the plasma are mostly too large to pass through the basement membrane of the capillaries,
    d. they are actively transported out of the filtrate by the cells of the proximal convoluted tubule.

15. Which of the following statements is correct?
    a. Sodium ions are actively transported out of the ascending limb and actively transported into the descending limb.
    b. As sodium ions are actively transported out of the ascending limb water follows due to osmosis.
    c. Sodium ions are actively transported out of the descending limb causing water to diffuse into the descending limb.
    d. As sodium ions are actively transported out of the ascending limb water moves by osmosis out of the descending limb.

16. Which of the following statements is correct?
    a. If the blood concentration rises less water is reabsorbed in the proximal tubule.
    b. ADH released from the pancreas increase the uptake of water in the descending limb.
    c. ADH released from the pituitary gland causes water reabsorption in the collecting duct.
    d. When blood concentration falls ADH is released from the pituitary gland and water channels are inserted in the collecting duct walls.

17. Solutes are transferred from the filtrate in the proximal tubule to the plasma by:
    a. active transport and diffusion,
    b. active transport and osmosis,
    c. osmosis and diffusion,
    d. diffusion only.

18. Filtration in Bowman's capsule is made more efficient by the presence of:
    a. fenestrated capillaries,
    b. podocytes,
    c. increased glomerular pressure,
    d. all of the above.

19. Which of the following is the function of the malpighian tubules in insects?
    a. excretion only,
    b. osmoregulation only,
    c. excretion and osmoregulation,
    d. absorption of the end products of digestion.

20. Which of the following statements describes osmoregulators?
    a. They allow their body fluid osmotic potential to mirror the environmental osmotic potential.
    b. They maintain an osmotic potential of their body fluids that is different from that of their environment.
    c. They excrete salt to maintain a high osmotic potential of the blood.
    d. The osmotic potential of their blood varies with the availability of water in the environment.

21. Which of the following statements is **not** correct?
    a. Animals living in fresh water excrete ammonia to reduce energy loss.
    b. Uric acid and ammonia are both soluble nitrogenous excretory compounds.
    c. Uric acid is excreted by birds because it is insoluble and can be removed as a solid.
    d. Excreting uric acid is a way of removing nitrogenous waste but reducing water loss.

22. When a patient with kidney failure is undergoing haemodialysis:
    a. blood is taken from an artery in the arm and returned to a vein,
    b. the haemodialysis fluid has the same composition as blood,
    c. the haemodialysis fluid has a higher concentration of glucose and salts,
    d. the haemodialysis fluid does not contain any urea.

Movement

1. Which of the following statements is true about skeletal muscle?
    a. The thick filament is made up of actin and myosin.
    b. The myosin heads are on the thin filament.
    c. The sarcomeres shorten in length when the muscle contracts.
    d. Neurotransmitter is stored in the sarcoplasmic reticulum.

2. During contraction of skeletal muscle:
    a. calcium ions diffuse out of the sarcoplasmic reticulum,
    b. calcium ions are actively transported out of the sarcoplasmic reticulum,
    c. calcium ions bind to myosin,
    d. calcium ions bind to actin.

3. During contraction of skeletal muscle:
    a. ATP is used to form the cross bridges between the actin and myosin,
    b. voltage gated calcium ion channels on the sarcoplasmic reticulum are opened,
    c. depolarisation of the sarcoplasmic reticulum causes it to release sodium ions into the muscle cells,
    d. the actin and myosin filaments become shorter.

4. Which of the following statements is correct?
    a. Ligaments join muscle to bone.
    b. Cartilage joins muscle to bone.
    c. Tendons join bone to bone.
    d. Ligaments join bone to bone.

5. The function of synovial fluid is to:
    a. fill the gap between presynaptic and postsynaptic membranes,
    b. act as a lubricant at a joint,
    c. fill the gap between the actin and myosin fibres,
    d. act as a lubricant within muscle myofibrils.

6. Which of the following statements is correct?
    a. The biceps is attached to the ulna.
    b. The triceps is attached to the radius.
    c. The joint capsule secretes synovial fluid.
    d. The knee joint is a ball and socket joint.

7. Striated muscle tissue is unusual because:
    a. The cells form long lines.
    b. Each cell contains many mitochondria.
    c. The cytoplasm is multinucleate.
    d. The sarcoplasmic reticulum stores calcium ions.

8. Which of the following statements is correct about muscle contraction?
    a. The Z lines move further apart.
    b. The actin filaments get shorter.
    c. The dark band stays the same width.
    d. The sarcomeres stay the same width.

9. Which of the following statements is correct?
    a. Tropomyosin is a fibrous protein.
    b. During muscle contraction calcium ions bind to tropomyosin.
    c. Calcium ions block formation of the actin-myosin cross bridge.
    d. The calcium pump in the sarcoplasmic reticulum is activated by depolarisation of the sarcolemma.

10. During cross-bridge formation the myosin head:
    a. binds to an adjacent myosin head,
    b. binds to tropomyosin,
    c. binds to troponin,
    d. binds to actin.

Reproduction

1. In the male reproductive system:
    a. the epididymis assists in sperm production,
    b. the urethra can transport both urine and semen,
    c. the seminal vesicles are temporary storage places while the sperm mature,
    d. the vas deferens carries urine from the bladder to the outside.

2. In the female reproductive system:
    a. the urethra can transport both urine and oocytes,
    b. the oviducts join the uterus next to the cervix,
    c. the lining of the uterus is called the endometrium,
    d. the cervix connects the uterus to the oviducts.

3. The hormone that causes the pre-natal development of the genitalia in girls is:
    a. oestrogen,
    b. progesterone,
    c. luteinising hormone,
    d. follicle stimulating hormone.

4. Testosterone is produced by the:
   a. seminal vesicles,
   b. prostate gland,
   c. interstitial cells,
   d. epididymis.

5. Which of these structures produces progesterone?
   a. anterior pituitary gland,
   b. posterior pituitary gland,
   c. follicle,
   d. corpus luteum.

6. In the menstrual cycle:
   a. the follicle produces the hormone oestrogen,
   b. growth of the follicle is stimulated by oestrogen,
   c. follicle stimulating hormone has a negative feedback on the pituitary gland,
   d. oestrogen causes the endometrium to break down.

7. In the menstrual cycle:
   a. Ovulation is stimulated by a surge in luteinising hormone.
   b. Progesterone from the corpus luteum initiates the repair of the uterus lining.
   c. Oestrogen stimulates the conversion of the empty follicle into the corpus luteum.
   d. Progesterone has a positive feedback on the pituitary gland to stimulate the release of luteinising hormone.

8. Which of the following statements about gametogenesis is correct?
   a. Polar bodies are formed to increase the number of secondary oocytes.
   b. A primary spermatocyte is diploid whereas a primary oocyte is haploid.
   c. A primary oocyte undergoes meiosis to produce an ovum and polar bodies.
   d. Sertoli cells are required in order for oogenesis to complete.

9. Which of the following is released at ovulation?
   a. primary oocyte,
   b. secondary oocyte,
   c. ovum,
   d. polar body.

10. Which of the following statements about sperm structure is correct?
    a. The acrosome contains mitochondria for energy production for swimming.
    b. Enzymes in vesicles in the midpiece are required for the process of fertilisation.
    c. The head contains the diploid nucleus.
    d. The acrosome contains enzymes required for fertilisation.

11. Which of the following structures implants into the endometrium?
    a. blastocyst,
    b. zygote,
    c. embryo,
    d. secondary oocyte.

12. Which of the following statements about polyspermy is correct?
    a. It is a way of producing more sperms than eggs.
    b. It is a mechanism to ensure the best sperm fertilises the egg.
    c. It is prevented by formation of the fertilisation membrane.
    d. It is a mechanism to increase the probability of fertilisation occurring.

13. During the acrosome reaction:
    a. enzymes are released from the cortical granules in the sperm head,
    b. enzymes released from the sperm head dissolve the zona pellucida,
    c. the cortical granules release enzymes to produce the fertilisation membrane,
    d. the fertilisation membrane spreads over the surface of the plasma membrane.

14. Which of the following statements about the structure of the secondary oocyte is correct?
    a. Cortical granules are small vesicles in the cytoplasm near the plasma membrane.
    b. Cortical granules are small vesicles in the zona pellucida.
    c. One or more polar bodies can be seen in the cytoplasm.
    d. The zona pellucida contains enzymes which are needed to release the nucleus from the sperm head.

15. Which of the following statements about human chorionic gonadotrophin (hCG) is correct?
    a. It is produced by the endometrium.
    b. It is a protein which is small enough to be filtered by the kidney and can be found in the urine.
    c. It stimulates the corpus luteum to maintain production of oestrogen.
    d. It is produced by the pituitary gland to stimulate gametogenesis.

16. During birth which of these processes takes place?
    a. The plasma level of progesterone rises and the level of oestrogen falls.
    b. The plasma level of oestrogen rises and the level of progesterone falls.
    c. Uterine contractions are inhibited by oxytocin.
    d. Progesterone has a positive feedback effect causing increased uterine contractions.

17. During IVF treatment:
    a. LH is injected to stimulate multiple ovulation,
    b. FSH is injected to regulate the menstrual cycle,
    c. FSH is injected to stimulate growth of several follicles,
    d. progesterone is injected to stimulate growth of several follicles.

Chapter Six

Plant Biology

Plants may appear to be simple but they form the basis of almost all food webs due to their ability to convert simple inorganic compounds into complex organic compounds that can be utilised by animals. This chapter looks briefly at their structure and reproduction.

Transport in plants

Key points
- Plants have two transport systems:
  - xylem - transports water and dissolved minerals from the roots upwards through the plant.
    - the water is used to replace that lost from transpiration.
    - the mechanism is passive and no ATP is used.
  - phloem - transports dissolved minerals and organic molecules both up and down through the plant from sources to sinks.
    - the mechanism is active and energy from ATP is required.

Xylem transport
- Xylem vessels:
  - dead and have no cytoplasm,
  - have varying degrees of lignin thickening in their walls,
  - end walls are dissolved leaving a continuous tube.

2 Water evaporates from the surface of the spongy mesophyll cells into the air spaces and then leaves via the stomata. As a molecule evaporates it pulls another molecule behind it creating tension forces. This transpiration pull extends to the xylem vessels in the veins of the leaf and stem.

3 Water is pulled up the stem in xylem vessels as the transpiration stream. The water molecules are held together by hydrogen bonds. (Refer back to page 20). This is called cohesion and is a very powerful force as the columns of water in tall trees are continuous. The strengthening in the walls of the xylem vessels is necessary to prevent them collapsing under the tension. (Same principle as the supporting cartilage in the air passages to the lungs). Also water molecules adhere to the sides of the xylem vessels and other cells, and this adhesion creates a strong force which holds up the considerable mass of water.

1 Mineral ions are taken up by active transport. This lowers the water potential in the roots causing water to be taken up by osmosis through the root hairs.
This creates root pressure that pushes water a short distance up the stem.
The root hairs create a large surface area.

6.1 Root hairs

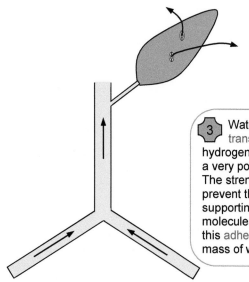

guard cell with chloroplasts   stoma   epidermis cell

6.2 Surface layer of a leaf.

Guard cells can absorb or lose water. This allows them to regulate transpiration by altering the size of the stoma.

Stomata are also the point of gas exchange so transpiration is an inevitable consequence of gas exchange.

Guard cells gain water:
- stoma large,
- transpiration high.

Guard cells lose water:
- stoma small,
- transpiration low.

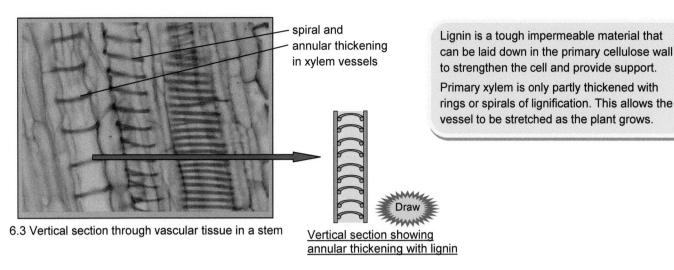

spiral and
annular thickening
in xylem vessels

Lignin is a tough impermeable material that can be laid down in the primary cellulose wall to strengthen the cell and provide support.

Primary xylem is only partly thickened with rings or spirals of lignification. This allows the vessel to be stretched as the plant grows.

6.3 Vertical section through vascular tissue in a stem

Draw

Vertical section showing
annular thickening with lignin

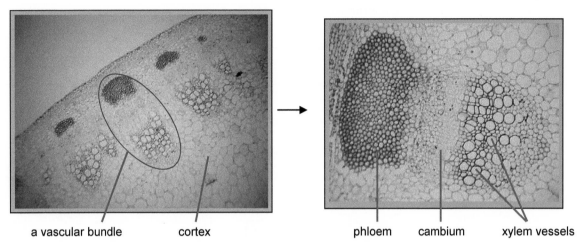

a vascular bundle   cortex

phloem   cambium   xylem vessels

6.4 Horizontal section through a stem of a dicotyledonous plant.
The vascular bundles are distributed around the edge.

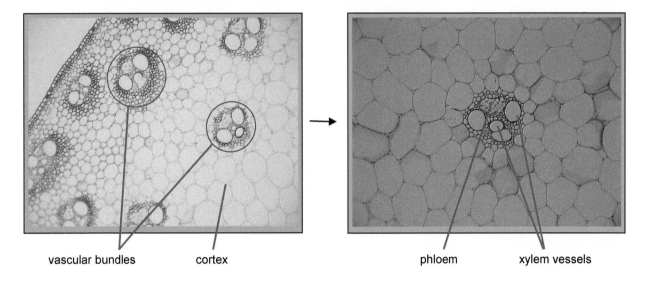

vascular bundles   cortex

phloem   xylem vessels

6.5 Horizontal section through a stem of a monocotyledonous plant.
The vascular bundles are distributed over the whole cross section.

Water conservation

Deserts

Key points
- Rainfall is low.
- Water sources may be deep in the ground.
- Temperatures are high during the day.
- High temperatures increase transpiration.

> Plants adapted to dry conditions are called **xerophytes.**

Adaptations

Adaptation	Mechanism
Thick waxy cuticle on leaves.	Wax is waterproof so a thick layer prevents water evaporating from the leaf surfaces.
Stomata buried in pits.	Water vapour accumulates in the pit above the stoma and prevents transpiration.
Rolled leaves.	Air inside the rolled up leaf becomes saturated with water vapour which prevents transpiration.
Reduction in leaves.	Leaves are reduced in size, have become spines or been lost altogether so surface area for transpiration is greatly reduced.
Thick fleshy leaves.	Used to store water.
Hairy leaves.	The hairs reduce the flow of air over the leaves and trap water vapour so reducing transpiration.

6.6 A desert barrel cactus in Arizona.
The leaves have been reduced to spines.

6.7 A Sedum in Madeira. Thick fleshy leaves store water.

6.8 A xerophytic shrub in the Galapagos Islands. The leaves are very small and covered in a dense mass of hairs to reduce transpiration.

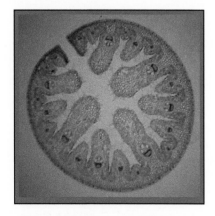

6.9a Low power view of Marram grass, *Psamma*.
This grows on sand dunes. The leaf is rolled up.

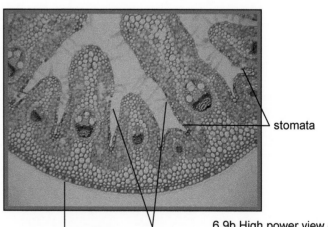

thick waxy cuticle on the outside to prevent water loss

hairs to trap humid air

stomata

6.9b High power view of Marram grass, showing xerophytic features.

Saline (salty) soils

Key points

➤ Water is absorbed into roots by osmosis.
➤ If the soil water has a high concentration of salt, i.e. it has a lower water potential than the root cell cytoplasm, water will be drawn out of the root cells by osmosis.

Adaptation

➤ Salts are actively transported into the root cells to lower the water potential to less than that of the soil solution.
➤ Water enters the roots by osmosis.
➤ The excess salt is either:
  • stored in the vacuoles,
  • excreted onto the leaf surface by special salt glands.

> Plants adapted to salty conditions are called **halophytes.**

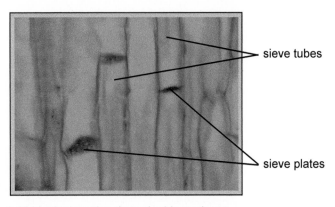

6.10 Shadscale saltbush *Atriplex confertifolia* in Arizona.
The saltbush is both a halophyte and xerophyte.

Phloem transport – translocation

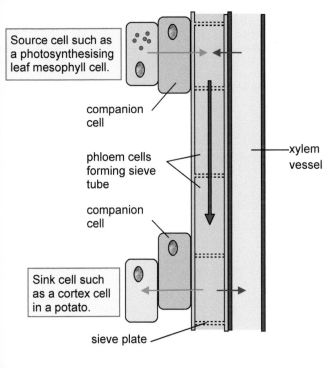

Source cell such as a photosynthesising leaf mesophyll cell.

companion cell

phloem cells forming sieve tube

companion cell

Sink cell such as a cortex cell in a potato.

xylem vessel

sieve plate

Key features

➤ Phloem cells form long sieve tubes.
➤ Nuclei and most other organelles are lost.
➤ Modified cytoplasm remains.
➤ Plasma membrane remains.
➤ End walls partially dissolved forming sieve plates.
➤ They have associated cells called companion cells that are used to provide active transport of solutes.

Mechanism

➤ Organic solutes such as sucrose and amino acids from the source cell actively transported into the sieve tube. ⟶
➤ This creates an osmotic gradient so water (from xylem) enters the sieve tube increasing pressure. ⟵
➤ Solutes from the sieve tube actively transported out into the sink cell and converted to, e.g. starch. ⟵
➤ This creates an osmotic gradient so water leaves the sieve tube decreasing pressure. ⟶
➤ The pressure gradient within the sieve tube causes a hydrostatic pressure flow* from source to sink.
➤ This can work in either direction, i.e. the source can be below ground e.g. a root cell or seed, and the sink at the growing shoot tip or developing fruit.

* This is possible because water is incompressible.

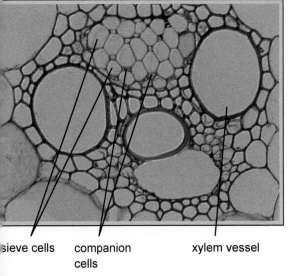

sieve cells   companion cells   xylem vessel

6.11 Cross section of a vascular bundle of a monocotyledonous plant

sieve tubes

sieve plates

6.12 Vertical section through phloem tissue

Growth from meristems

Key similarities
➢ Meristematic tissue contains small undifferentiated cells that can undergo mitosis.
➢ After cytokinesis one cell differentiates and the other remains in the meristem – see cell cycle page 92.
➢ The differentiated cell can:
  • extend the length of the stem or root,
  • develop into leaves or flowers.
➢ They can result in indeterminate growth of the plant.

Key differences
➢ Apical meristems are found at the shoot and root tips.
➢ They result in growth in length of the shoot or root.
➢ Lateral meristems are the strips of cambium in the vascular bundles – see page 217.
➢ They result in growth of diameter of the shoot or root.

meristematic region outlined in yellow contains cells undergoing mitosis

root cap

6.13 Vertical section through a root tip

Tropisms

Be careful not to confuse tropism with trophic as in trophic level.

Key points
➢ A tropism is a response of the plant either towards or away from a directional stimulus in the environment.
➢ Stimuli include light (phototropism) or gravity (gravitropism).
➢ Tropisms are controlled by the plant hormone called auxin.
➢ Auxin can be moved from cell to cell by integral membrane proteins called **auxin efflux pumps**.

Phototropism

6.14 Seedlings in a pot on a windowsill. Note how the leaves face the light.

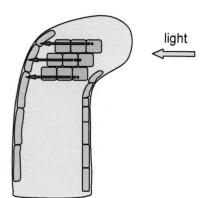

light

Key points
➢ Auxin is produced by cells just behind the apical meristem.
➢ Light is absorbed by proteins in the apex called **phototropins**.
➢ These influence cells by switching on certain genes.
➢ These genes result in the formation of auxin efflux pumps.
➢ An uneven distribution of light stimulates the formation of efflux pumps on the illuminated side resulting in auxin being pumped across to the shaded side of the shoot.
➢ An increase in auxin concentration alters the pattern of gene expression by causing an increase in the length of cells behind the apical meristem.
➢ This causes the shoot to bend towards the light – positive phototropism.
➢ This allows the leaves to collect more light for photosynthesis.

<u>Diagrammatic representation of auxin transport</u>
The arrows show the effect of the auxin efflux pumps transporting auxin to the shaded side and the increased growth of cells there causing bending.

Micropropagation

➢ This is taking a small amount of tissue from the plant apex and inducing it to grow into a new plant.
➢ This requires:
  • nutrient agar,
  • plant hormones.
➢ This allows growers to increase rapidly the number of plants of –
  • a new variety,
  • virus-free strains,
  • rare / endangered species such as orchids.

Flowering plants
Flower structure

6.15 A micropropagation cabinet

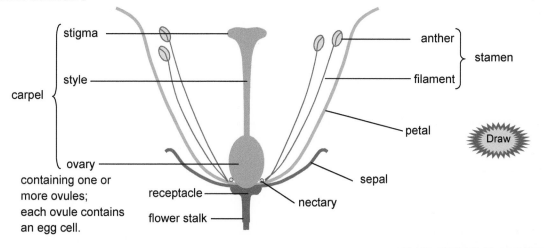

Draw

➢ Success in plant reproduction depends on pollination, fertilisation and seed dispersal.
➢ Most flowering plants have a mutualistic relationship with pollinators.

6.16 This open flower can be pollinated by many types of insect

6.17 This tubular flower is pollinated by bumble bees

6.18 This bird of paradise flower is pollinated by birds

6.19 A honey bee covered in pollen

Pollinators
Most are insects but some bird, bat and mammal species can act as pollinators.

Mutualism
This is a close relationship between two organisms where both benefit from the relationship.
The flower is pollinated but the pollinator can gain nectar and/or pollen as food.

Pollination	Fertilisation	Seed Dispersal
Transfer of pollen from an anther to the stigma.	Fusion of a male gamete from the pollen grain with a female gamete in an ovule inside the ovary.	Spreading the seeds away from the parent plant.

6.20 Dandelion seeds being dispersed by wind

Control of flowering
Key points
➢ Flowering involves a change in gene expression in the shoot apex.
➢ The switch to flowering is in response to the relative lengths of light and dark periods.
➢ Plants can be divided into two groups – long-day and short-day.
➢ This is controlled by **phytochrome**.
➢ There are two forms of phytochrome – P_r which absorbs red light and
– P_{fr} which absorbs far red light
➢ In red or white light P_r is **rapidly** converted to P_{fr}.
➢ In darkness P_{fr} is **slowly** converted back to P_r.
➢ P_r inhibits flowering in long-day plants.
➢ P_r promotes flowering in short-day plants.
➢ Flowering in short-day plants is stimulated by the length of the dark period and not the length of the light period.

$$P_r \xrightleftharpoons[\text{darkness – slow}]{\text{red or white light – fast}} P_{fr}$$

Let's see how this works.

Light period	Dark period	Quantity of P_r	Quantity of P_{fr}	Flowering
Short P_r converted to P_{fr} rapidly	Long Most of the P_{fr} is converted back to P_r	High	Low	Short-day plants stimulated to flower

➢ Plants can be induced to flower 'out of season' by growing them in greenhouses where the length of the dark period can be controlled.
➢ An example of a short-day plant is Chrysanthemum.

6.21 Chrysanthemum flowers

Seed structure

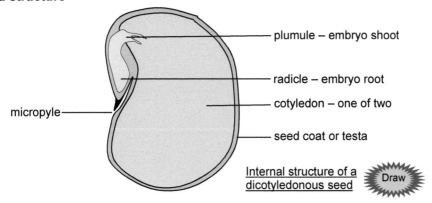

plumule – embryo shoot

radicle – embryo root

cotyledon – one of two

seed coat or testa

micropyle

Internal structure of a dicotyledonous seed

Draw

Dicotyledonous means two cotyledons.
Cotyledons are modified leaves found in the seed and used for storing food for germination.

Conditions necessary for seed germination

1. Moisture

    Seeds dry out for dispersal. At germination the cells need to absorb water to rehydrate so that metabolic reactions can take place.
    The water is absorbed through a tiny hole, the micropyle.

2. Warmth

    Many of the metabolic events of germination use enzymes. These are sensitive to temperature. Temperature is often used as a trigger for germination – e.g. many seeds from temperate climates only germinate after being exposed to cold temperatures for several days before being given warmer temperatures. Hence they germinate in Spring.

3. Oxygen

    Many of the metabolic events of germination use energy. This is produced by aerobic respiration.

1. State the name of the water transport system in plants.	2. State the name of the food transport system in plants.	3. What is the difference between the two in terms of direction of transport?
4. What is the name for the evaporation of water from the surface of the leaf?	5a. Name the force that holds water molecules together.	5b. What is this force due to?
6. Name the structures in the leaf through which water evaporates.	7. Name the process by which water enters the roots.	8. List 4 water conservation adaptations used by desert plants.
9. How do plants living in salty soils lower the water potential of their cytoplasm?	10a. Name the mechanism by which organic solutes are moved into a sieve tube.	
10b. Name the type of cell that carries out this transporting.	10c. Name two examples of this type of cell.	11a. Name the region of the plant which contains actively dividing cells.

11b. What type of cell division is occurring here?	12. What is a tropism?	13. Name the plant hormone that controls phototropism.
14. What is the effect of this hormone on cells?	15a. What is the name given to growing new plants from tissue samples?	15b. Name two ingredients required for this.
16. What is pollination?	17. Name the flower structure that produces pollen.	18. Name the flower structure that contains the egg cells.
19a. Name the substance that controls flowering.	19b. State the two forms of this substance.	19c. Which form is required in high concentration for short-day plants to flower?
20. List the parts of a seed.	21. List three conditions required for seed germination.	22. Two solutions are separated by a partially permeable membrane. In which direction will the water move? low water potential ┊ high water potential

Glossary

ADHESION	Attraction between water molecules and different molecules.
COHESION	Hydrogen bonding between water molecules.
COMPOUND	A substance made from two or more elements chemically combined.
COVALENT BOND	A strong chemical bond between molecules, e.g. between the sugar and phosphate and the sugar and base in a nucleotide.
INDETERMINATE GROWTH	Not fixed in extent compared to determinate growth such as in growth of a flower which has a defined shape.

Answers to Grey Box Questions   Underlined words are required.

1. Xylem.   2. Phloem.
3. Xylem transports up only; phloem transports in both directions.
4. Transpiration.   5a. Cohesion.   5b. Hydrogen bonding.
6. Stomata.   7. Osmosis.
8. Thick waxy cuticle; Stomata in pits; rolled leaves; reduced leaves.
9. Actively transporting salt into the cytoplasm.   10a. Active transport.
10b. Source cell.   10c. Photosynthesising leaf cell; storage cell in root, stem or seed.
11a. Meristem.   11b. Mitosis.
12. A response by a plant to a directional stimulus.   13. Auxin.
14. Increased growth.   15a. Micropropagation.   15b. Nutrient agar; plant hormones.
16. Transfer of pollen from anther to stigma.   17.
18. Ovule / ovary.   19a. Phytochrome.   19b. P_r and P_{fr}.
19c. P_r.   20. Micropyle; testa / seed coat; cotyledon; plumule; radicle.
21. Warmth; moisture; oxygen.   22. From right to left.

Self-test Quiz:

1. Phloem transport requires energy. This energy is provided by cells next to the sieve cells. These cells are called
    a.   active cells,
    b.   companion cells,
    c.   company cells,
    d.   associated cells.

2. A xerophyte is type of plant that:
    a.   possesses modified xylem tissue,
    b.   loses its leaves in winter,
    c.   has a reduced rate of photosynthesis,
    d.   is adapted to dry conditions.

3. Water is taken into a plant:
    a.   through active uptake by the xylem tissue,
    b.   through water loss as a result of respiration in the root cells,
    c.   by osmosis through the root hairs,
    d.   by the active evaporation of water causing transpiration in the leaves.

4. Which of the following statements about meristems is correct?
    a.   They protect the root as it grows through the soil.
    b.   They regulate flowering.
    c.   They allow indeterminate growth.
    d.   They control translocation.

5. A halophyte is a type of plant that:
    a.   is adapted to salty conditions,
    b.   has a reduced number of leaves,
    c.   has a thick waxy cuticle,
    d.   has a reduced rate of photosynthesis.

6. Which of the following best describes transpiration?
    a.   The loss of water vapour from the leaves and stem of the plant.
    b.   The movement of water into the leaves of the plant.
    c.   The transport of water through the phloem tissue.
    d.   The uptake of water via the root hairs of the plant.

7. Translocation is best described as:
    a.   transport of food substances up the stem from storage cells in the root,
    b.   loss of water vapour from the leaves of a plant,
    c.   transport of organic substances within the plant using energy,
    d.   uptake of water from the roots via root hairs.

8. Which of the following statements is correct?
    a.   Fertilisation is growth of the pollen on the stigma of the flower.
    b.   Pollination is transfer of the male gamete to the ovule.
    c.   Fertilisation is growth of the seed from the ovum.
    d.   Pollination is transfer of pollen from anther to stigma.

9. Which of the following statements correctly describes seed dispersal?
    a.   The transfer of seeds from anther to stigma.
    b.   Formation of seeds from the ovules within the ovary.
    c.   Release and spreading of seed from the parent plant.
    d.   Growth of seeds following absorption of water.

10. Which statement correctly describes a difference between transport cells in xylem tissue and phloem tissue?
    a. Xylem cells have completely lost their end walls but phloem cells still have a partial end wall.
    b. Xylem cells contained a modified cytoplasm but phloem cells contain normal cytoplasm.
    c. The nucleus in xylem cells is non-functional but the nucleus in phloem cells is important in regulating active transport.
    d. Phloem cells have lignified walls to assist in support and xylem cells do not.

11. Which of the following statements about the control of flowering is correct?
    a. Long day plants flower because long days result in a high concentration of P_r.
    b. Short day plants flower because long nights result in a high concentration of P_r.
    c. P_{fr} causes flowering in long day plants because sunlight changes it to P_r.
    d. Short day plants flower because high levels of P_{fr} block the effect of P_r.

12. Which of the following conditions is not normally necessary for seed germination?
    a. light,
    b. moisture,
    c. warmth,
    d. oxygen.

13. When stomata open to allow transpiration to occur what is a further consequence of this?
    a. respiration,
    b. photosynthesis,
    c. translocation,
    d. gas exchange.

14. Rolling up a leaf reduces transpiration because:
    a. it makes the stomata close up,
    b. it reduces the surface area of the leaf,
    c. it reduces the amount of light reaching the stomata,
    d. it raises the humidity around the stomata.

15. Translocation requires source cells and sink cells. A difference between these cells is that:
    a. sink cells are only found in roots,
    b. only photosynthesising cells can act as source cells,
    c. sink cells transport organic solutes out of sieve tubes,
    d. only source cells use active transport.

Chapter Seven

Ecology

Ecology is the study of the environment – species, communities, and all the ways they interact with each other and their non-living (abiotic) environment. Since the human species is having a major, sometimes catastrophic, impact on our planet, the study of ecology becomes increasingly important. Global warming, deforestation and ocean acidification are just three of the important issues.

Species, communities and ecosystems

Species
➢ Species are groups of organisms that can potentially interbreed to produce fertile offspring.
➢ Members of a species may be reproductively isolated in separate populations.

Example – Ramshorn snails living in one pond may have the potential to breed with the Ramshorn snails living in a nearby pond but are isolated from them by the dry land between the ponds.

Sometimes different species can interbreed but the offspring are infertile. Example – a mule is a horse x donkey.

7.1 A mule

Population
➢ This is a group of organisms of the same species living in the same place.

Community
➢ This is formed by populations of different species living together and interacting with each other.

You need to know how to use the chi-squared test on data collected from random sampling. Revise Chapter One, page 11.

Ecosystem
➢ This is formed by the interaction of a community with its abiotic environment.

Ways of feeding

Autotroph – an organism that synthesises its organic molecules from simple inorganic substances which are obtained from the abiotic environment.

7.2 Wild flowers

Heterotroph – an organism that obtains organic molecules from other organisms.

7.3 Hyena, Tanzania

Saprotroph – a heterotrophic organism that lives on or in non-living organic matter, secreting digestive enzymes onto it and absorbing the products of digestion.

7.4 Fungi on a rotting log

Consumer – a heterotrophic organism that ingests other organic matter that is living or recently killed.

Detritivore – a heterotrophic organism that ingests detritus.

7.5 Giant millipede, Borneo

Saprotrophs and detritivores are **decomposers.**

Food chains
Key points
➢ A food chain shows a linear relationship of one organism feeding on another.
➢ Each organism is on a particular feeding or **trophic level** depending on what it is eating – see food web.
➢ Chemical energy in carbon compounds flows through the food chain.
➢ All food chains end with decomposers.

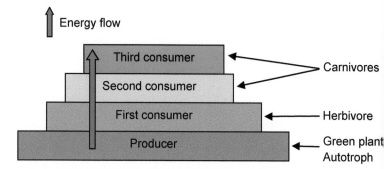

Energy flow

Third consumer — Carnivores
Second consumer —
First consumer — Herbivore
Producer — Green plant Autotroph

Decomposers

➢ Animals produce faeces.
➢ All organisms may die and not be eaten by a consumer.
➢ All these organic compounds are broken down by decomposers.

7.6 Fungi growing in cow dung

Examples of food chains

A marine ecosystem:

phytoplankton ⟶ copepod ⟶ herring ⟶ tuna
(zooplankton)

A rainforest ecosystem:

fig tree fruit ⟶ vervet monkey ⟶ eagle

A freshwater lake ecosystem:

algae ⟶ tadpole ⟶ dragonfly nymph ⟶ perch ⟶ heron

Food webs

Key points
➢ A food web is a series of interlinking food chains.
➢ An omnivore is an animal that is both a herbivore and a carnivore.
➢ Omnivores and carnivores can change their feeding level depending on what they are eating.

Look at the food web below.

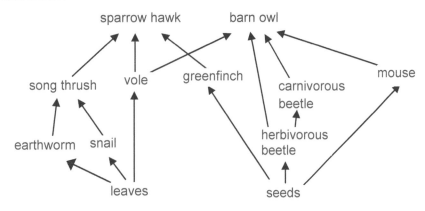

1. On the food web above deduce the feeding level of:	2. What is an organism that synthesises its organic molecules from simple inorganic substances?
a. The snail. _____	
b. The carnivorous beetle. _____	
c. The mouse. _____	
d. The sparrow hawk eating the vole. _____	3. What is an organism that obtains organic molecules from other organisms?
e. The sparrow hawk eating the song thrush. _____	
f. The barn owl eating the herbivorous beetle. _____	
g. The barn owl eating the carnivorous beetle. _____	

4. An earthworm is eating dead leaves. What type of organism is it?	5. A fungus is feeding on dead wood. What type of organism is it?	6. What is the second level in a food chain?

7. What is a species?	8. What is a community?

Mesocosms

➢ These are small scale investigations.
➢ They are self-sustaining natural systems.
➢ They are a bridge between a controlled laboratory experiment and the more variable uncontrolled field investigation.
➢ They allow a greater number of key variables to be controlled and manipulated to evaluate how organisms or communities may respond to changing environmental conditions.
➢ They provide sufficient biological complexity relative to the natural environment being modelled.

7.7a An aquatic mesocosm

7.7b A rainfall mesocosm

Energy flow

Energy, nutrients and ecosystems

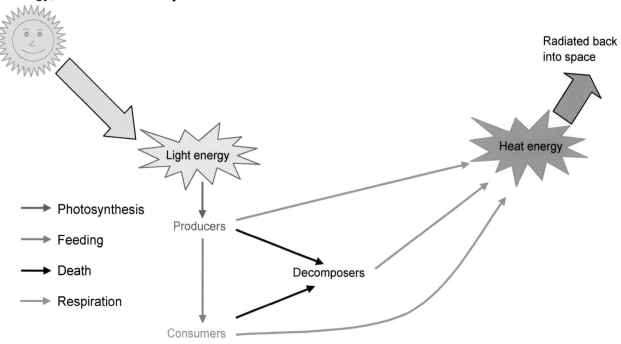

Key points – energy

➢ Energy enters most ecosystems as sunlight energy trapped by photosynthesis.
➢ Sunlight energy is continuous but variable.
➢ Photosynthesis converts the light energy to chemical energy.
➢ This chemical energy is stored in organic carbon compounds.
➢ The chemical energy in carbon compounds flows through food chains by feeding.
➢ The chemical energy is used by organisms through respiration but is converted to heat energy.
➢ As it flows through it is eventually all converted to heat energy and this leaves the ecosystem.
➢ Organisms cannot convert the heat energy to other, useable, forms of energy so it radiates into space.

The following diagram illustrates energy flow and losses in a food chain:

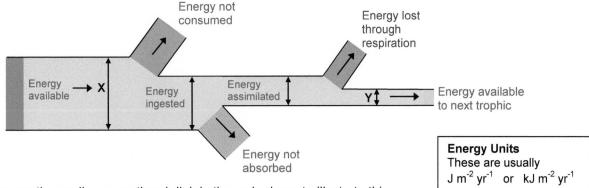

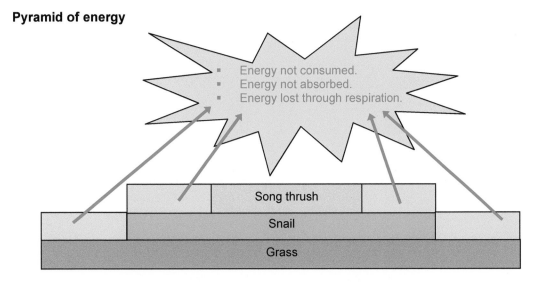

We can use the snail — song thrush link in the web above to illustrate this.

- The energy available is all the leaves in the place where the snail lives. ■
- But it will not eat all of the leaves. ☐
- After digesting and absorbing some of the leaf material it has eaten some will pass out of its gut as faeces. ☐
- The snail moves around and therefore uses up some of the energy it has consumed. ■
- The remainder of the energy is used for growth. This is what is available to the song thrush. ☐

Efficiency of energy flow

In the diagram above the amount of energy available at the start of the trophic level is X. The amount available to the next trophic level is Y. The efficiency is best calculated as a percentage.

$$\text{Efficiency} = \frac{Y}{X} \times 100$$

Key points

➤ The efficiency of energy transfer from one trophic level to the next one is never 100%.
➤ Commonly it is 10–20%.
➤ The energy losses between trophic levels restrict the length of food chains because a point comes when there is insufficient energy available to support a further trophic level.
➤ The biomass of higher trophic levels diminishes due to the loss of carbon dioxide through respiration of organic compounds, and loss of excretory organic compounds, e.g. urea.

Pyramid of energy

The yellow boxes represent the energy lost through a simple food chain.

Example – energy flow through a forest ecosystem:

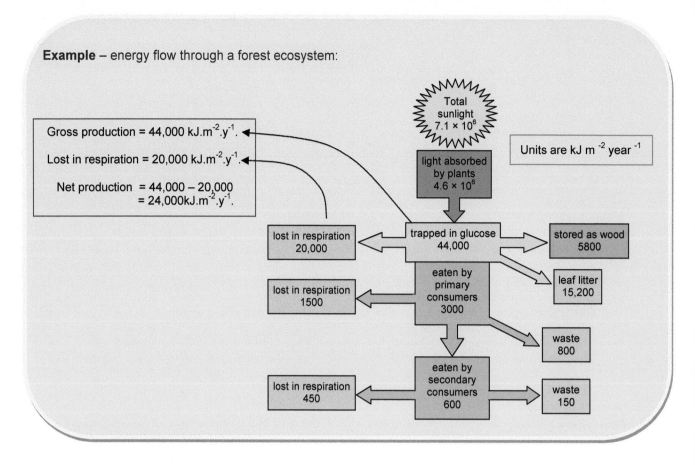

Gross production = 44,000 kJ.m^{-2}.y^{-1}.

Lost in respiration = 20,000 kJ.m^{-2}.y^{-1}.

Net production = 44,000 – 20,000
= 24,000kJ.m^{-2}.y^{-1}.

Total sunlight 7.1 × 10^6

Units are kJ m^{-2} year^{-1}

light absorbed by plants 4.6 × 10^6

lost in respiration 20,000

trapped in glucose 44,000

stored as wood 5800

leaf litter 15,200

lost in respiration 1500

eaten by primary consumers 3000

waste 800

lost in respiration 450

eaten by secondary consumers 600

waste 150

Constructing a pyramid of energy

Key points

➢ Energy pyramids are **always** a stepped pyramid shaped because energy is lost going from one trophic level up to the next.
➢ The lowest bar represents gross primary productivity or gross production.
➢ The width of the bars must be drawn to scale.
➢ The height of the bars is not significant but they should be uniform.
➢ The bars are centred.

Using the data from the forest ecosystem above.

Trophic Level	Energy / kJ m^{-2} year^{-1}
Producers	44000
Primary consumers	3000
Secondary consumers	700

Scale 1mm = 300 kJ m^{-2} year^{-1}

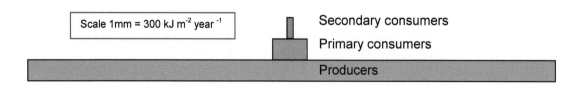

Secondary consumers

Primary consumers

Producers

Ecosystems

Key points

➢ An ecosystem is formed by the interaction between a community and its abiotic environment.
➢ An ecosystem has the potential to be sustainable over long periods of time if:
  • sufficient sunlight falls on the ecosystem,
  • the nutrients are recycled / replenished,
  • the community is not damaged.
➢ Nutrients are obtained from the abiotic environment.
➢ The supply of nutrients is finite and limited.
➢ When organisms die and decompose the nutrients are returned to the environment.
➢ The nutrients can then be recycled.

Summary

Energy enters an ecosystem (usually) as light energy and leaves as heat energy.

Nutrients are recycled within the ecosystem.

Nutrients may leave one ecosystem, for example, by being washed or blown out, but they then usually enter another ecosystem – see blue box.

7.8 A pond ecosystem

7.9 A dust storm on the Bodélé Depression

Dust blown from a vast dried lake bed, the Bodélé Depression, in central Africa supplies essential nutrients to rainforest in the Amazon basin.

9. Name the trophic level of the organisms that start food chains.	10. What is the most common source of energy for ecosystems?	11. In what form is energy transferred within a food web?
12. List three ways energy is lost when passing through a trophic level.	13. State the approximate % efficiency of energy transfer through a trophic level.	14. In what form does energy leave an ecosystem?
	15. What is a population?	16. What is an abiotic environment?
17. What do you get when a community interacts with its abiotic environment?		
	18. What is meant by the term reproductive isolation?	

Carbon cycling

The carbon cycle
➢ Carbon cycles in two main forms, carbon dioxide and methane.
➢ Peat and fossil fuels link to the carbon dioxide cycle.
➢ These are shown separately as combining them would make the diagram too complex.
➢ The boxes with the brown outline link the three.
➢ The cycle starts with carbon dioxide in the atmosphere.

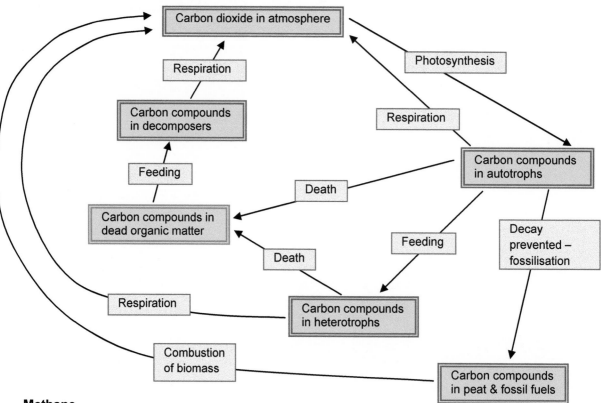

Methane
Key points
➢ In anaerobic conditions dead organic matter is converted to methane by methanogens.
➢ These are organisms belonging to the Domain Archaea.

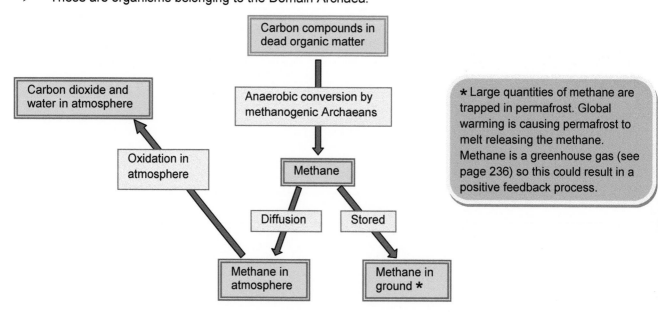

* Large quantities of methane are trapped in permafrost. Global warming is causing permafrost to melt releasing the methane. Methane is a greenhouse gas (see page 236) so this could result in a positive feedback process.

Peat, coal, oil and gas

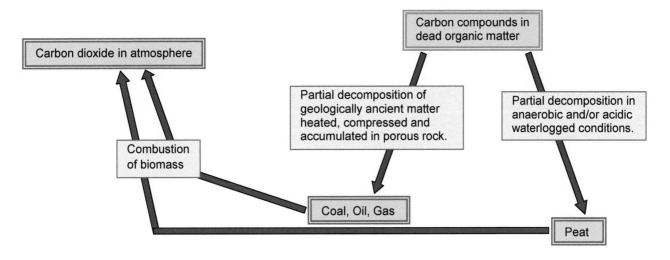

Large quantities of peat have been extracted from drained peat bogs and used as fuel or for gardening where it decomposes. In Indonesia large areas of dried peat are burning underground.

19. Name the process that converts atmospheric carbon dioxide to organic carbon compounds.	20. List two ways carbon dioxide is returned to the atmosphere in the carbon cycle.	21. Where do reef building corals obtain their carbon from?
22. Name the process by which organic compounds in autotrophs are transferred to heterotrophs.	23. In the carbon cycle what happens to biomass if decay is prevented?	24. What happens to carbon compounds in dead organisms?
25. What type of respiration do methanogenic bacteria use?	26. What does oxidation do to atmospheric methane?	27. Which Domain do methanogenic organisms belong to?

Climate change

The greenhouse effect

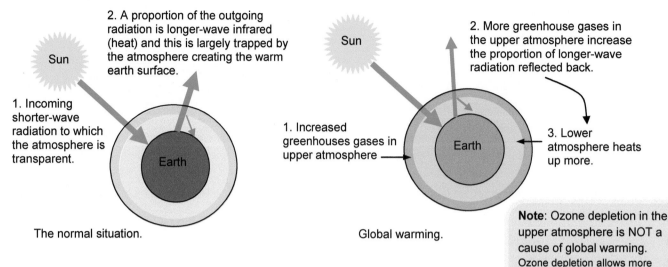

2. A proportion of the outgoing radiation is longer-wave infrared (heat) and this is largely trapped by the atmosphere creating the warm earth surface.

1. Incoming shorter-wave radiation to which the atmosphere is transparent.

The normal situation.

2. More greenhouse gases in the upper atmosphere increase the proportion of longer-wave radiation reflected back.

1. Increased greenhouses gases in upper atmosphere

3. Lower atmosphere heats up more.

Global warming.

Note: Ozone depletion in the upper atmosphere is NOT a cause of global warming. Ozone depletion allows more harmful UV radiation to reach the Earth's surface which increases the incidence of skin cancer.

Key points

➢ The greenhouse effect is a natural phenomenon and has helped to create a warm atmosphere that allowed evolution of life on the planet.

➢ The main greenhouse gases are carbon dioxide and water vapour.

➢ Other greenhouse gases which have less impact include methane and nitrogen oxides.

➢ The impact of a gas depends on:
- its ability to absorb long wave radiation,
- its concentration in the atmosphere.

➢ Carbon dioxide levels have been rising due to increasing use of fossil fuels in power stations, motor vehicles, aircraft and shipping.

➢ Aircraft also produce water vapour trails (contrails) which have an effect equal to their carbon dioxide emissions.

➢ Analysis of air bubbles trapped in Antarctica ice showed carbon dioxide levels remained fairly constant from 500BC to mid-1800s, the start of the industrial revolution.

7.10 Aircraft contrails

Date	Carbon dioxide concentration /ppm	% increase from 1880
1880	270	
1958	315	16.7
2000	360	33.3
2004	375	38.9
2006	382	41.5
2008	386	42.9
2010	390	44.4
2013	396	46.7

Table showing increase in atmospheric carbon dioxide since 1880.

Data from the Mauna Loa monitoring station in Hawaii. (ppm = parts per million)

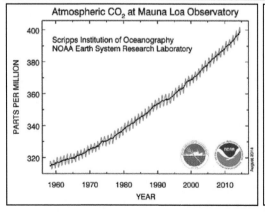

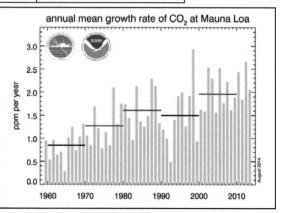

7.11 Graphs showing changes in atmospheric carbon dioxide since 1960 at Mauna Loa Observatory

- The gases in the upper atmosphere reflect back some of the heat rising from the Earth.
- This causes the atmosphere to heat up.
- Global temperatures and climate patterns are influenced by concentrations of greenhouse gases.
- This rising temperature can:
  - influence climate patterns:
    - increase frequency and severity of storms and hurricanes,
    - alter rainfall patterns causing droughts in some areas and flooding in others.
  - cause increased melting of glaciers, polar ice caps and sea ice leading to a rise in sea level,
  - cause a rise in sea levels due to thermal expansion of the oceans,
  - cause a rise in sea temperatures which leads to coral bleaching (death of coral),
  - increase evaporation so more atmospheric water vapour to increase greenhouse effect,
  - melt permafrost causing release of trapped methane,
  - enhance plant growth where plants have adequate water and minerals,
- Rising carbon dioxide levels increase acidity of the oceans causing weakening of coral reefs.

Human activities and climate change – evaluation
Activity and effect
- Burning fossil fuels to supply energy:
  - produces carbon dioxide and nitrogen oxides.
- Cutting down tropical rainforest:
  - reduces uptake of carbon dioxide due to photosynthesis,
  - increases carbon dioxide output from burning and rotting vegetation.
- Increase in cattle farming:
  - cattle produce methane.
- Increase in rice paddies:
  - anaerobic breakdown of organic compounds in the mud releases methane.
- Waste tips:
  - anaerobic breakdown of waste releases methane.

> A report from The Royal Institute of International Affairs in December 2014 stated that emissions from cattle equalled that of emissions from transport.

Key points
- Climate change is a better term than global warming because some regions of the globe will get colder as a result of increasing greenhouse gases.
- The graph below indicates that there is a close correlation between the rise in carbon dioxide concentration and the rise in global temperatures.

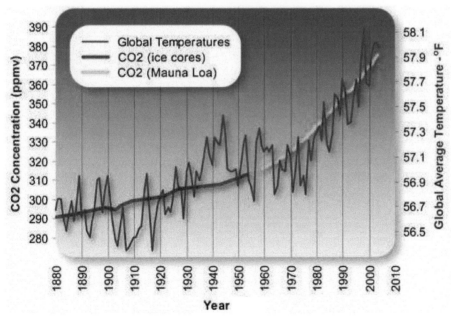

7.12 Graph showing the relationship between atmospheric carbon dioxide levels and global average temperature

American Secretary of State John Kerry said in a speech in Jakarta, Indonesia on 21st September 2014:
'In a sense, climate change can now be considered the world's largest weapon of mass destruction, perhaps even, the world's most fearsome weapon of mass destruction.'

Destruction of the rainforests

Accurate figures are difficult to obtain and it varies each year, but scientists generally agree that we are losing about 80,000 acres of tropical rainforest **daily**, and in addition significantly degrading a further 80,000 acres every day. Along with this plant loss go all the animals.

To put it another way a report in September 2014 stated that between 2000 and 2012 an area of rainforest equivalent to 5 football pitches was destroyed every **minute**. This is mostly driven by the demand for timber, leather, beef, soy and palm oil.

Healthy rainforest on the left and on the right cleared for palm oil plantations.

7.13 Rainforest destruction in Borneo

Coral reefs

Coral reefs are wonderfully diverse and productive ecosystems. They provide a vital resource for many coastal communities, provide breeding grounds for many fish species, and also protect the shoreline from the ocean waves.

Ocean acidification due to rising atmospheric carbon dioxide means corals are unable to absorb the calcium carbonate needed for their skeletons. Not only does this slow their growth but it weakens them making them more susceptible to wave damage. The oceans are now 30% more acidic than they were in 1750.

7.14 Reef damaged by waves. Fagatele Bay, American Samoa

Carbon fluxes

Key points

➢ Carbon flux is the flow of carbon from one carbon reservoir to another.
➢ There are four major carbon reservoirs:
  • atmosphere,
  • oceans,
  • Earth's crust,
  • terrestrial ecosystems.
➢ The net flux is the difference between input to the reservoirs and output from the reservoirs.
➢ The information above shows that the overall net flux is not only out of balance but getting worse.

Diagram of carbon reservoirs and fluxes

Carbon stores in the coloured boxes are in gigatonnes, and the fluxes are in gigatonnes per year. (1 gigatonne = 1000,000,000,000kg)

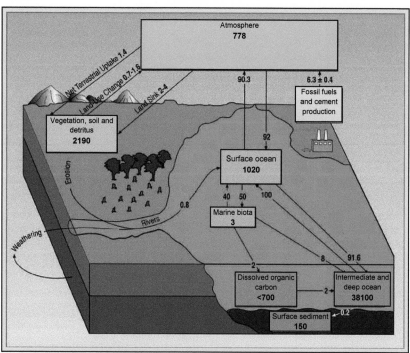

© Kevin Saff at en.wikipedia [Public domain], from Wikimedia Commons.

"It is not so much that we are systematically annihilating life on this planet, but that there is nothing really being done about it, and worse still, nobody cares.

Indeed for governments throughout the world, the environment is little more than an embarrassment. Their main preoccupation is to earn the necessary foreign currency required to assure the economic development on which their prestige, power and future must depend. To this end they will sacrifice anything – their forests, their land, their topsoil, not to mention their traditions, their culture, their religion, indeed all that their ancestors, for countless generations, held to be most holy."

Edward Goldsmith, The retreat from Stockholm. *The Ecologist* (1982). p98. (Reprinted with permission).

28. What does plant matter that is partial decomposed in waterlogged anaerobic and/or acidic conditions become?	29. What happens to shorter wave radiation from the sun when it hits the Earth?	30. List the two main greenhouse gases.
31. List two additional greenhouse gases.	32. Why do greenhouse gases increase atmospheric temperatures?	33. List five effects of global warming.
34. What is a carbon reservoir?	35. List the four carbon reservoirs.	
36. What is meant by the term carbon flux?	37. What is meant by the term net carbon flux?	

Glossary

ABIOTIC	The non-living component of the environment.
DETRITUS	Non-living organic matter.
PPMV	Parts per million by volume.

Answers to Grey Box Questions

1a. First consumer. b. Second consumer. c. First consumer. d. Second consumer. e. Third consumer. f. Second consumer. g. Third consumer.

2. Autotroph.   3. Heterotroph.   4. Detritivore.

5. Saprotroph.   6. First consumer.

7. Organisms that can potentially interbreed to produce fertile offspring.

8. Populations of different species living together and interacting with each other.

9. Producer / autotroph.   10. Sunlight.   11. Chemical.

12. Not consumed. Not assimilated. Respiration.   13. 10-20%

14. Heat.   15. A group of organisms of the same species living in the same place.

16. Non-living.   17. Ecosystem.

18. Members of a population that are unable to breed with a population of the same species due to some isolating factor, usually geographic.

19. Photosynthesis.   20. Respiration, burning, atmospheric oxidation of methane.

21. Dissolved carbon dioxide / hydrogen carbonate ions.   22. Feeding.

23. Peat and fossil fuels.   24. Consumed by decomposers.   25. Anaerobic.

26. Converts it to carbon dioxide and water.   27. Archaea.   28. Peat.

29. It becomes longer wave radiation.   30. Carbon dioxide. Water vapour.

31. Methane. Nitrogen oxides.   32. They reflect back to Earth more of the longer wave radiation.

33. Influence climate patterns / increase frequency and severity of storms and hurricanes / alter rainfall patterns causing droughts in some areas and flooding in others.
Cause increased melting of glaciers, polar ice caps and sea ice leading to a rise in sea level.
Cause a rise in sea levels due to thermal expansion of the oceans;
Cause a rise in sea temperatures which leads to coral bleaching (death of coral).
Increase evaporation so more water vapour to increase greenhouse effect;
Melt permafrost causing release of trapped methane.
Enhance plant growth where plants have adequate water and minerals.
34. A place where carbon is stored.
35. Atmosphere. Ocean. Earth's crust. Terrestrial ecosystems.
36. Movement of carbon between reservoirs.
37. The difference between input to reservoirs and the output from them.

Self-test Quiz

1. Food chains generally start with:
    a. herbivores,
    b. green plants,
    c. carnivores,
    d. decomposers.

2. In an ecosystem:
    a. energy is recycled,
    b. pyramids of energy always start with first consumers at the base,
    c. there are always three trophic levels,
    d. elements are recycled.

3. In an ecosystem which of the following is true?
    a. Respiration is part of the carbon cycle but photosynthesis is not.
    b. Green plants do not depend on decomposers.
    c. Green plants are affected by abiotic factors.
    d. Energy loss at each trophic level limits the number of trophic levels in a food chain to three.

4. A community can be defined as:
    a. a group of populations living with each other in an area,
    b. a group of organisms that can interbreed,
    c. the habitat in which the organisms are found,
    d. a group of populations living and interacting with the abiotic environment.

5. Which of the following statements is true?
    a. The trophic level of an organism is the height above ground where it is found.
    b. The transfer of energy from one trophic level to the next is never 100% efficient.
    c. There are always more carnivores in a food chain than herbivores.
    d. A food web always contains at least 10 organisms.

6. The initial source of energy for most communities is:
    a. light energy,
    b. chemical energy,
    c. green plants,
    d. producers.

7. Decomposers are:
    a. saprotrophic fungi and bacteria,
    b. producers,
    c. piles of dead plant and animal material,
    d. detritivores.

8. The greenhouse effect is due to:
    a. an increase in the amount of heat energy reflected from the earth's surface,
    b. an increase in the heat output of the sun,
    c. a decrease in the proportion of solar energy radiated back into space from the earth's atmosphere,
    d. an increase in heat output from the earth's surface due to the rise in human population.

9. A food web is:
    a. a complex food chain,
    b. food chains that include decomposers,
    c. all of the producers in a community,
    d. a group of interlinking food chains.

10. A pyramid of energy is always pyramid shaped because:
    a. there are always more consumers than producers,
    b. energy is lost between one trophic level and the next one up,
    c. most food chains start with light energy from the sun,
    d. carnivores consume more energy finding food than herbivores.

11. Look at the following food chain and select the correct statement.
    seeds → rat → cobra → mongoose
    a. The mongoose is a fourth consumer.
    b. The rat is a carnivorous consumer.
    c. The cobra is a second consumer.
    d. The rat is a producer.

12. Which of the following are greenhouse gases?
    a. water vapour , methane, carbon dioxide, nitrogen oxide,
    b. nitrogen oxide, carbon dioxide, hydrogen, oxygen,
    c. methane, carbon dioxide, nitrogen oxide, ozone,
    d. nitrogen oxide, water vapour, methane, ozone.

13. The efficiency of energy transfer within a food web:
    a. is determined by the length of the food chains,
    b. is about 50%,
    c. is determined by the efficiency of the producers,
    d. is about 10%.

14. An ecosystem is formed as a result of:
    a. an interaction between a population and its abiotic environment,
    b. an interaction between a community and its abiotic environment,
    c. an interaction between a population and a community,
    d. an interaction between different species.

15. Which of the following statements about the carbon cycle is correct?
    a. Carbon dioxide diffuses into water and can be used by aquatic autotrophs.
    b. Carbon dioxide is used by decomposers to make organic carbon compounds.
    c. Photosynthesis releases carbon dioxide which is used by plants to make organic compounds.
    d. Carbohydrates are converted to organic carbon compounds by respiration in decomposers.

16. Which of the following statements is correct?
    a. Methanogenic Archaea convert methane into carbon dioxide.
    b. Methanogenic Archaea convert carbon dioxide in the atmosphere into methane.
    c. Methane in the atmosphere can be oxidised into water and carbon dioxide.
    d. Water and carbon dioxide in the atmosphere can be oxidised into methane.

17. Which of the following is correct concerning global warming?
    a. It can adversely affect climate.
    b. It can lead to increased acidification of the oceans.
    c. It can cause increased melting of polar ice caps and sea ice.
    d. All of the above.

18. The net carbon flux can be described as:
    a. The change in the atmospheric carbon dioxide concentration.
    b. The difference between the flow of carbon into a reservoir and the flow of carbon out of it.
    c. The transfer of carbon to the atmospheric reservoir.
    d. The transfer of carbon from the ocean and Earth's crust reservoirs.

19. Increasing the dissolved carbon dioxide in the oceans can result in:
    a. damage to coral reefs due to the decrease in pH,
    b. an increase in the melting of the polar ice caps,
    c. an increase in the longer wavelength radiation from the sun radiated from the ocean surface,
    d. a reduction in the number of hydrogen carbonate ions available for marine Molluscs to use for shell building.

20. Look at the left graph (7.11) on page 236. The reason for the annual fluctuation is:
    a. Tropical rainforest trees lose their leaves in the winter.
    b. There is a greater uptake of carbon dioxide in the northern hemisphere forests in summer.
    c. Light intensity in the northern hemisphere fluctuates more than in the southern hemisphere.
    d. Temperatures in the tropics are higher than in higher latitudes.

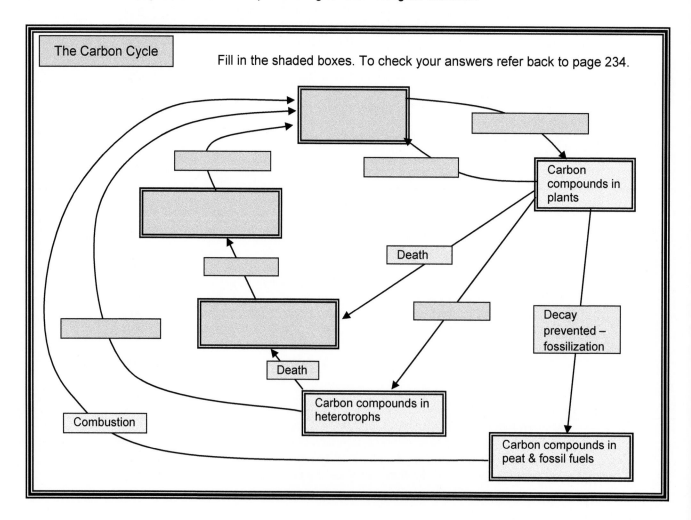

The Carbon Cycle

Fill in the shaded boxes. To check your answers refer back to page 234.

Chapter Eight

Genetics

This is the story of heredity, how information is passed from parents to offspring. Experimental work on genetics was started in the nineteenth century, and Gregor Mendel is considered to be the founding father. He was the first person to make thorough, quantitative observations of the patterns of inheritance along with mechanisms to explain them. His work studying the garden pea led to the development of his two simple laws.

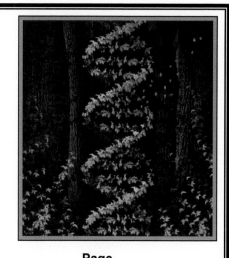

Chromosomes

Key points
➤ Prokaryotes have a single circular chromosome.
➤ Some prokaryotes have plasmids – small circular pieces of DNA in the cytoplasm – see page 74.
➤ Eukaryotes have linear chromosomes associated with histone proteins – see page 43.
➤ The number of chromosomes is a characteristic of members of a species.
➤ Eukaryotic nuclei can be diploid or haploid:
  • A diploid nucleus has pairs of chromosomes called homologous pairs:
    ▪ Homologous chromosomes carry the same sequence of genes but not necessarily the same alleles of those genes.
  • A haploid nucleus has one chromosome from each homologous pair.
➤ Some eukaryotes have a pair of chromosomes called **sex chromosomes** that determine gender.
➤ The chromosomes other than the sex chromosomes are called **autosomes**.
➤ Chromosomes can be arranged into a karyogram – see page 101.

> A human female has 44 autosomes + the sex chromosomes XX,
> A human male has 44 autosomes + the sex chromosomes XY.

Genes, alleles and mutations
Key points
➤ A **gene** is a heritable factor that consists of a length of DNA on a chromosome and influences a specific characteristic.
➤ A gene occupies a specific position on a chromosome called its locus.
➤ The different forms of a gene are called **alleles**.
➤ Alleles differ from one another by one or only a few bases.
➤ New alleles are formed by **mutations**.
➤ Mutations can be at the gene level, (see page 245) or at the chromosome level – see page 100.
➤ Meiosis mixes alleles to produce variety in sexual reproduction – see page 100.
➤ **Genome** is the whole of the genetic information of an organism.
➤ **Genome size** is the total length of DNA in an organism and includes all the non-coding sequences.
➤ The human genome project determined the entire base sequence of all the human chromosomes.

> Gene: flower **colour**,
> Alleles: **red** colour, **blue** colour.

> **Genome**
> In prokaryotes it is all the information in the single circular chromosome plus any plasmids.
>
> In eukaryotic animals it is all the information in a haploid set of chromosomes plus mitochondrial DNA.
>
> In eukaryotic plants it is all the information in a haploid set of chromosomes plus mitochondrial DNA plus chloroplast DNA.

> **Human genome project**
> This was started in 1990 as an international collaboration to determine the entire base sequence of the human genome. The sequence of the 3 billion base pairs was completed in 2003. Work continues on mapping the location of specific genes and the positions and functions of other base sequences.
> Outcomes
> ▪ Improved knowledge of how human genes function.
> ▪ Improved diagnosis of genetic disease.
> ▪ Increased potential for gene therapy.
> ▪ Increased potential to design drugs to combat genetic malfunctions.

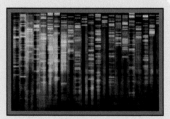

8.1 DNA sequencing

Sickle cell anaemia – a base substitution mutation

Key points
➤ Caused by a mutation in one of the two haemoglobin genes.
➤ An amino acid called glutamic acid has been replaced by one called valine.
➤ The triplet CTC has mutated to CAC.
➤ When the triplet is transcribed the normal mRNA codon GAG becomes GUG.
➤ GAG would be translated into glutamic acid but GUG is translated into valine.

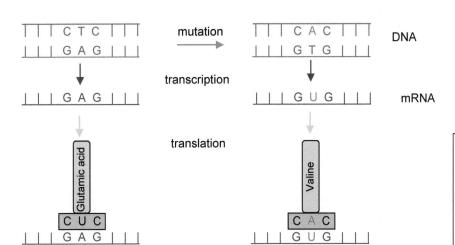

Hints:
- GAG has become GTG. **A** comes before **T** in the alphabet.
- **g** for glutamic acid becomes **v** for valine and **g** comes before **v** in the alphabet.

Refer to the codon table on page 52 and look up the codons for these two amino acids.

If you **substitute** the A of the glutamic acid triplet with a U you will get a codon for valine.

Comparing diploid chromosome numbers of different species

Species	Diploid Number of Chromosomes
Parascaris equorum (parasitic worm)	2
Oryza sativa (rice)	24
Homo sapiens (human)	46
Pan troglodytes (chimpanzee)	48
Canis familiaris (domestic dog)	78

Human ancestors had the same number of chromosomes as chimpanzees – 48. By comparing chimp and modern human chromosomes it looks as though human chromosome 2 is a fusion of two smaller chimp chromosomes giving us 46.

Comparing chromosome and gene numbers of different species

Species	Number of Chromosomes	Estimated Number of Genes
Escherischia coli (bacterium)	One circular chromosome	1700 – 3000
Arabidopsis thaliana (plant)	10	23,000 – 25,000
Homo sapiens (human)	46	19,000 – 20,000
Drosophila melanogaster (fruit fly)	8	15,682
Mus musculus (House mouse)	40	25,000

Comparing genome size of different species

Species	Genome Size in Base Pairs
T2 bacteriophage (a bacterial virus)	0.17×10^6
Escherischia coli (bacterium)	4.6×10^6
Drosophila melanogaster (fruit fly)	130×10^6
Homo sapiens (human)	3200×10^6
Paris japonica (Japanese canopy plant)	$150,000 \times 10^6$

8.2 Flowers of *Paris japonica*

- ➢ The number of chromosomes is highly variable between species.
- ➢ There is some correlation between size and number – the smaller the size the greater the number.
- ➢ The number of genes is highly variable between species.
- ➢ There is a positive correlation between genome size and complexity in prokaryotes.
- ➢ There is a positive correlation between genome size and complexity in eukaryotes but only in the more simple phyla.
- ➢ In the higher phyla there is much greater variability
- ➢ This is due to different proportions of non-coding DNA and repetitive sequences – see pages 46 and 56.
- ➢ Humans and most other mammals so far sequenced have roughly the same number of base pairs and genes.

Cairn's technique for measuring DNA molecules
Principles
- ➢ Thymidine is one of the four building blocks used in DNA replication – see page 44.
- ➢ It can be labelled with the radioactive form of hydrogen called tritium, ^{3}H.
- ➢ When tritium decays it emits a particle that marks a photographic plate.
- ➢ If cells are allowed to replicate in the presence of tritiated thymidine, [^{3}H]-T, the DNA becomes radioactive.

Key points
- ➢ Cairns used bacteria for his investigations.
- ➢ He cultured them with [^{3}H]-T.
- ➢ They were then treated with a hypotonic solution to lyse them (split them open).
- ➢ This would release the DNA.
- ➢ The solution was then spread on a photographic plate and left in the dark for many days to form an autoradiogram.
- ➢ After developing the film black dots could be seen where the bacterial chromosome had been.
- ➢ Since the experimental material was bacteria these dots formed circles.
- ➢ The circle could be measured to determine the length of the DNA molecule.

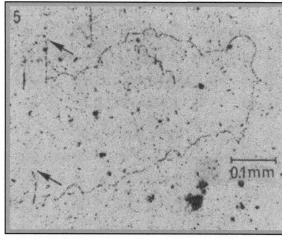

8.3 An autoradiogram of a Chinese hamster chromosome using Cairn's technique
From arrow to arrow it is 1.6mm long. Exposure time was 3 months.

Radiation and gene mutation

Ionising radiation, X-rays, UV light and many chemicals are mutagens, i.e. they cause mutations. Scientists tracked the effects of ionising radiation after the Hiroshima and Nagasaki nuclear bombs, the nuclear power plant explosions at Chernobyl and Three Mile Island, and more recently at Fukushima due to the tsunami.

Hiroshima and Nagasaki
- ➢ Nuclear bombs were detonated over these Japanese cities in August 1945.
- ➢ Early in 1948 studies were begun to determine the after-effects of radiation using a city 29km south of Hiroshima as the control.
- ➢ It was found that birth defects were not significantly higher.
- ➢ However 200 cases of leukaemia (blood cancer) and 1,700 cases of solid cancers could be attributed to radiation damage.

Chernobyl

➢ In April 1986 nuclear reactor No. 4 at Chernobyl exploded and caught fire.
➢ Several tons of radioactive material was released into the atmosphere, made worse by being carried up in the heat from the fire.
➢ 400× more radioactive material was released than from the Hiroshima bomb.
➢ This spread over huge areas of land, mainly Belarus, but also Ukraine, Russia, Germany, Scandinavian countries, southern Europe and the UK.
➢ Workers in the plant, and rescue and firefighter personnel were either killed quickly or died within a few weeks from very high doses of radiation.
➢ Millions of people received increased doses of radiation.
➢ Mutations in new born farm animals in the fall-out area increased.
➢ Groundwater, and hence reservoirs, became contaminated as well as upland areas where contaminated rain fell.
➢ This led to food chain livestock – reindeer, sheep, cattle, wild boar – becoming contaminated with caesium-137.
➢ About 100,000km^2 of land was significantly contaminated.
➢ Thyroid cancer in children due to iodine-131 rose to over 6000 by 2005 with predictions of it rising very much higher.
➢ A report stated that there had been no increase in the rate of human birth defects or solid cancers.
➢ However it raised the possibility of long term genetic defects due to a large increase in tandem repeat mutations among children born in 1994.

Genetic modification and biotechnology

Tandem repeats
Key points

➢ A tandem repeat is a short sequence of bases in the DNA which are repeated, e.g. GGTGGTGGTGGT.
➢ The repeats are in tandem, i.e. clustered together.
➢ Individual repeats can be removed or added through recombination or replication errors.
➢ This results in alleles with different numbers of repeats.
➢ On each side of the repeats are segments of non-repetitive bases which allow the sections to be extracted with restriction endonuclease enzymes.

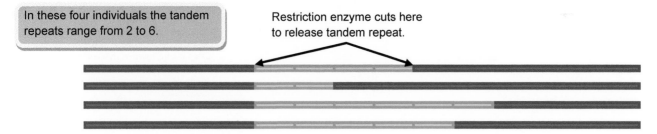

In these four individuals the tandem repeats range from 2 to 6.

Restriction enzyme cuts here to release tandem repeat.

The polymerase chain reaction (PCR)
Key points

➢ This copies and amplifies minute quantities of DNA.
➢ Only specific parts of the DNA molecule are amplified.
➢ This is done by adding specific primers which bind to the complementary regions of DNA.
➢ The machine is automatically programmed to amplify the DNA.
➢ The DNA can then be used for profiling using gel electrophoresis.

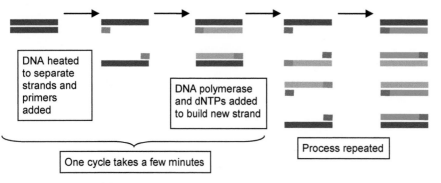

DNA heated to separate strands and primers added

DNA polymerase and dNTPs added to build new strand

One cycle takes a few minutes

Process repeated

8.4 A group of PCR machines

The stages of the PCR.

Gel electrophoresis
Key points
➢ The PCR is used to amplify the amount of DNA.
➢ The DNA is cut into fragments using restriction endonucleases.
➢ The fragments have a small negative charge.
➢ They will move through a gel towards a positive electrode.
➢ The smaller the fragment the further it will move.
➢ The DNA bands are stained.

> Restriction endonucleases are a group of enzymes obtained from bacteria that recognize very specific sequences of DNA and cut both of the DNA strands at this point.

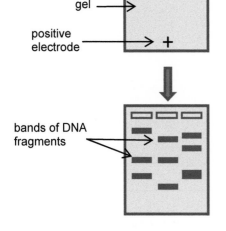

wells

gel

positive electrode

bands of DNA fragments

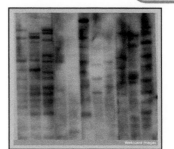

8.5a The original autoradiograph, discovered by Professor Alec Jeffreys at Leicester University

For a larger image go to
http://wellcomeimages.org/
Image number b0005956

The first DNA fingerprint. The first three lanes contain DNA from a woman, her mother and her father respectively. Lanes 4–11 contain DNA from assorted other species including mouse, baboon, lemur, cow, grey seal and tobacco (last lane). The DNA probe used in this experiment detected tandemly repeated short stretches of DNA called minisatellites whose length varies between individuals.

8.5b An example produced using school equipment

DNA profiling
Principles
➢ Tandem repeats are short sequences of DNA repeated many times.
➢ They vary between individuals so much that the probability of two individuals being the same is zero, excluding identical twins.
➢ PCR may be used to increase the amount of DNA.
➢ Great care to prevent contamination is required as the PCR will also amplify contaminant DNA.
➢ DNA is cut up with restriction endonucleases.
➢ Gel electrophoresis separates the DNA fragments.
➢ The banding patterns are compared.

Uses
➢ Paternity – sometimes a woman is unsure who the father of her child might be, or the man disputes being the father, or wants to know if he is the father. DNA profiling from a mouth swab is used.
➢ Forensic investigations – often tiny samples of DNA can be found such as a drop of blood or saliva, a hair follicle, scrapings under a finger nail, and the DNA can be amplified using the PCR before profiling.

- ➤ Family relationships for immigrants – a male immigrant may wish to bring his wife and children into the country. DNA profiling can be used to determine if the man and his wife are the natural parents of the children.
- ➤ Determining if rare birds and other animals being sold as captive bred have actually been captive bred or been stolen from the wild.
- ➤ Comparing DNA from fossils with modern organisms.
- ➤ Determining the contents of manufactured foods, especially those containing meat.

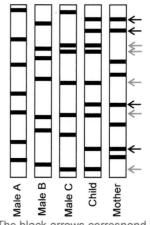

An example of how DNA profiling has been used to determine paternity

Male A Male B Male C Child Mother

The black arrows correspond to the mother.
The red arrows show that the father of the child is male C.

Production of human insulin using gene transfer

Key requirements
- ➤ The insulin gene.
- ➤ A plasmid.
- ➤ A host bacterium (*E.coli*).
- ➤ Four enzymes - reverse transcriptase,
  - DNA polymerase,
  - a restriction endonuclease,
  - DNA ligase.

> When genes are transferred between species the amino acid sequence of polypeptides translated from them is unchanged because the genetic code is universal.

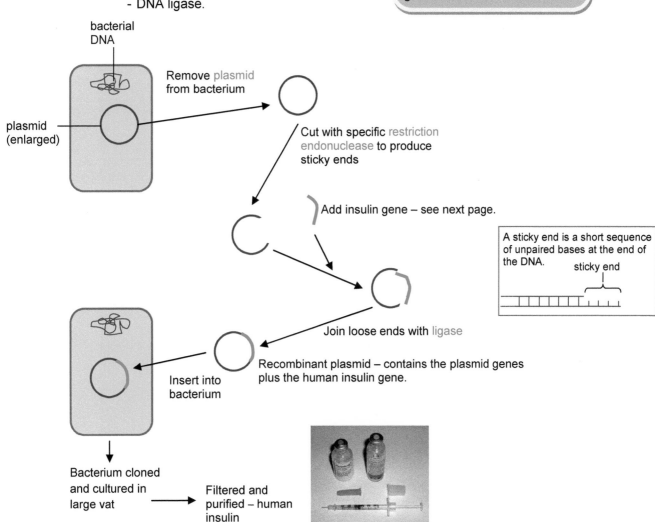

bacterial DNA

Remove plasmid from bacterium

plasmid (enlarged)

Cut with specific restriction endonuclease to produce sticky ends

Add insulin gene – see next page.

A sticky end is a short sequence of unpaired bases at the end of the DNA.
sticky end

Join loose ends with ligase

Recombinant plasmid – contains the plasmid genes plus the human insulin gene.

Insert into bacterium

Bacterium cloned and cultured in large vat → Filtered and purified – human insulin

8.6 Insulin syringes are marked in 'insulin' units.

The insulin gene

➢ The gene cannot be cut from the beta cell DNA because it will produce primary RNA which contains introns – see page 50.

➢ Insulin mRNA from the cytoplasm is obtained.

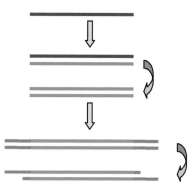

➢ The enzymes reverse transcriptase and DNA polymerase are used to make a DNA molecule from the mRNA.

➢ A specific sequence of bases is added at each end and then cut with the same restriction endonuclease as used on the plasmid to make the same sticky ends.

Genetically modified organisms (GMOs)

Key points

➢ Since the genetic code is (nearly) universal genetic information can be transferred between organisms.
➢ New varieties can be produced much more quickly than through conventional breeding.
➢ Novel genes can be introduced which are not in the species' genome.
➢ It does raise questions of ethics and safety.

Examples currently in commercial use

Soybean	Tolerance to the herbicide glyphosate by inserting a gene from a soil bacterium.
Corn	Resistance to insect pests, specifically the corn borer, by inserting a gene from a bacterium which produces a toxic protein.
Altered fatty acid composition in canola beans	High laurate levels achieved by inserting a gene from the California bay tree. (Laurate is used in soap manufacture.)
Virus resistance in plum	Resistance to plum pox virus conferred by inserting a coat protein gene from the virus.

Examples in development

Golden rice	Modified using three genes to produce high levels of beta-carotene, a precursor for vitamin A.
Vaccines	Tobacco engineered to produce hepatitis B antigen for vaccine production.
Oral vaccine for chickens	Corn engineered to produce a protein from the Newcastle disease virus in its seeds induced an immune response in chickens when fed to them.

Benefits of GM

Corn
The added gene comes from the bacterium *Bacillus thuringiensis* so the GM variety is called Bt corn. Caterpillars eating any part of the plant will be killed by the bacterial toxin.
Benefit – the toxin is specific to pests eating the plant and does not harm other animals. The crop does not have to be sprayed with insecticides which would kill beneficial insects. This also reduces costs associated with manufacture and application of the insecticide.

Soybean
Glyphosate is a biodegradable general herbicide. The soybean crop is allowed to germinate and then sprayed once with glyphosate. The weeds are killed and then continued growth of the soybean out-competes any new weeds that germinate.
Benefit – reduced competition for soil nutrients increases crop yield.

Canola
Canola is a variety of rapeseed which is normally low in laurate. Laurate for soap making has been obtained from coconut, palm and laurel oils.
Benefit – GM canola can be grown easily and cheaply and in large quantities. Palm oil plantations have resulted in vast areas of tropical rainforest being destroyed, so using GM canola can reduce this destruction.

Bt corn
The toxin is expressed in all parts of the plant including the pollen. The plant is wind pollinated so the pollen blows around and lands on the leaves of other plants leading to concerns that it could kill insects feeding on those leaves. Research was done with larvae of the Monarch butterfly that feeds on milkweed. Laboratory tests showed that the larvae were indeed harmed when Bt corn pollen was sprinkled on the milkweed leaves. However the tests were shown to have used amounts of pollen that would not be encountered in the field and Bt corn was licenced for continued use.

Golden rice
Potential benefit: Large numbers of people have a limited range of foods in their diet and rice is the mainstay. Vitamin A deficiency is a common problem. Golden rice could provide sufficient beta carotene to overcome this deficiency.

Newcastle disease
This is a highly contagious and virulent virus and is found worldwide. Chickens are an important source of eggs and low fat meat for humans.
Potential benefit. Immunising both small and large flocks would be simple and productivity would be greatly increased.

Nature, January 2015 – GM microbes created that can't escape the lab
Genetically engineered micro-organisms are used in Europe, the US and China to produce drugs under controlled industrial conditions. Preventing these micro-organisms from escaping into the environment – biocontainment – has been an important area of research. Two laboratories in the US have recoded the *E. coli* bacteria genome so that they require a synthetic amino acid in order to make an essential protein. Without this amino acid they cannot make the protein and without the protein they die. Work is continuing to increase the number of synthetic amino acids required.

Risks of GM
- See Bt corn above.
- Widespread use of pest resistant crop plants may result in the pests developing resistance to the toxin, though this frequently happens with other forms of pest control.
- There are concerns that the proteins from transgenic genes could be toxic or cause allergic reactions in livestock or humans if they would not normally have encountered them.
- During the procedure to transfer genes into bacteria antibiotic resistance genes are used to test whether the desired gene has been transferred. These antibiotic resistance genes would be dangerous if they spread to pathogenic bacteria.
- Transferred genes could mutate and create problems. During the risk assessment for the transfer mutations would be difficult to predict and could not therefore be included in the assessment.
- Transferred genes in plants could spread to other species through cross pollination. These plants could then become toxic to wildlife or become uncontrollable weeds.
- Herbicide resistant plants could grow the following year from spilled seed. This would be a nuisance if the new crop was different as plants of the previous crop growing in amongst the new crop could not be controlled.

Cloning
Key points

➢ A clone is a group of cells or organisms that are genetically identical because they have come from a single parent.

➢ Many plant species and some animal species have natural methods of cloning.

➢ Horticulturists can increase the numbers of a new plant variety or of an endangered plant by taking cuttings or micropropagation – see page 221.

➢ Cloning can be done with animals after IVF. When the zygote divides the cells can be separated and each will develop into an embryo.

➢ This can be done several times to produce a number of embryos.

> Cloning can happen naturally resulting in identical twins.

These are the stems from the parent plant.

Buds grow into new plants which put down roots and can eventually break off from the parent.

8.7 Strawberry runners

8.8 A cluster of greenfly on a rose
Female greenfly give birth to live young without fertilisation, a process called parthenogenesis.

Somatic cell nuclear transfer (SCNT)
Key points

➢ This is a technique for cloning an adult animal.

➢ The first steps were done by John Gurdon on amphibians.

➢ He removed nuclei from body cells of *Xenopus* tadpoles and transplanted them into enucleated egg cells.

➢ The egg cells behaved as though they were zygotes and developed into mature frogs.

➢ It was first done in a mammal by Dr Ian Wilmut who created Dolly the sheep in 1996.

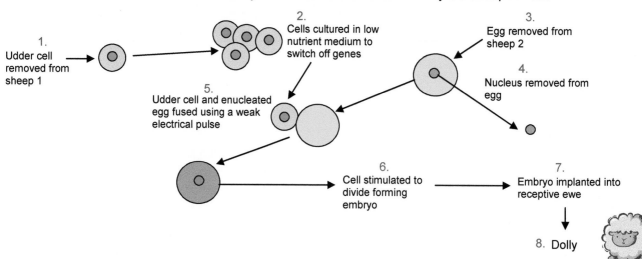

1. Udder cell removed from sheep 1

2. Cells cultured in low nutrient medium to switch off genes

3. Egg removed from sheep 2

4. Nucleus removed from egg

5. Udder cell and enucleated egg fused using a weak electrical pulse

6. Cell stimulated to divide forming embryo

7. Embryo implanted into receptive ewe

8. Dolly

➢ To date human SCNT has met with very limited success partly due to very strict regulations and the failure to find the right protocol to stimulate development.

➢ Creating an embryo from a patient would mean being able to harvest pluripotent embryonic stem cells which could be used to treat the patient – refer back to pages 71 and 102.

➢ However techniques were developed in 2006 to induce adult cells to become pluripotent stem cells, negating the need for SCNT.

Theoretical genetics
Key vocabulary

> The definitions are critical and really must be learnt or you will not be able to understand genetics problems or write good answers.

GENE	A heritable factor that controls a specific characteristic.
ALLELE	A specific form of a gene, occupying the same gene locus as other alleles of that gene, but differing from other alleles by small differences in its base sequence.
DOMINANT ALLELE	An allele that has the same effect on the phenotype when in either the homozygous or heterozygous state.
RECESSIVE ALLELE	An allele that only has an effect on the phenotype when it is in the homozygous state.
GENOTYPE	The alleles possessed by an organism.
PHENOTYPE	The characteristics of an organism.
HETEROZYGOUS	Having two different alleles at a gene locus.
HOMOZYGOUS	Having two identical alleles at a gene locus.
CODOMINANT	Pairs of alleles that both affect the phenotype when present in the heterozygous state.
LOCUS	The specific position on a homologous chromosome of a gene. (Plural loci).
CARRIER	An individual that has a recessive allele of a gene that causes an adverse effect when homozygous.
SEX LINKAGE	The pattern of inheritance characteristic of genes located on the sex chromosomes.
TEST CROSS	Testing a phenotypically dominant phenotype to determine if it is heterozygous or homozygous.
PURE OR TRUE BREEDING	A parent where the dominant phenotype is homozygous.
F_1	First filial generation, i.e. offspring from the parental generation.
F_2	Second filial generation only obtained by crossing F_1 with F_1.

Inheritance

> Mendel discovered the principles of inheritance using the garden pea and established his two Laws.

Mendel and Inheritance

Gregor Mendel was a monk in a monastery in Brno in what is now the Czech Republic. He approached the problem of inheritance from a mathematical point of view and during the 1850s and 60s used the common garden pea to obtain the large numbers he needed for mathematical analysis. The pea also had the advantage that there were many distinct varieties of flower colour, seed colour and shape, and plant height. This meant he could carry out many cross breeding experiments in order to find patterns and deduce the principles of inheritance. Mendel did not know about chromosomes or genes – he used the term 'factors' which we now call genes. Although he published his work in 1865/6 it was not well known and dismissed or ignored by other biologists. The principles of genetics were 'discovered' again in 1900 but the researchers then found Mendel's publication and realised he had discovered the principles 35 years earlier.

8.9 The garden pea

Key principles

➤ Most gamete producing cells are diploid.
➤ Therefore alleles are in pairs.
➤ Gametes are produced by meiosis.
➤ Therefore gametes are haploid and contain only one allele from a pair.
➤ Fusion of haploid gametes to form the zygote restores the diploid number.
➤ Random fertilisation mixes alleles.

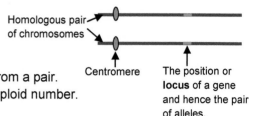

Homologous pair of chromosomes

Centromere

The position or **locus** of a gene and hence the pair of alleles.

The reason that alleles are in pairs

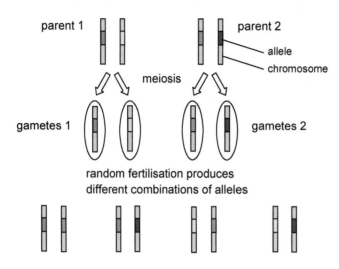

meiosis

parent 1   parent 2

allele
chromosome

gametes 1   gametes 2

random fertilisation produces
different combinations of alleles

Genetics problems

Key points for answering genetics problems

➤ **ALWAYS** choose a letter to represent a gene where the upper and lower case are distinct. When you are quickly writing out a problem you could easily get them muddled when you have separated them into gametes.
➤ Always set out a genetics answer fully and clearly showing:
  ♦ key
  ♦ the parental phenotype
  ♦ the parental genotype
  ♦ the gametes in circles
  ♦ the first filial generation

  and if required:
  ♦ the second gametes, G_2
  ♦ the second filial generation, F_2.
➤ A phenotype is expressed in words.
➤ A genotype is expressed in letters.

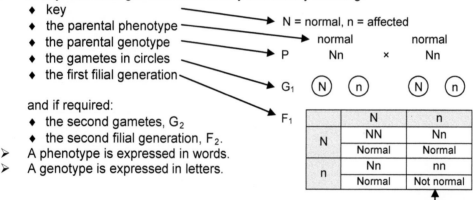

N = normal, n = affected

	N	n
N	NN / Normal	Nn / Normal
n	Nn / Normal	nn / Not normal

This is called a **Punnett grid.** Note that it includes both genotypes and phenotypes.

Key points for solving genetics problems

➤ Genetics problems are easy if you know the clues to look for.
➤ All problems you will be asked to solve fall into seven types:
  1. Monohybrid.
  2. Codominance.
  3. Multiple alleles.
  4. Sex linkage.
  5. Dihybrid.
  6. Linkage without crossing over.
  7. Linkage with crossing over.

One worked example is given for each type of cross and then there is a second problem for you to try. The answer is at the end of the Chapter.

Genetic disorders in humans

➤ Many have been identified but most are rare.
➤ Most are on the autosomes but some are sex linked.

Disorder	Chromosome	Dominant or recessive
Huntingdon's	4	Dominant
Haemophilia	X	Recessive
Colour blindness	X	Recessive
Cystic fibrosis	7	Recessive
Duchenne muscular dystrophy	X	Recessive
Phenylketonuria	12	Recessive
Sickle cell	11	Codominant
Tay-Sachs	15	Recessive

Some human genetic disorders. You need to know the coloured boxes.

The test cross

Key points

➤ This is done in order to determine whether a dominant phenotype is homozygous or heterozygous.
➤ This is **always** crossed with the homozygous recessive.
➤ If the dominant phenotype is heterozygous we would expect 50% of the offspring to show the recessive phenotype.

P   Long winged   x   Short wing
         Ll   ll

G   (L)   (l)   (l)

F$_1$

	l
L	Ll
	50% long winged
l	ll
	50% short winged

Each box contains a definition. State the word being defined. Check your answers on page 253.	1. An allele that has the same effect on the phenotype when in either the homozygous or heterozygous state.	2. A specific form of a gene, occupying the same gene locus as other alleles of that gene.
3. The alleles possessed by an organism.	4. The specific position on a homologous chromosome of a gene.	5. Having two different alleles at a gene locus.
6. A heritable factor that controls a specific characteristic.	7. The characteristics of an organism.	8. An allele that only has an effect on the phenotype when it is in the homozygous state.
9. The pattern of inheritance characteristic of genes located on the sex chromosomes.	10. Testing a phenotypically dominant phenotype to determine if it is heterozygous or homozygous.	11. A parent where the dominant phenotype is homozygous.
12. An individual that has a recessive allele of a gene that causes an adverse effect when homozygous.	13. Having two identical alleles at a gene locus.	14. Pairs of alleles that both affect the phenotype when present in the heterozygous state.

Monohybrid crosses

- This is the basic cross. Make sure you master this before going further.

PROBLEM
Pure breeding long winged flies are crossed with short winged flies and all the offspring are long winged. Long wings is dominant. When these offspring are crossed with short winged flies approximately one half of the offspring have short wings. Explain fully.

SOLUTION
We are told long wings is dominant so we can choose letters.
We are also told the long winged flies are pure breeding which means the genotype is homozygous. The genotype must be LL. The short wing parents must be ll as l is recessive.

Key L = long, l = short.

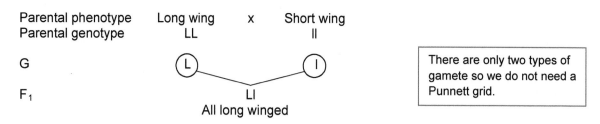

| Parental phenotype | Long wing | x | Short wing |
| Parental genotype | LL | | ll |

G

F$_1$ Ll
All long winged

There are only two types of gamete so we do not need a Punnett grid.

Notice that on the gametes row we only need to write one L and one l. This is because all the gametes from each parent are the same and so there is no need to write more.

Now for the second part of the problem. Since we are not crossing offspring amongst themselves we have to start with P again.

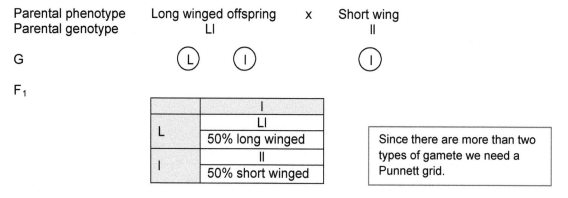

| Parental phenotype | Long winged offspring | x | Short wing |
| Parental genotype | Ll | | ll |

G

F$_1$

		l
L		Ll
		50% long winged
l		ll
		50% short winged

Since there are more than two types of gamete we need a Punnett grid.

In theory we get a 50:50 or 1:1 ratio. In the actual cross we get approximately 50:50 and so, allowing for random fertilisation, our actual or observed ratio fits our ratio predicted from the Punnett grid above.

PROBLEM 1

The Under Dog normally has very short legs but there is also a recessive mutation that has long legs. A Dog homozygous for short legs was crossed with one with long legs. The F$_1$ puppies were crossed with Dogs that were heterozygous for short legs. Predict the outcome of these F$_1$ crosses.

Answer page 271.

Codominance

- Codominance simply means that **both** alleles have an effect on the phenotype.
- Do NOT describe them as both being dominant.
- The alleles are shown in a different way from a monohybrid cross. A capital letter is used for the gene with a capital suffix for the allele.

PROBLEM

A mouse with white fur was crossed with one with black fur and all the offspring have grey fur. Show this cross in a genetics diagram and deduce the phenotypes and phenotype ratio of the F_2 generation.

SOLUTION.

There are three phenotypes so this clearly indicates codominance, the grey being a blend of white and black. This means that both the white and the black parents have to be homozygous. To choose the symbol we can use F for fur and W and B for the colours.

Key F^W = white, F^B = black.

P   White fur   x   Black fur
            $F^W F^W$ $F^B F^B$

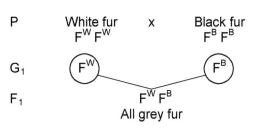

G_1

F_1 $F^W F^B$
                 All grey fur

'Parent phenotype' and 'Parent genotype' have been simplified to 'P'.

Second cross

Grey fur   x   Grey fur
$F^W F^B$ $F^W F^B$

This is a cross of F_1 x F_1 and so the offspring are F_2.

G_2

F_2

	F^W	F^B
F^W	$F^W F^W$	$F^W F^B$
	white	Grey
F^B	$F^W F^B$	$F^B F^B$
	grey	Black

Adding the phenotypes to the table makes it easier to count the ratio.

The F_2 ratio is 1 white : 2 grey : 1 black.

PROBLEM 2

The cannabis plant, Cannibis sativa, produces two chemicals, THC and CBD, controlled by a pair of codominant alleles. A heterozygous plant produces both chemicals in equal quantities. Two heterozygous plants were crossed and 460 seeds collected. When these were grown approximately 230 of the plants produced THC and CBD in equal amounts. Deduce the approximate numbers of plants that produced only THC and only CBD.

Answer page 272.

Multiple alleles

- Usually within a population there are many alleles of a gene and this is logically called **multiple alleles**.
- However any one individual can only have two of these alleles because it has only one pair of loci for any given gene.
- The example you have to know is the ABO blood grouping.
- There are three alleles – I^A, I^B, and i.
- This is an unusual case though because they also show codominance – alleles I^A and I^B are codominant.
- This results in four different phenotypes or blood groups.

Genotypes	Phenotype or blood group
$I^A I^A$ or $I^A i$	A
$I^B I^B$ or $I^B i$	B
$I^A I^B$	AB
ii	O

PROBLEM

Claire is blood group A and her husband Clive is blood group O. Celine is blood group AB and her husband David is blood group B. At the hospital Claire and Celine's baby girls were born at the same time but Claire feels the staff accidentally muddled them up. Baby Melissa given to Celine is blood group O. Explain how this could solve the difficulty.

SOLUTION

If the baby is blood group O it's genotype must be ii. Celine is blood group AB and therefore has the genotype $I^A I^B$ so she cannot give an i allele to the baby. Claire is blood group A and so either has the genotype $I^A I^A$ or $I^A i$. Clive has to have the genotype ii. This means that baby Melissa must belong to Claire and Clive.

	Claire	Clive		Celine		David	
P	$I^A i$	ii		$I^A I^B$		$I^B i$	
G	I^A , i	i		I^A , I^B		I^B , i	

We will assume David is $I^B i$ although he could be $I^B I^B$.

F$_1$

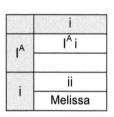

	i
I^A	$I^A i$
i	ii — Melissa

	I^B	i
I^A	$I^A I^B$ — Group AB	$I^A i$ — Group A
I^B	$I^B I^B$ — Group B	$I^B i$ — Group B

None of these genotypes is ii and so cannot be Melissa even if David is $I^B i$.

PROBLEM 3

Sufyan is blood group A and Chiara is group B. Their first baby is group O and their second group AB. Explain how this is possible.

Answer page 272.

Sex linkage

- In humans (and some other organisms) two chromosomes, the sex chromosomes, determine gender.
- All the other chromosomes are called autosomes.
- The female sex chromosomes are XX and the male sex chromosomes are XY.
- Sex linked genes are only found on the X chromosome and not on the shorter Y chromosome.

This region of the X chromosome carries the sex linked genes.

- Only females can be heterozygous or homozygous with respect to sex linked genes.
- Individuals have two phenotypes – the characteristic on the X chromosome **and** the gender.
- Males produce X sperm and Y sperm and therefore determine the gender of the offspring.
- A female carrier must be heterozygous as one X chromosome has the dominant allele and the other has the recessive allele. $X^A X^a$.
- The sex ratio in the offspring is always 1:1.

The commonest mistake with sex linkage problems is that students forget that the Y chromosome does **not** carry an allele.

A simple way of avoiding this mistake is to write the symbol Y^-.

Writing $-$ next to the Y will prevent you from putting an allele there.

You need to know:
Colour-blindness and haemophilia are examples of sex linked characteristics.
Both are recessive.

PROBLEM
Ethan had haemophilia but Sasha, his wife, was normal and not a carrier. Their daughter Karen married Jacob who also had haemophilia. Determine the phenotypes of their sons and daughters.

SOLUTION
Ethan must have had the genotype $X^h Y^-$ since he had haemophilia. Karen inherited his X^h chromosome, but her other X chromosome from her mother was normal X^H. Thus Karen had the genotype $X^H X^h$ so she was a carrier. Jacob had to be $X^h Y^-$ as he had haemophilia.

Key H = the normal allele, h = the haemophilia allele.

Filling in names and phenotypes helps to get the genotypes correct.

The genotype shows both gender and characteristic.

	First generation		Second generation	
	Ethan	Sasha	Karen	Jacob
	Haemophilia	Normal	Carrier	Haemophilia
P	$X^h Y^-$	$X^H X^H$	$X^H X^h$	$X^h Y^-$
G	X^h	X^H	X^H X^h	X^h Y^-

F₁

	X^H
X^h	$X^H X^h$
	Karen

	X^h	Y^-
X^H	$X^H X^h$	$X^H Y^-$
	Female, carrier	Male, normal
X^h	$X^h X^h$	$X^h Y^-$
	Female with haemophilia	Male with haemophilia

PROBLEM 4
A man with normal colour vision married a woman who also had normal colour vision. However two of their five children were colour blind. Explain how this could have arisen, showing which children they were.

Answer page 273.

Pedigree charts

- This is another way of showing genetic crosses but for several generations.
- Gametes are not shown.
- There are standard symbols.

Normal female   Normal male   Affected female   Affected male

Heterozygotes may be shown as

The symbol for a heterozygous individual is rather variable. Sometimes half the square or circle is filled in, sometimes there is a black dot in the middle of the square or circle. The question will have a key, or if **you** draw it **you** have to provide a key.

Example

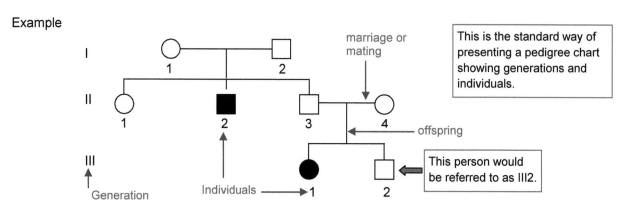

marriage or mating

This is the standard way of presenting a pedigree chart showing generations and individuals.

offspring

This person would be referred to as III2.

Generation   Individuals

Some information has deliberately been missed from the above diagram but we can deduce it. Two common questions are – 1. Is the disorder dominant or recessive? 2. Is the disorder sex linked?

The disorder has to be recessive since neither individual in generation I has it but II2 does have it. Similarly III1 has it but neither of her parents.

Is it sex linked? Remember that sex linked alleles are only on the X chromosome. If we give the symbol n to the disorder then III1 must be X^nX^n. One X^n must have come from her father making him X^nY. He should show the disorder but he doesn't, and thus from this we can deduce that the gene is not sex linked. A useful hint is that it is often a male that provides the essential clue.
We can now continue to deduce that both I1 and I2 must be heterozygous, and also II3 and II4. We could now show this in a Punnett grid. Use N for the dominant normal allele and n for the recessive disorder allele.

Parent I2

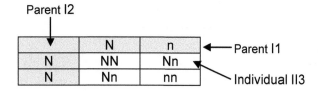

	N	n
N	NN	Nn
N	Nn	nn

Parent I1

Individual II3

PROBLEM 5

The pedigree chart below shows the inheritance of hairy ears in rabbits. An open symbol is hairy and a black symbol is smooth. Deduce whether smooth ears is dominant or recessive.

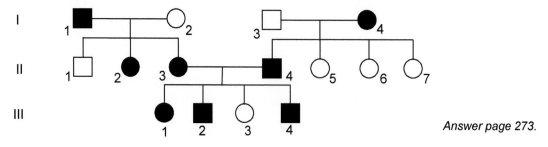

Answer page 273.

Dihybrid crosses

➤ Two genes are involved.
➤ Therefore there are two pairs of homologous chromosomes.
➤ Therefore there are four alleles.
➤ Therefore each gamete must contain two alleles.
➤ The two alleles must be one from each pair.

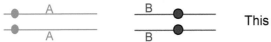 This genotype would be written as AABB.

The table below shows all the possible allele combinations and the resulting gametes.

Parental genotype	Gamete types
AABB	AB
AAbb	Ab
aaBB	aB
aabb	ab
AABb	AB and Ab
AaBB	AB and aB
Aabb	Ab and ab
aaBb	aB and ab
AaBb	AB and Ab and aB and ab

When both characteristics are homozygous then only one type of gamete is produced.

When one characteristic is homozygous and the other heterozygous then two types of gamete are produced.

When both characteristics are heterozygous then four types of gamete are produced.

Note it is number of **types** of gamete; for genotype AABB you do not need to write gamete AB twice or four times – they are all the same and it wastes time in exams.

An important point to remember is that the numbers of each type of gamete are equal, eg AABb gives gametes AB and Ab in the ratio 1 : 1, and AaBb gives gametes AB, Ab, aB, and ab in the ratio 1 : 1 : 1 : 1. Knowing this allows us to determine numbers of phenotypes from a Punnett grid.

Example
    Key R = round, r = square; T = tall, t = short.

G

		RT	Rt	rT	rt
rt		RrTt	Rrtt	rrTt	rrtt
		round, tall	round, short	square, tall	square, short

Simply counting the numbers we can see that there is one of each phenotype and the ratio is 1 : 1 : 1 : 1.

Always put alleles in their pairs, i.e. RRTt and <u>never</u> simply by 'joining' the gametes, i.e. RTRt.

A fly with pink eyes and short wings was crossed with a pure breeding one that had red eyes and long wings. Assuming that red eyes and long wings are dominant, determine genotype and phenotype ratios in both the F_1 and F_2 generations.

SOLUTION

Pink and short are both recessive and hence the genotype must be homozygous.
We are told that red and long is pure breeding and hence must also be homozygous.

Key R = red eyes and r = pink eyes, L = long wings and l = short wings

	pink, short	x	red, long
P	rrll		RRLL
G	(rl)		(RL)
F_1		RrLl	

All the F_1 have the doubly heterozygous genotype RrLl and therefore red eyes and long wings.

F_1	RrLl	x	RrLl
G	(RL) (Rl) (rL) (rl)		(RL) (Rl) (rL) (rl)

F_2

	RL	Rl	rL	rl
RL	RRLL	RRLl	RrLL	RrLl
Rl	RRLl	RRll	RrLl	Rrll
rL	RrLL	RrLl	rrLL	rrLl
rl	RrLl	Rrll	rrLl	rrll

> To prevent mistakes always follow a pattern – notice the gametes are always in the same order.

- 9 red eyes, long wings R_L_
- 3 red eyes, short wings R_ll
- 3 pink eyes, long wings rrL_
- 1 pink eyes, short wings rrll

The _ means the allele could either be dominant or recessive.

> You need to know how to use the chi-squared test on dihybrid crosses so revise this in Chapter One, pages 9-10.

PROBLEM 6

In the mongoose red eyes and striped tail are dominant characteristics, with brown eyes and plain tail being the corresponding recessives.
A mongoose with brown eyes and plain tail was crossed with one with red eyes and striped tail. Over a period of years the total number of offspring was 30 made up as below.
    7 red eyes, plain tail,
    8 brown eyes, plain tail,
    8 red eyes, striped tail,
    7 brown eyes, striped tail.
Determine the genotypes of the parents.   *Answer page 274.*

Mendel and Morgan

Mendel seemed to be very lucky with his choice of characteristics in the pea plant as they all behaved in the way his laws predicted.

The fruit fly *Drosophila* is used a great deal in genetics as it has a great many mutations, only has four pairs of chromosomes, and can breed very quickly in large numbers. Thomas Hunt Morgan started studies of fruit fly genetics in 1904. During these investigations a male with a mutation for white eyes appeared. (The normal eye colour is red). Morgan crossed this male with red eyed females and the F_1 were all red eyed indicating the mutation was recessive. In the F_2 he predicted a ratio of 1 red M: 1 red F: 1 white M: 1 white F. Instead he found no white eyed females. He began to suspect that these characteristics might have something to do with the two chromosomes that determined gender, the X and Y chromosomes.

He now crossed the white eyed male with F_1 females and this time there were white eyed females. He deduced that the white allele was on the larger X chromosomes and not on the smaller Y chromosome. If this was the case then a cross white eyed female with red eyed males should produce only white eyed males and only red eyed females. This proved to be correct.

All of these four crosses are shown on page 277.

Morgan deduced that these must be linked genes and so could not follow Mendelian laws which required genes to behave independently. He also proposed the idea of crossing over between linked genes and the recombination of alleles.

8.10 The fruit fly *Drosophila*.

This section deals with the more difficult genetics. The rules in general still apply but with some modifications. There is some new vocabulary to learn as well.

Key vocabulary

LINKAGE	The tendency for some parental alleles to be inherited together.
LINKAGE GROUP	All the genes on a particular chromosome.
AUTOSOMES	All those chromosomes other than the sex chromosomes.
AUTOSOMAL LINKAGE	Linkage involving the autosomes.
CHIASMA	The site of crossing over and exchange of sections of DNA between homologous chromatids. (Plural chiasmata)
CROSSING OVER	When non-sister chromatids of a homologous pair exchange alleles.
PARENTAL COMBINATION	The combination of alleles found in the parents.
RECOMBINATION	The reassortment of alleles into different combinations from those in the parents as a result of crossing over.
RECOMBINANT	An organism produced as a result of recombination.

Autosomal linkage

- Organisms have many more genes than chromosomes – see page 245.
- Therefore each chromosome must carry many genes.
- All the genes on a chromosome form a linkage group.
- Linked genes cannot assort independently.
- A linkage cross is a dihybrid but only involving **one** pair of chromosomes.
- This is why it gives monohybrid ratios in the offspring.

Recognition feature:
You will normally be told if the genes are linked. If not then look for a monohybrid ratio, 1:1 or 3:1, in the offspring.

The homologous pairs of chromosomes below illustrate this situation.

Here we have two pairs of homologous chromosomes, one pair carrying the genes A and D, and the other pair carrying the gene B. Genes A and B are unlinked as are genes D and B and they will assort independently. Genes A and D are however linked and will not assort independently.

A B C D E F G H

Here the genes A to H form a **linkage group.**

In a normal dihybrid cross the genotype letters can be written in a line, e.g. AaBb. With linked genes however you cannot tell what the linkage pattern is and this is why the genotype must be written in a different way.

$\underline{A\ D}$ $\underline{A\ d}$
a d   a D

You will see that this resembles their positions on the homologous chromosomes, the short lines representing the loci.

The significance of this format is that it shows the linkage pattern. Take the linked genes A and D, and the genotype AaDd. In this format, AaDd, you cannot tell if A and D are linked on the same chromosome, or A and d are linked on the same chromosome. If you use the alternative format you can.

This format is absolutely crucial to linkage problems.

This is the format that will be used in exams and examiners will expect you use it too.

PROBLEM
The snowy gull commonly has white feathers and a yellow beak, but some birds have black feathers and an orange beak. Black and orange are recessive and the genes are linked.
A pure breeding bird with white feathers and yellow beak was mated to one with black feathers and orange beak. The offspring had white feathers and yellow beak. Two of these were mated and 75% of the offspring had the dominant phenotypes and the other 25% had the recessive phenotype. Explain fully using genetics diagrams.

SOLUTION
The white, yellow bird is pure breeding and so has a homozygous genotype. Since black and orange are recessive the genotype of this bird must also be homozygous.
The genes are linked so we **must** use the alternative format for writing the genotype.

Key H = white, h = black; Y = yellow, y = orange.

We cannot use W for white because W and w are too similar.

	white, yellow	x	black, orange	
P	$\dfrac{H\ Y}{H\ Y}$		$\dfrac{h\ y}{h\ y}$	First cross
G_1	(HY)		(hy)	
F_1		$\dfrac{HY}{hy}$		

	white, yellow	x	white, yellow	
F_1	$\dfrac{HY}{hy}$		$\dfrac{HY}{hy}$	Second cross – notice it is F_1 x F_1 going to F_2.
G_2	(HY) (hy)		(HY) (hy)	

F₂

	HY	hy
HY	$\underline{HY}$ / HY	$\underline{HY}$ / hy
	white feathers, yellow beak	white feathers, yellow beak
hy	$\underline{HY}$ / hy	hy / hy
	white feathers, yellow beak	black feathers, orange beak

White feathers, yellow beak, and black feathers, orange beak are in the ratio 3:1 which is the 75% to 25% stated in the problem.

White, yellow and black, orange are parental combinations. Note the absence of recombinations because no crossing over has taken place,.

PROBLEM 7

The Quad Rat is normally square and has furry whiskers, but the recessive characteristics of triangular and smooth whiskers also exist. The genes are known to be both on chromosome 2. A homozygous square Rat with smooth whiskers was crossed with a homozygous triangular Rat with furry whiskers. All the offspring were square with furry whiskers. When each of these was crossed with a triangular Rat with smooth whiskers the offspring were always 50% square with smooth whiskers and 50% triangular with furry whiskers. Deduce the genotypes of the parent Rats.

Answer page 273.

Linkage and crossing over

Key points

➢ Crossing over occurs through the formation of chiasmata.
➢ Some homologous pairs never form chiasmata; others may have many.
➢ Chiasma formation and crossing over occurs during prophase I of meiosis.
➢ The effect of this is to mix linked alleles within the homologous pair.

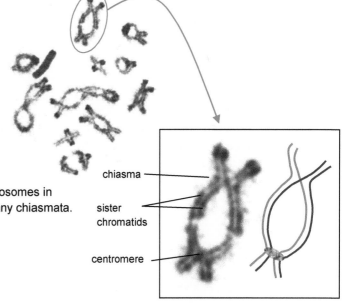

8.11 A group of chromosomes in prophase I showing many chiasmata.

8.12 A homologous pair of chromosomes with a single chiasma.
The drawing alongside shows the arrangement of the chromatids.

Explanation

We will start with the bivalent, the pair of homologous chromosomes that have replicated and lined up together.

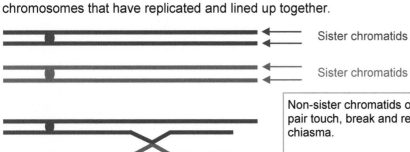

Sister chromatids

Sister chromatids

Non-sister chromatids of the homologous pair touch, break and rejoin at the chiasma.

Part of the blue chromatid has now joined to the pink one and vice versa. These will contain the recombinant alleles.

The upper and lower unchanged chromatids will contain the parental combination of alleles.

How does this appear with actual alleles? We will use the genotype $\frac{A\ D}{a\ d}$.

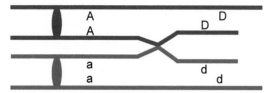

After completion of the crossing over process we get:

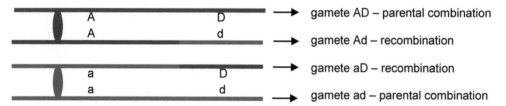

And finally after completion of meiosis we get the gametes AD; ad; Ad; aD – four different types. If you look back at the table on page 261 and the genotype AaBb we get the similar four types of gamete. **However, there is a crucial difference**. The four types of gamete from AaBb are in **equal** proportions because the numbers are determined by the random positioning of the homologous pairs on the equator at metaphase I. With the linked genes the numbers of gametes are in two **unequal** pairs. The first two, AD and ad, are the **parental gametes** because that is way they are linked on the parental chromosomes. They are the **large** pair of numbers. The other two Ad and aD are the **recombinant gametes** because the alleles have *recombined* in a different way and are a **small** pair of numbers.

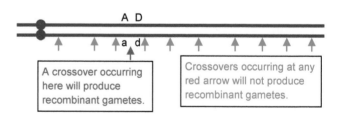

gamete AD – parental combination

gamete Ad – recombination

gamete aD – recombination

gamete ad – parental combination

As an example of where linkage and crossing over have occurred the numbers of gametes formed might be:

| AD | = | 110 | | Ad | = | 5 |
| ad | = | 110 | | aD | = | 5. |

The large difference between the two pairs is because the probability of a cross-over occurring between the two gene loci is very small and the gametes Ad and aD will **only** appear if a cross-over has occurred between the two loci. A cross-over occurring anywhere else on the chromosome will not produce these two types of gamete.

A D

A crossover occurring here will produce recombinant gametes.

Crossovers occurring at any red arrow will not produce recombinant gametes.

The numbers of AD and ad gametes will be equal, as will the numbers of Ad and aD gametes because the cross-over has to produce one of each. Any slight differences in the offspring ratios will be due to random fertilisation.

Summary

Genotype AaBb gives gametes AB, Ab, aB, and ab in **equal** proportions.

Genotype $\frac{A\ D}{a\ d}$ with no crossing over gives gametes AD and ad in equal proportions,

        but with crossing over gives gametes AD and ad, and also Ad and aD.

                                                in equal   in equal
                                                proportions, proportions,
                                                large number. small number.

Genotype $\frac{A\ d}{a\ D}$ with no crossing over gives gametes Ad and aD in equal proportions,

        but with crossing over gives gametes Ad and aD, and also AD and ad.

                                                in equal   in equal
                                                proportions, proportions,
                                                large number. small number.

Parental combinations

In a problem if you are not told the linkage pattern then how can you tell? It is very simple – look at the numbers. The large pair is the parental combination, i.e. the linkage pattern.

T = tall, t = short; R = round, r = square.
Two different homozygous tall round are test crossed.

Cross 1 F_1 = 211 tall, round; 201 short, square;   Linkage pattern = $\frac{T\ R}{t\ r}$ tall, round linked
                 24 tall, square; 22 short, round.   short, square linked

Cross 2 F_1 = 199 tall, square; 193 short, round;   Linkage pattern = $\frac{T\ r}{t\ R}$ tall, square linked
                 18 short, square; 20 tall, round.   short, round linked

> **Recognition features:**
> - The offspring of a test cross will have four phenotypes.
> - There will be one pair of large numbers which are the parental combinations.
> - There will be one pair of small numbers which are the recombinants.

Transparent wings and clubbed antennae are autosomal linked dominant alleles in the Fairy fly. Grey wings and smooth antennae are the characteristics resulting from being homozygous for both the recessive alleles.

A fly with grey wings and smooth antennae was mated to a pure breeding fly with transparent wings and clubbed antennae.

These offspring were all mated to flies with grey wings and smooth antennae and the total offspring were:

| 227 transparent wings, clubbed antennae, | 231 grey wings, smooth antennae, |
| 10 transparent wings, smooth antennae, | 7 grey wings, clubbed antennae. |

Deduce the genotypes of all the flies giving clear genetics diagrams.

SOLUTION

The clear give-away is the non-Mendelian ratio in the numbers of offspring – this is the classic one large pair of numbers and one small pair of numbers indicating linkage **and** crossing over. The parent with the dominant characteristics is pure breeding and therefore homozygous, and the other one has to be homozygous as it has the recessive phenotype.

Key T = transparent, t = grey; B = clubbed, b = smooth.

P   transparent, clubbed   x   grey, smooth
$\frac{TB}{TB}$ x $\frac{tb}{tb}$

G_1 (TB)   (tb)

F_1 $\frac{TB}{tb}$

The second cross is again with the homozygous recessive $\frac{tb}{tb}$.

P $\frac{TB}{tb}$ x $\frac{tb}{tb}$

G_1 (TB)   (tb)   (Tb)   (tB)   (tb)

F_1

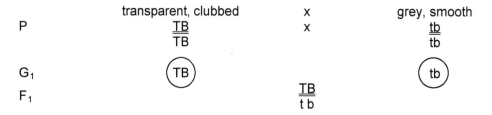

	TB	tb	Tb	tB
Tb	$\frac{TB}{tb}$	$\frac{tb}{tb}$	$\frac{Tb}{tb}$	$\frac{tB}{tb}$
	transparent, clubbed 227	grey, smooth 231	transparent, smooth 10	grey, clubbed 7

These are the parental combinations and form the large pair of numbers.   These are the recombinants and form the small pair of numbers.

Notice in the F_1 Punnett grid the order of the gametes is different from the simple dihybrid cross. Look back at pages 261 and 262. The order is – parental gametes first, then recombinant gametes with the double line between to emphasise the separation. This means the numbers of phenotypes in the first two boxes <u>must</u> be the large pair of numbers, the parental combinations, and the numbers of phenotypes in the second two boxes <u>must</u> be the small pair of numbers, the recombinations.

PROBLEM 8

The Chocolate Moose can have brown or yellow fur and either a rounded nose or a pointed one. Brown and round are the dominant characteristics and the genes are linked. A Moose pure breeding for brown fur and round nose was crossed with one with yellow fur and pointed nose. All the baby Moose born had brown fur and a round nose. One of these was test crossed and the offspring numbers were :

| 21 brown fur and round nose; | 20 yellow fur and pointed nose; |
| 2 brown fur and pointed nose; | 3 yellow fur and round nose. |

Explain these results and identify the recombinants.   *Answer page 276.*

Polygenic inheritance

Key points

➢ Two or more genes influence the characteristic.

➢ The basic Mendelian principles still apply but the end result can be continuous variation.

If we have one gene with a pair of alleles controlling a characteristic then an individual will either have the characteristic controlled by the allele or it will not. This is called discrete (or discontinuous) variation. All the genetics so far has been discrete. If though two or more genes control the characteristic then intermediate forms can occur resulting in discontinuous variation.

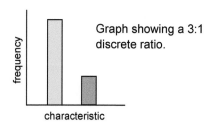

Graph showing a 3:1 discrete ratio.

Example 1

Seed colour in wheat is controlled by around six genes. For this first example we will look at the effect of just two of these at two pairs of unlinked loci, but the second example of human skin colour on the next page does look at the effect of six genes.

The seed colour can vary from white through to dark red, so we can use the letters W and R to represent the genes. The genotype WWWW will produce a white seed whereas the genotype RRRR will produce a dark red seed.

Genotype	Seed colour
WWWW	white
WWWR	pale pink
WWRR	mid pink
WRRR	dark pink
RRRR	red

We are going to cross two wheat plants that produce mid pink seeds and have the genotype

$$\frac{W}{R}\ \frac{W}{R}$$

Therefore each parent can produce the gametes – WW, WR, RW, and RR.

F_1

	WW	WR	RW	RR
WW	WWWW	WWWR	WWWR	WWRR
WR	WWWR	WWRR	WWRR	WRRR
RW	WWWR	WWRR	WWRR	WRRR
RR	WWRR	WRRR	WRRR	RRRR

	Seed colour				
	white WWWW	pale pink WWWR	mid pink WWRR	dark pink WRRR	red RRRR
Number	1	4	6	4	1

If we now plot this as a bar chart we get a shape that is looking approximately like a normal distribution, or continuous variation.

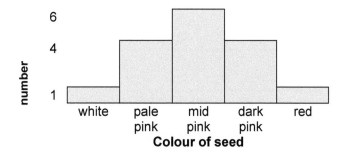

Example 2

Polygenes determine human skin pigmentation. It is thought that around 20 pairs of loci are involved but for this illustration I will show only 3 pairs with alleles A,B,C and a,b,c.

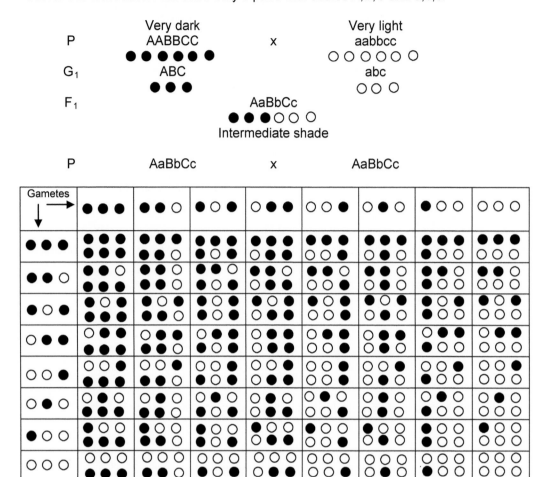

When these are grouped we end up with the numbers below.

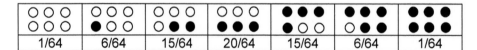

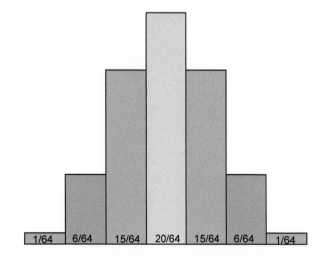

This looks closer to a normal distribution. It should be obvious therefore that the greater the number of genes controlling the characteristic the closer the distribution will be to a normal distribution.

Human height is another polygenic characteristic but clearly nutrition will have a major influence on this. Other modifying factors could be expression of the growth hormone and thyroxin genes, and perhaps also any maternal epigenetic influences.

Solutions to chapter problems

PROBLEM 1

The Under Dog normally has very short legs but there is also a recessive mutation that has long legs. A Dog homozygous for short legs was crossed with one with long legs. The F₁ puppies were crossed with Dogs that were heterozygous for short legs. Predict the outcome of these F₁ crosses.

SOLUTION
We are told the short leg dog is homozygous, and the dog with long legs also has to be homozygous because long is recessive.

Key: T = short, t = long.

> We cannot use S for short because S and s are too similar.

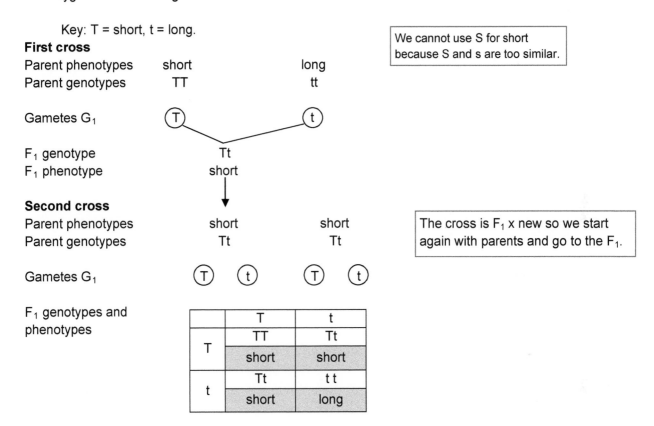

> The cross is F₁ x new so we start again with parents and go to the F₁.

For the first cross all the F₁ Under Dogs will be heterozygous and therefore have short legs. In the second cross though there will be a ratio of three Dogs with short legs to one Dog with long legs. One third of the Dogs with short legs will have a homozygous genotype and two thirds will have a heterozygous genotype.

PROBLEM 2

The cannabis plant, Cannibis sativa, produces two chemicals, THC and CBD, controlled by a pair of codominant alleles. A heterozygous plant produces both chemicals in equal quantities. Two heterozygous plants were crossed and 460 seeds collected. When these were grown approximately 230 of the plants produced THC and CBD in equal amounts. Deduce the approximate numbers of plants that produced only THC and only CBD.

SOLUTION

Key C^T = THC plants; C^C = CBD plants

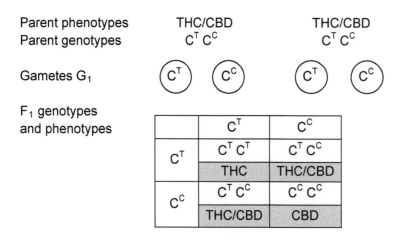

Parent phenotypes THC/CBD   THC/CBD
Parent genotypes $C^T C^C$ $C^T C^C$

Gametes G_1

F$_1$ genotypes and phenotypes

		C^T	C^C
C^T		$C^T C^T$	$C^T C^C$
		THC	THC/CBD
C^C		$C^T C^C$	$C^C C^C$
		THC/CBD	CBD

The ratio is 1THC : 2THC/CBD : 1CBD. 25% or approximately 115 plants will only produce THC, and the same for plants only producing CBD.

PROBLEM 3

Sufyan is blood group A and Chiara is group B. Their first baby is group O and their second group AB. Explain how this is possible.

SOLUTION
Since their first baby is group O it must have the genotype ii, and therefore both Sufyan and Chiara must have an i in their genotype. Sufyan is group A and therefore must have an I^A allele as well, so his genotype is I^Ai. Similarly Chiara must have the genotype I^Bi.

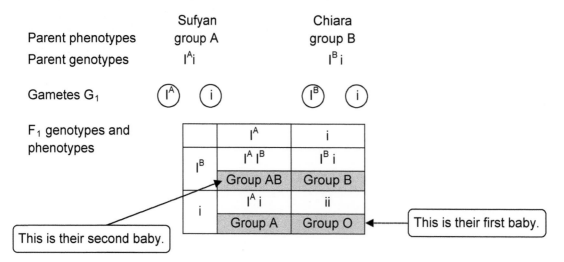

Parent phenotypes
Parent genotypes

Sufyan
group A
I^Ai

Chiara
group B
I^Bi

Gametes G_1

F$_1$ genotypes and phenotypes

		I^A	i
I^B		$I^A I^B$	I^B i
		Group AB	Group B
i		I^A i	ii
		Group A	Group O

This is their second baby.

This is their first baby.

PROBLEM 4

A man with normal colour vision married a woman who also had normal colour vision. However two of their five children were colour blind. Explain how this could have arisen, showing which children they were.

SOLUTION

The only possibility here is for the woman to be a carrier. She will then pass a recessive colour blind allele to half of her sons. Since the man has normal vision none of their daughters can be colour blind though half of them will be carriers.

Key: N = normal vision, n = colour blindness.

Parent phenotypes	woman, carrier	man, normal
Parent genotypes	$X^N X^n$	$X^N Y^-$

Gametes G_1 (X^N) (X^n) (X^N) (Y^-)

F$_1$ genotypes and phenotypes

	X^N	X^n
X^N	$X^N X^N$	$X^N X^n$
	daughter normal	daughter, carrier
Y^-	$X^N Y^-$	$X^n Y^-$
	son, normal	son, colour blind

PROBLEM 5

The pedigree chart below shows the inheritance of hairy ears in rabbits. An open symbol is hairy and a black symbol is smooth. Deduce whether smooth ears is dominant or recessive.

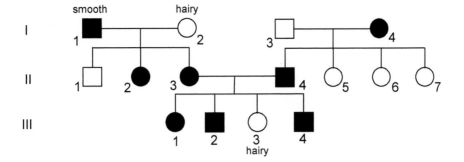

SOLUTION

There is nothing in either generation I or II to help as the pedigree will work with smooth ears being either dominant or recessive. The answer lies with generation III. If the smooth ear allele is recessive then II3 and II4 are both homozygous recessive. Therefore they could not have had III3 since this has hairy ears and must have at least one dominant allele. The smooth ear allele is therefore dominant. We can check this by working backwards. Then II3 and II4 are heterozygous. I1 and I4 must also be heterozygous.

PROBLEM 6

In the mongoose red eyes and striped tail are dominant characteristics, with brown eyes and plain tail being the corresponding recessives.
A mongoose with brown eyes and plain tail was crossed with one with red eyes and striped tail. Over a period of years the total number of offspring was 30 made up as below.

      7 red eyes, plain tail,
      8 brown eyes, plain tail,
      8 red eyes, striped tail,
      7 brown eyes, striped tail.
Determine the genotypes of the parents.

SOLUTION
The genotype of the mongoose with brown eyes and plain tail has to be doubly homozygous recessive, rrtt.
The genotype of the other parent is R_T_ because it has red eyes and a striped tail.
If we look at the offspring we see that there are some that have brown eyes and striped tail. Thus they have the genotype rrtt. One r and one t have come from the rrtt parent and the other r and t must have come from the other parent. This means that this parent must have been RrTt.
Finally we prove this by drawing out the Punnett grid.

Key R = red, r = brown; T = striped, t = plain.

> We cannot use S for striped because S and s are too similar.

                 red, striped   brown, plain
P   RrTt   x   rrtt

G   (RT)   (Rt)   (rT)   (rt)   (rt)

F₁

	RT	Rt	rT	rt
rt	RrTt	Rrtt	rrTt	rrtt
	red, striped	red, plain	brown, striped	brown, plain

1 RrTt red eyes, striped tail,   1 rrTt brown eyes, striped tail,
1 Rrtt red eyes, plain tail,   1 rrtt brown eyes, plain tail.

The actual numbers observed – 8, 7, 8, 7, – can be taken as a 1:1:1:1 ratio because the small difference will be due to random fertilisation.
Thus our expected ratio fits with our actual results, confirming that the genotypes of the two parents are RrTt and rrtt.

PROBLEM 7

The Quad Rat is normally square and has furry whiskers, but the recessive characteristics of triangular and smooth whiskers also exist. The genes are known to be both on chromosome 2. A homozygous square Rat with smooth whiskers was crossed with a homozygous triangular Rat with furry whiskers. All the offspring were square with furry whiskers. When each of these was crossed with a triangular Rat with smooth whiskers the offspring were always 50% square with smooth whiskers and 50% triangular with furry whiskers. Deduce the genotypes of the parent Rats.

SOLUTION
We are told both parents are homozygous.

Key: Q = square, q = triangular; F = furry, f = smooth.

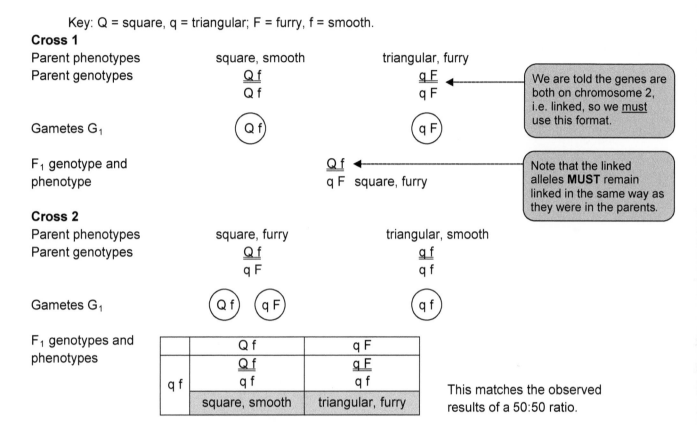

Cross 1

Parent phenotypes	square, smooth	triangular, furry
Parent genotypes	$\underline{Q\ f}$ $Q\ f$	$\underline{q\ F}$ $q\ F$

We are told the genes are both on chromosome 2, i.e. linked, so we __must__ use this format.

Gametes G₁   (Q f)   (q F)

F₁ genotype and phenotype $\underline{Q\ f}$
 $q\ F$ square, furry

Note that the linked alleles **MUST** remain linked in the same way as they were in the parents.

Cross 2

Parent phenotypes	square, furry	triangular, smooth
Parent genotypes	$\underline{Q\ f}$ $q\ F$	$\underline{q\ f}$ $q\ f$

Gametes G₁   (Q f) (q F)   (q f)

F₁ genotypes and phenotypes

	Q f	q F
q f	$\underline{Q\ f}$ q f square, smooth	$\underline{q\ F}$ q f triangular, furry

This matches the observed results of a 50:50 ratio.

IBHL Biology 2016 © Ashby Merson-Davies

275

PROBLEM 8

The Chocolate Moose can have brown or yellow fur and either a rounded nose or a pointed one. Brown and round are the dominant characteristics and the genes are linked. A Moose pure breeding for brown fur and round nose was crossed with one with yellow fur and pointed nose. All the baby Moose born had brown fur and a round nose. One of these was test crossed and the offspring numbers were :   21 brown fur and round nose;   20 yellow fur and pointed nose;
                                          2 brown fur and pointed nose;   3 yellow fur and round nose.
Explain these results and identify the recombinants.

SOLUTION

Key: B = brown fur, b = yellow fur; R = round nose, r = pointed nose.

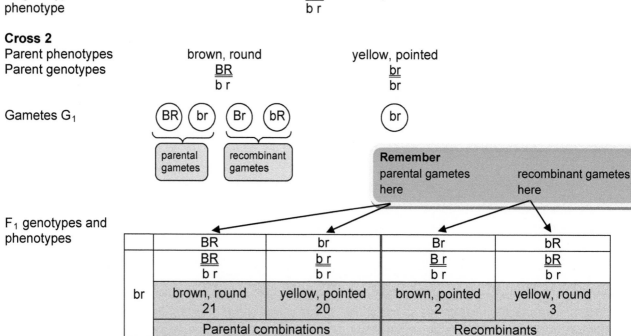

Cross 1

	yellow, pointed	brown, round
Parent phenotypes		
Parent genotypes	br / br	BR / BR
Gametes G₁	br	BR
F₁ genotype and phenotype		BR / b r brown, round

Cross 2

	brown, round	yellow, pointed
Parent phenotypes		
Parent genotypes	BR / b r	br / br
Gametes G₁	BR br Br bR	br

parental gametes   recombinant gametes

Remember
parental gametes here   recombinant gametes here

F₁ genotypes and phenotypes

	BR	br	Br	bR
	BR / b r	b r / b r	B r / b r	bR / b r
br	brown, round 21	yellow, pointed 20	brown, pointed 2	yellow, round 3
	Parental combinations		Recombinants	

This matches the observed results.

Glossary

CONTAGIOUS	Easily spread by contact.
ENUCLEATED	A cell that has had its nucleus removed.
GENOME SIZE	The total number of DNA base pairs in one copy of a haploid genome.
MUTATION	A spontaneous permanent change in the base sequence of DNA.
VIRULENT	Violent.

Morgan's fruit fly crosses

Key: R = red, r = white

Cross 1 – mutant male × normal female

	white male $X^r Y$	red female $X^R X^R$

G

F_1

	X^r	Y^-
X^R	$X^R X^r$ red, female	$X^R Y^-$ red, male

Cross 2 – F_1 × F_1

	red male $X^R Y^-$	red female $X^R X^r$

G

F_1

	X^R	Y^-
X^R	$X^R X^R$ red, female	$X^R Y^-$ red, male
X^r	$X^R X^r$ red, female	$X^r Y^-$ white, male

Cross 3 – white male × F_1 female

	white male $X^r Y^-$	red female $X^R X^r$

G

F_1

	X^r	Y^-
X^R	$X^R X^r$ red, female	$X^R Y^-$ red, male
X^r	$X^r X^r$ white, female	$X^r Y^-$ white, male

Cross 4 – red male × white female

	red male $X^R Y^-$	white female $X^r X^r$

G

F_1

	X^R	Y^-
X^r	$X^R X^r$ red, female	$X^r Y^-$ white, male

Test Problems

Many of the organisms used here are imaginary to make a change from all the ones on mice, rabbits and fruit flies. Treat the genetics in the normal way though. The answers are in Appendix 2 on page 306.

1. Two black female mice were crossed with a grey male. In several litters female A produced 19 black and 18 grey young. Female B produced 25 black young.
    What can you deduce about the nature of black and grey fur colour in mice, and what are the genotypes of the parents?

2. Two yellow Bandycoots were thought by their keeper to be homozygous for coat colour. When they were mated all the babies were yellow. However when these offspring were later mated amongst themselves. The F_2 generation, some of these offspring were orange. This meant that one of the grandparents was heterozygous.
    How would you find out which grandparent was heterozygous?

3. In the Giant Boring beetle (*Coleopsis yawnii*) green eyes are dominant over blue. A blue-eyed beetle, both of whose parents had green eyes, was mated with a green-eyed beetle. They have one baby beetle which is blue-eyed. Deduce the genotypes of all these five individuals? If they have another baby beetle could it be green-eyed, and if so determine its genotype.

4. Once upon a time a Quoll with luminous eyes met a Quoll with blue eyes. Shortly afterwards several little Quolls were born and they all had luminous eyes. Deduce the genotypes of the parents and the offspring.
    Later on in life the little Quolls grew up and all but one met luminous eyed Quolls. All their babies had luminous eyes. The one lonely Quoll however met a beautiful blue-eyed Quoll and some of their babies had blue eyes. Deduce the genotypes of the lonely Quoll, his beautiful mate, and their babies.

5. In humans the ability to taste phenylthiourea depends on the presence of a dominant allele. The gene is not sex linked.
    a. Construct a pedigree chart to show a homozygous taster man and a non-taster woman and their two children, one son and one daughter.
    b. Their son marries a person of the same genotype for this gene. Continue the pedigree chart to show this and their three children, a son and two daughters. Each child has a different genotype.

6. Grandpa has blood group O. His first child, Horace, married a group O woman and they had two children, Belinda and Bertha, who were both group B.
    Grandpa's second child was group A, but the third child in the family, Clint, was group O. Grandpa thought it wise to tell his children before they studied this revision guide that the third child had been adopted.
    a. Deduce Granny's genotype showing all your reasoning.
    b. Why did Grandpa decide to say that Clint was adopted?

7. Web feet is a sex linked characteristic in Dingbats. Female Dingbats are XX and males XY. A webbed male is crossed with a homozygous normal female and the baby Dingbat is a female with normal feet.
    Deduce whether the web allele is dominant or recessive.
    If their next baby is a male determine whether it will have web or normal feet.

8. The genotypes in a particular variety of tomato were TtHh, Tthh, ttHh and tthh. The genes are not linked. Which two pairs would a plant breeder select in order to obtain a phenotype ratio of 1:1:1:1?

9. In the Squishy plant yellow fruit is dominant over green, and bumpy fruit dominant over smooth. Explain how a cross between a plant with green bumpy fruits and one with yellow smooth fruits gave:
    25 plants with green bumpy fruits,
    26 plants with green smooth fruits,
    24 plants with yellow bumpy fruits,
    25 plants with yellow smooth fruits.

10. The Administrator beetle (*Regis tra*) has black wing cases and short antennae. Two beetles with these characteristics were crossed and the offspring were:

     19 black, short antennae,

     6 black, long antennae,

     5 white, short antennae,

     1 white, long antennae.

    Determine the genotypes of the parents.

11. Frumpy plants have small flowers with green petals and these are the dominant characteristics. Large white flowers are recessive, and the genes are not linked. A plant with small green flowers was crossed with one with large white flowers and the offspring had either small green flowers or large green flowers. Determine the genotypes of the parents.

    If the plants with large green flowers were allowed to self-pollinate, determine the genotypes and phenotype ratio of the offspring.

12. A plant breeder crossed a Pogwort with red flowers with one with white flowers and all the offspring were pink. Determine the flower colours and proportions of the F_2 generation.

13. A Tarsus rat was taken from a group that was known to breed true for black and straight hair. It was then bred with a rat of unknown genotype and the offspring were:

Black, straight hair	1315
Red, curly hair	1370
Red, straight hair	21
Black, curly hair	19

    Determine the genotype of the unknown parent and give a genetic explanation of the results.

14. The Zye Goat has yellow legs and large eyes as dominant characteristics. White legs and small eyes are recessive. The genes are linked and crossing over occurs in both sexes. A goat with the dominant phenotype was test crossed. The results are below.

	F_1 results
Yellow legs, large eyes	275
Yellow legs, small eyes	6
White legs, large eyes	8
White legs, small eyes	290

    Explain genetically how these results were produced and state which of the F_1 are the recombinants.

15. There are two types of Zom Bee, one with red legs and one with blue legs. The characteristic is carried on the X chromosome. If red is dominant, what is the F_2 ratio if red-legged female bees are crossed with blue-legged males, the F_1 males all being red-legged? (Genetically, Zom Bees are the same as the fruit fly Drosophila).

16. Blue flowers of the Whoopsy Daisy are dominant to white, and tall plant recessive to short. A tall white flowered plant crossed with a short blue flowered plant gave the following offspring.

Short, blue	11
Tall, white	12
Short, white	113
Tall, blue	110

    Explain these results fully.

17. In the Dead Sloe (*Rigor mortis*) the allele for round fruit is dominant over long fruit, and the allele for complex flower recessive to simple flower. A cross was made between two varieties, Purplepear (long fruit and simple flower) and Grapecluster (round fruit and complex flower). All the F_1 plants produced round fruits and had simple flowers.

    A test cross on the F_1 gave the following results:

Round fruit, simple flowers	23
Long fruit, simple flowers	93
Round fruit, complex flowers	89
Long fruit, complex flowers	19

(a) Explain these results fully.

(b) If the alleles were not linked what numbers would you predict for each phenotype for the F_1 test cross. Base your calculation on the same total number of offspring as the actual test cross.

18. The Paraceta Mole has dominant alleles for white fur and black feet but there are recessive alleles for yellow fur and pink feet.

A pure breeding (remember that this means homozygous) white mole with black feet was crossed with a yellow mole with pink feet. As expected all the offspring were white with black feet. When these offspring were crossed amongst themselves many times they produced a total of 113 white with black feet, 32 yellow with pink feet, 7 white with pink feet and 8 yellow with black feet. What do these results indicate and what numbers would you have expected in the F_2?

Self-test Quiz

1.   A gene can best be described as:
      a.   a heritable factor that consists of a length of DNA,
      b.   part of a chromosome,
      c.   a homologous pair of alleles,
      d.   lengths of DNA linked by exons.

2.   With sex-linked (X-linked) genes:
      a.   both males and females are carriers,
      b.   only males are affected,
      c.   only females are carriers,
      d.   only twins are affected.

3.   A haploid cell is one in which:
      a.   only one of each pair of chromosomes is present,
      b.   there are 23 pairs of chromosomes,
      c.   the sex chromosomes are missing,
      d.   there is no nucleus.

4.   Sickle cell anaemia is:
      a.   a human genetic disease caused by an extra chromosome 21,
      b.   a genetic disease only inherited by a son from his father,
      c.   caused by the production of a faulty protein,
      d.   due to non-disjunction.

5.   The probability that a family of four children born to the same parents consists only of boys is:
      a.   a quarter,
      b.   a half,
      c.   an eighth,
      d.   a sixteenth.

6.   A mother of a child is blood group A and the father is blood group B. The child could have blood group:
      a.   A,
      b.   B,
      c.   A or B,
      d.   A, B, AB, or O.

7.   A father has one copy of the allele for Huntingdon's disease and the mother no copies. What is the probability that their second child will have the allele?
      a.   an eighth,
      b.   a quarter,
      c.   a half,
      d.   zero.

8.   Cystic fibrosis is caused by:
      a.   a dominant gene mutation,
      b.   a recessive gene mutation,
      c.   a base substitution mutation,
      d.   a sex linked gene.

9.   Sickle cell anaemia is caused by:
      a.   a dominant gene mutation,
      b.   a chromosome mutation,
      c.   a base substitution mutation,
      d.   a sex linked gene.

10. Two chromosomes that carry the same genes but not necessarily the same alleles are called:
    a. homozygous chromosomes,
    b. homologous chromosomes,
    c. sex chromosomes,
    d. codominant chromosomes.

11. A woman has one haemophilia allele and one normal allele. Which of the following statements is true?
    a. She is a carrier for the haemophilia allele.
    b. She will develop haemophilia.
    c. The probability of passing the haemophilia allele to her sons is 100%.
    d. All of her daughters will have the same genotype as herself.

12. Haemophilia is caused by:
    a. a dominant gene mutation,
    b. non-disjunction,
    c. a base substitution mutation,
    d. a sex linked gene.

13. A man has a sex linked recessive allele. His wife does not. What is the probability that their second son will also have the sex linked recessive allele?
    a. 100%,
    b. 75%,
    c. 25%,
    d. 0%.

14. A woman is homozygous for a recessive allele found on chromosome 20. Her husband is heterozygous. The probability that she will have a son who is also heterozygous is:
    a. 50%,
    b. 0%,
    c. 25%,
    d. 75%.

15. Chiasma formation and crossing over can take place during:
    a. Prophase I,
    b. Prophase II,
    c. Metaphase I,
    d. Anaphase I.

16. Recombination can best be defined as:
    a. the appearance amongst the offspring of combinations of characteristics due to mutations,
    b. the reassortment of alleles as a result of crossing over,
    c. combinations of characteristics in the offspring due to random alignment during metaphase I,
    d. formation of new characteristics as a result of non- disjunction during anaphase II.

17. Autosomes are:
    a. those chromosomes that carry homologous genes,
    b. those chromosomes that do not determine the sex of the individual,
    c. those chromosomes that do determine the sex of the individual,
    d. the only chromosomes where crossing over can take place.

18. A pedigree chart is used to show:
    a. if an allele is sex linked,
    b. if an allele is dominant or recessive,
    c. genetic relationships within a family tree,
    d. genetic relationships between different families.

19. A plasmid is:
    a.   a small circular piece of DNA found in some prokaryotes,
    b.   a genetic mutation,
    c.   part of the bacterial nucleus,
    d.   a prokaryotic organelle.

20. A linkage group is:
    a.   the group of chromosomes found in any one nucleus,
    b.   the combinations of genes produced as a result of crossing over,
    c.   all the genes found on one chromosome,
    d.   all the different alleles of a gene.

21. Polygenic inheritance can result in:
    a.   formation of linkage groups,
    b.   crossing over,
    c.   mutations,
    d.   continuous variation.

22. The purpose of crossing over is to:
    a.   mix alleles between sister chromatids,
    b.   mix alleles between chromosomes of the homologous pair,
    c.   increase the phenotypic variation in the parents,
    d.   mix genes between the chromosomes of non-homologous pairs.

23. Alleles are best described as:
    a.   different genes,
    b.   genes found on different chromosomes,
    c.   different forms of a gene,
    d.   genes only found on homologous chromosomes.

24. The gametes that can be produced from the genotype RrTt are:
    a.   Rr, RT, rt and Tt,
    b.   RTrt,
    c.   RrTt,
    d.   RT, Rt, rT and rt.

25. An organism has the genotype A b.
                                    a B
    The table shows genotypes and numbers for the gametes. Which is the correct line?

a.	AB	Ab	aB	ab
	100	105	101	99
b.	AB	Ab	aB	ab
	14	210	208	12
c.	AB	Ab	aB	ab
	135	45	45	15
d.	AB	Ab	aB	ab
	210	14	12	208

Chapter Nine

Evolution and Biodiversity

The theory of evolution was put forward at nearly the same time by Charles Darwin and Alfred Russel Wallace and was the most outstanding biological theory of the 19th century. Biodiversity is of tremendous importance at the present time given the global damage to habitats by humans.

Evolution

Charles Darwin and Alfred Russel Wallace

Charles Darwin joined HMS Beagle under Captain FitzRoy as the ship's naturalist. The ship sailed from Devonport 18th December 1831 on its 5 year mapping voyage for the British Admiralty.

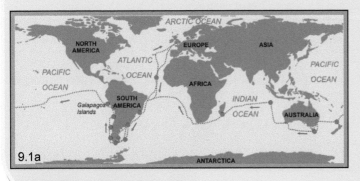

9.1a

At every opportunity Darwin studied the plants, animals and geology of the places visited, sometimes leaving the ship for days and travelling overland. It was during this time that he began to formulate his ideas on variation. His observations on the tortoises and mocking birds of the Galapagos Islands reinforced these ideas and over the following 20 years at his house in Downe, Kent in the UK he accumulated more evidence and finally in 1859 published his book *On the Origin of Species by Means of Natural Selection*.

9.1b An elderly Charles Darwin

9.1c Beagle being hailed by native Fuegians during the survey of Tierra del Fuego, painted by Conrad Martens

Alfred Russel Wallace was a contemporary of Darwin and a great traveller, naturalist and collector. Extensive observations in the Amazon River basin and Malay Archipelago led him to the same conclusions as Darwin and in 1858 he published *On the Tendency of Varieties to Depart Indefinitely from the Original Type*. It was this which prompted Darwin to publish. The Wallace Line is a line running between Borneo and Sulawesi, and between the Indonesian islands of Bali and Lombok. The distance between these two islands is only about 35km yet Wallace observed a distinct difference in plant and animal species between them. To the West are Asiatic species and to the East a mix of Asiatic and Australian species. We now know that this is the junction between two tectonic plates and in the geological past the islands were a long distance apart.

9.2

Key steps
The Darwin–Wallace principle of evolution by natural selection

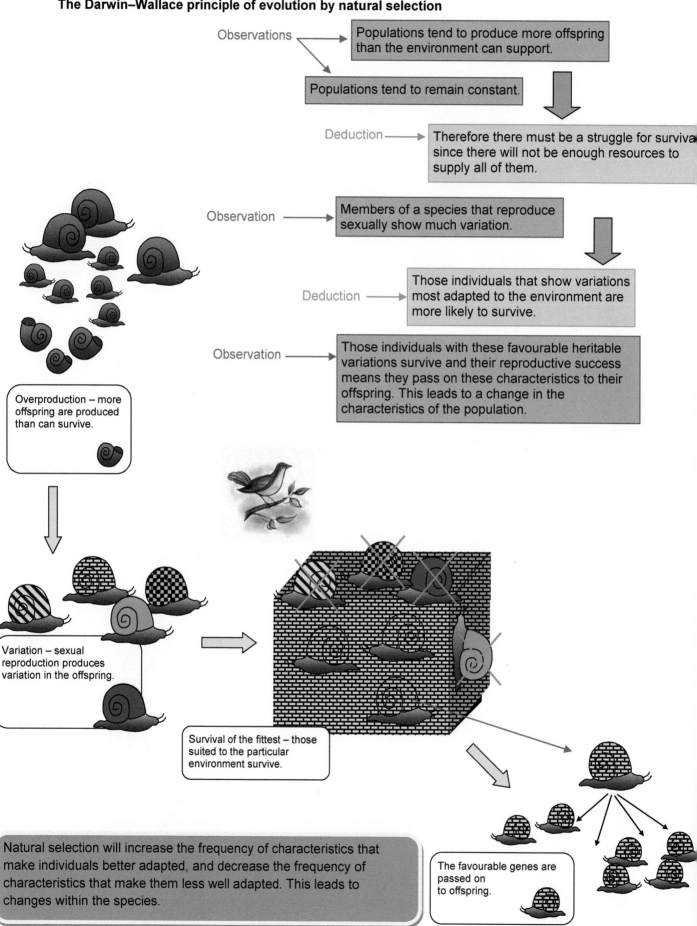

Observations → Populations tend to produce more offspring than the environment can support.

Populations tend to remain constant.

Deduction → Therefore there must be a struggle for surviva since there will not be enough resources to supply all of them.

Observation → Members of a species that reproduce sexually show much variation.

Deduction → Those individuals that show variations most adapted to the environment are more likely to survive.

Observation → Those individuals with these favourable heritable variations survive and their reproductive success means they pass on these characteristics to their offspring. This leads to a change in the characteristics of the population.

Overproduction – more offspring are produced than can survive.

Variation – sexual reproduction produces variation in the offspring.

Survival of the fittest – those suited to the particular environment survive.

Natural selection will increase the frequency of characteristics that make individuals better adapted, and decrease the frequency of characteristics that make them less well adapted. This leads to changes within the species.

The favourable genes are passed on to offspring.

Variation
➢ The original source of variation is mutation which alters the genetic code.
➢ This variation is then shuffled around by:
- crossing over during meiosis – see page 265,
- random assortment during meiosis – see page 100,
- random fertilisation.

Evolution in response to environmental change

- **Example 1 – Multiple antibiotic resistance in bacteria**

Methicillin-resistant *Staphylococcus aureus*, MRSA, and *Clostridium difficile* are two bacteria that have developed resistance and are a potential threat to human health.

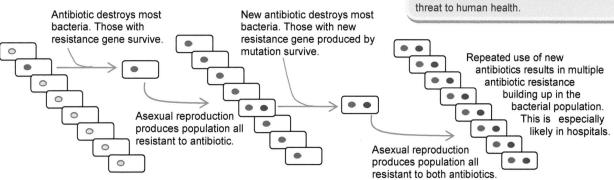

Antibiotic destroys most bacteria. Those with resistance gene survive.

New antibiotic destroys most bacteria. Those with new resistance gene produced by mutation survive.

Asexual reproduction produces population all resistant to antibiotic.

Asexual reproduction produces population all resistant to both antibiotics.

Repeated use of new antibiotics results in multiple antibiotic resistance building up in the bacterial population. This is especially likely in hospitals.

- **Example 2 – Changes in finch beaks on the Galapagos**

General points
➢ The Galapagos Islands are a small group of 14 volcanic islands 926km west of Ecuador.
➢ A flock of finches from Ecuador were probably blown onto the islands in a storm many years ago.
➢ As the population expanded there would be competition for food.
➢ Natural variations in beak shapes and sizes would allow exploitation of the different food sources available.
➢ Over time this would lead to speciation – see page 290.

Charles Darwin visited the islands in 1835 on HMS Beagle. The 13 species of finches found amongst the islands are named after him.

The Island of Daphne Major
➢ This is a small, fairly isolated island susceptible to climate changes.
➢ Two species of finch, the large and medium ground finches, have been studied for many years by Peter and Rosemary Grant.

9.3a Medium ground finch. The beak is short and thick, ideal for small and medium seeds.

9.3b Large ground finch. The beak is better adapted for larger seeds.

- The original finch on the island was the medium ground finch.
- It had a range of beak sizes allowing it to exploit seeds of different sizes.
- In 1982 a few large ground finches flew to the island from a neighbouring one and fed on the larger seeds.
- Since the two species fed primarily on different sized seeds there was only a small level of competition between the large finch and any members of the medium finch population which had larger beaks.
- Two years of drought in 2003–4 drastically reduced plant growth and the lack of seeds caused both populations to fall dramatically.
- Medium finches with smaller beaks were able to find small seeds which finches with larger beaks could not pick up.
- Medium finches with large beaks were strongly competing for the larger seeds with the large finch.
- Smaller beaked birds survived better than larger beaked birds.
- A strong shift towards smaller beak size occurred with the medium finch in the following years, along with a change in foraging behaviour which focused towards smaller seeds.
- Thus there was an even greater divergence in beak size between the medium and large finches.

Evidence for evolution

1. Fossils
- The fossil remains of extinct species provide evidence that species are continuously evolving.
- Older rocks contain simpler organisms and species that are no longer living.
- Younger rocks contain species that resemble those that are alive today.
- It is not a perfect record of the evolution of species, but it does show that changes in species have taken place in the past.

9.4 Shell fossils

The first fossil is simply a print of a shell in mud which has hardened. In the other two the organism has been replaced with hard minerals.

2. Homologous structures
- These have the same evolutionary origin but now have different functions.
- Example – the pentadactyl limb.
- So called because it typically has five digits.
- Found in all four classes of vertebrates – amphibians, reptiles, birds and mammals.

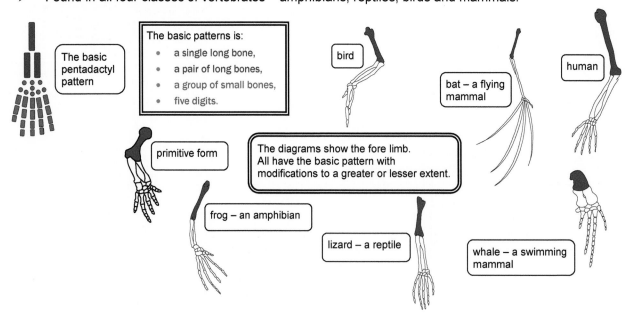

The basic pentadactyl pattern

The basic patterns is:
- a single long bone,
- a pair of long bones,
- a group of small bones,
- five digits.

bird

bat – a flying mammal

human

primitive form

The diagrams show the fore limb. All have the basic pattern with modifications to a greater or lesser extent.

frog – an amphibian

lizard – a reptile

whale – a swimming mammal

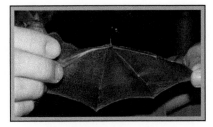
9.5 A bat wing

9.6 A Mesosaurus fossil from the early Permian 299-271mya.
This clearly shows the pentadactyl limb.

3. Development of melanism in insects
- Example – The Peppered moth *Biston betularia*. This moth is common in England.
- The normal form has white wings covered in black specks.
- Dark forms in which the black specks had merged to varying degrees first appeared during the industrial revolution in the mid-19th century.
- The moth rests during the day on lichen covered tree trunks and the normal form would be well camouflaged.

dark form

normal form

On a lichen covered tree trunk the normal form is well camouflaged.

9.7 a

- As the trees near industrial areas became dirty with soot the dark forms would be camouflaged but the normal speckled form would be easily seen and eaten by birds.
- In clean country areas the dark form would be seen and eaten.
- As particular areas became industrialised the population of the dark form increased and that of the speckled form decreased.
- In 1956 the Clean Air Act was passed and gradually the soot was washed off the trees.
- Selection pressure started to work against the dark forms and over the next 30 years the speckled form became more common.

On a soot covered tree trunk the dark form is well camouflaged.

9.7b

9.7 The peppered moth

4. Selective breeding of domesticated animals
- Breeds have been produced for food production, working, pets, sport.
- Humans have selected a particular feature and used these animals to breed from.
- Offspring which showed an increase in this feature were bred from and the process repeated.
- Dogs – Chinese dog (food), sheep dog (working), dachshund (pet), greyhound (sport).
- Cattle – Jersey (milk), Aberdeen Angus (beef).
- If new varieties can be produced by Man selecting specific characteristics then the same can happen if the environment does the selecting.

9.8 Sheep dog

5. Continuous variation

> Gulls in the genus *Larus* can be found in a ring around the North Pole.
> It shows continuous variation of related populations across the geographical range.
> This matches the concept of gradual divergence.

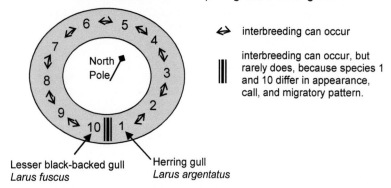

⟷ interbreeding can occur

‖ interbreeding can occur, but rarely does, because species 1 and 10 differ in appearance, call, and migratory pattern.

Herring gull
Grey back and pink legs

Lesser black-backed gull
Larus fuscus

Herring gull
Larus argentatus

The original species probably spread in one direction (in the diagram this would be anticlockwise) and selection produced minor variations along the way. When the end of the ring closed back at the starting point there was so much variation between the starting form and the final form that interbreeding was inhibited.

Lesser black-backed gull. Black back. Winter adults have pink legs; summer adults have yellow legs.

9.9 The two gull species at the ends of the North Pole gull cline

Speciation

Key points

> A gene pool consists of all the genes and their different alleles present in an interbreeding population.
> Speciation occurs when populations of species gradually diverge into separate species by evolution.
> Natural selection acts on each population gene pool in a different way.
> Evolution requires that allele frequencies change with time in populations.
> The populations must be isolated in some way by a barrier.
> The barrier could be:
>   - geographical – a river or mountain range separates the populations,
>   - temporal – different populations are around at different times,
>   - behavioural – mating rituals or calls could be different in different populations.
>   - food – different populations prefer different foodplants,
>   - environmental – if different aspects of the environment favour one form over another.
> Speciation can be gradual or abrupt.

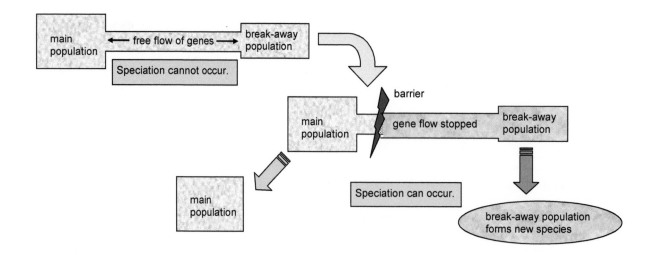

IBHL Biology 2016 © Ashby Merson-Davies

The pace of evolution – gradualism and punctuated equilibrium

Gradualism
A slow change from one form to another.

Punctuated equilibrium
Long periods with little change with intermittent short periods of rapid change.

Points for discussion

- Gradualism is a Darwinian approach.
- The fossil record indicates this to be true in some cases, e.g. the horse leg where the fossils show all the stages from the earliest horse to the modern horse.
- In other cases the fossil record shows no intermediates.
- Eldredge and Gould proposed (1972) that most evolutionary changes take place at the time of speciation.
- Small populations that become isolated do not contain the full gene pool and have different allele frequencies.
- Environmental differences encourage rapid speciation in these small populations and once established new genotypes resist change.
- The population enters a long period of stasis until punctuated by another change.
- An example of this would be the variety of Darwin's finches on the volcanic Galapagos Islands.
- Sometimes these changes can affect local populations such as a rise in sea level creating an island, or a major volcanic eruption that affects the global climate, e.g. after Krakatoa erupted in 1883 average global temperatures fell by $1.2^{0}C$.

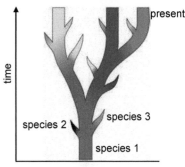

9.10 Gradualism

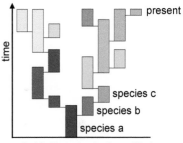

9.11 Punctuated equilibrium

Polyploidy

- This is having more than three sets of chromosomes in the nucleus.
- Polyploidy can result in self-sterility, e.g. meiosis in a triploid cell results in gametes with variable numbers of chromosomes because the chromosomes left over after pairs of homologous chromosomes have formed bivalents will end up randomly in the gametes.
- This results in reproductive isolation.

Polyploidy and speciation in Alliums

- The *Allium* genus includes onions, chives, leeks and garlic.
- They are highly variable in their chromosome numbers.
- Many *Allium* species reproduce asexually which, since it is done by mitosis, is not affected by chromosome numbers.

Some examples of Alliums

Species	2n	Ploidy level
A. aflatunense	16	2x
A. carinatum	16	2x
	24	3x
A. senescens	32	4x
A. oleraceum	40	5x
A. nutans	66	8x

Selection mechanisms

There are three categories of selection pressure:

- stabilising,
- directional,
- disruptive.

1. Stabilising

- Snail shells show a range of colours from very pale brown to dark brown.
- 'Forest snails' live in brown leaf litter.
- Snails with very pale or very dark shells can easily be seen by predators.
- Selection pressure will therefore favour mid brown shells.

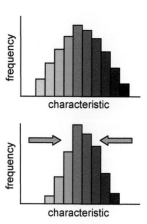

2. Directional

- Mice normally have brown coloured fur.
- The fur colour will show a range from very pale brown to dark brown.
- 'Beach mice' live on white sand dunes.
- Dark coloured mice can easily be seen by predators.
- Selection pressure will therefore favour pale fur.

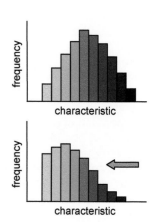

3. Disruptive

- The Peppered moth (see page 289) has white wings speckled with black.
- The amount of black speckling shows variation.
- Moths with lightly speckled wings survive best in clean countryside.
- Moths with heavy speckling survive best in countryside that has been polluted with soot from chimneys.
- This splits the mixed population.

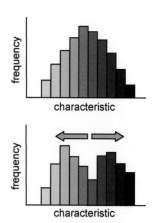

1a. What is the original source of genetic variation?	1b. List three ways that this genetic variation can be shuffled around.	2. What is the principle behind using fossils as evidence for evolution?
3a. What are homologous structures?	3b. State an example of homologous structures.	4. What is the name given to the development of black pigmentation in response to soot pollution?
5a. Name the process where a new species develops from an existing one.	5b. What key feature must exist for this to occur?	6. List the three types of selection mechanism.

Classification of biodiversity

Classification

Key points

➤ Organisms are grouped into three domains.

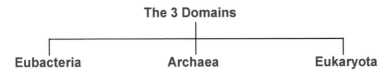

The 3 Domains

Eubacteria   Archaea   Eukaryota

All prokaryotic organisms (those without a true nucleus) used to be grouped together as 'bacteria'. In 1977 Carl Woese sequenced ribosomal RNA and discovered that one group of 'bacteria' were so different from the others that he proposed the three domain system. In fact the Archaea share many molecular features with the Eukaryota, e.g. their DNA is associated with histones.

➤ The Eukaryotes include protoctistans, fungi, plants and animals.
➤ Classification of an organism is done by putting it into a hierarchy of taxa.
➤ The genus and accompanying higher taxa contain all the species that have evolved from a single ancestral common species.
➤ Taxonomists sometimes reclassify groups of species when new evidence shows that a previous taxon contains species that have evolved from different ancestral species.
➤ A natural classification can help in identification of species and allow the prediction of characteristics shared by species within a group.

Natural classification:
This is classifying an organism based on its evolutionary relationships, i.e. kingdom to species.
Artificial classification:
This is sometimes used to group organisms which show similar characteristics due to convergent evolution, e.g. all organisms with wings.

The hierarchy of taxa

Kingdom
Phylum
Class
Order
Family
Genus
Species

One way to remember this is:
King
Philip
Classified
Over
Fifty
Green
Spiders

Examples

Taxonomic rank	Plant example	Animal example
Domain	Eukaryota	Eukaryota
Kingdom	Plantae	Animalia
Phylum	Angiospermophyta	Chordata
Class	Dicotyledonaea	Mammalia
Order	Ranales	Primates
Family	Ranunculacae	Hominidae
Genus	*Ranunculus*	*Homo*
Species	*acris*	*sapiens*
Common name	Meadow buttercup	Human

The binomial system

➢ Each organism has two Latin names, its genus and species.

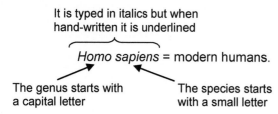

It is typed in italics but when hand-written it is underlined

Homo sapiens = modern humans.

The genus starts with a capital letter

The species starts with a small letter

> Other examples used so far in the is chapter:
>
> Large ground finch – *Geospiza magnirostris*
> Medium ground finch – *Geospiza fortis*
> Peppered moth – *Biston betularia*
> Lesser black-backed gull – *Larus fuscus*
> Herring gull – *Larus argentatus*
>
> Darwin was especially fascinated by beetles and 71 species are named after him. In 2002 a small moth discovered on the Galapagos island of San Cristobal was named *Galagete darwini*.

➢ The system is international.
➢ Names are agreed at congresses.
➢ All biologists use the same names.
➢ Misunderstandings through language differences are prevented.
➢ The first name is the genus name and shows which other species are closely related.

Plants

Group	Recognition Features	
Bryophyta Mosses and Liverworts	No roots or cuticle. No vascular system. Rhizoids similar to root hairs. Mosses with simple leaf-like structures. Liverworts have flattened shape called a thallus. Spores produced in capsules.	9.12a 9.12b
Filicinophyta Ferns	Roots. Leaves in fronds. Cuticle on leaves. Simple vascular tissue. Can form small trees, but not woody. Spores produced in structures called sporangia on the underside of the fronds (second photo).	9.12c 9.12d
Coniferophyta Conifers	Shrubs to very large trees. Roots, stems, leaves. Woody stems and roots. Produce pollen and ovules in cones. Produce seeds. Vascular tissue more advanced than the Filicinophyta.	9.12e
Angiospermophyta Flowering plants	Highly variable in structure – tiny herbaceous to large trees. Roots, stems, leaves, flowers. Can form woody tissue. Some parasitic. Produce pollen and ovules in flowers. Produce seeds. Fruits often produced for seed dispersal. Well formed vascular tissue.	9.12f

9.12 Major plant groups

Animals

Group	Recognition Features	
Porifera Sponges	No special shape. No mouth or anus. Lack tissues and organs. Collection of cells of different types organised into pores, canals and chambers.	 9.13a
Cnidaria Jellyfish, sea anemones and corals.	Two cell layers. Radial symmetry. Mouth. Two forms – medusa (jellyfish) and polyp (sea anemone). Some corals have hard calcareous cover. Tentacles with stinging cells.	 9.13b
Platyhelminthes Flatworms, flukes, tapeworms	Flat and unsegmented. Bilateral symmetry. Mouth but no anus. Rudimentary head. No vascular system.	 9.13c
Mollusca Snails, slugs, squids, octopus	Soft, flexible body with no obvious segmentation. Head, muscular foot and visceral hump. Hard rasping radula for feeding. Many with a single or double shell. Open circulatory system with simple heart.	 9.13d
Annelida Segmented worms, leeches	Segmented body. Bilateral symmetry. Mouth and anus. Vascular system with simple heart. Bristles (chaetae).	 9.13e
Arthropoda Crabs, spiders, scorpions, centipedes, insects	Segmented. Bilateral symmetry. Hard exoskeleton made of chitin. Jointed appendages. Vascular system with simple heart. Most land species have a system of tubes (trachea) throughout the body for gas exchange.	 9.13f 9.13g
Chordata Fish, amphibians, reptiles, birds, mammals.	Segmented. Bilateral symmetry. Endoskeleton of cartilage or bone. Well-developed vascular and gas exchange systems.	 9.13h

9.13 Major animal groups

Vertebrate animals

Group	Recognition Features
Fish	Mostly fully aquatic. Gas exchange through gills. Scaly skin. Skeleton of cartilage or bone. No limbs. External fertilisation. Ectothermic.
Amphibians Frogs, toads, newts, salamanders.	Land living but usually requiring a moist habitat. Simple lungs for gas exchange. Some use a moist skin for additional gas exchange. Adults with four limbs. External fertilisation. Aquatic gill breathing juvenile stages. Show metamorphosis. Ectothermic.
Reptiles Snakes, lizards, iguanas, chameleons, turtles, tortoises, crocodilians.	Mostly land living. Lungs for gas exchange. Dry scaly skin. Internal fertilisation. Eggs have a tough leathery coat. Ectothermic.
Birds	Skin with feathers. Scaly legs. Horny beak. Wings. Well developed lungs. Internal fertilisation. Eggs have a hard calcareous shell. Endothermic.
Mammals	Skin with fur / hair. Well developed lungs. Teeth. Internal fertilisation. Young develop internally. Produce milk from mammary glands. Endothermic.

9.14a

9.14b

9.14c

9.14d

9.14e

9.14 Major vertebrate groups

A dichotomous key

Key points

➤ Dichotomous means two, therefore each step is a pair of statements, and the number to the right directs you to the next pair.

➤ Each statement must be qualitative and not relative, e.g. 'long leaf blade' is meaningless but 'length of leaf blade greater than width' can be measured.

Example

1. Leaf with toothed margin ……………………………………… 2
   Leaf with smooth margin ……………………………………… 15
2. Lateral veins branch off midrib alternately left and right ……… 3
   Lateral veins branch off midrib in pairs …………………………… 7
3. Tip of leaf blade rounded …………………………………… apple
   Tip of leaf blade pointed …………………………………… 10

©Ashby Merson-Davies

7. List the three domains.	8. List the hierarchy of taxa.	9. Which taxa are used in the binomial system?
10. List 4 advantages to scientists of the binomial system.		11. Which group of plants have leaves in fronds and a simple vascular system?
	12. Which group of plants have flowers?	13. Which group of plants produce seeds in cones?
14. Which group of animals have flat and unsegmented bodies and bilateral symmetry?	15. Which group of animals have a head, muscular foot and visceral hump?	16. Which group of animals have gills and use external fertilisation?
17. Which group of animals have jointed limbs and an exoskeleton?	18. Which group of animals are radially symmetrical and have tentacles with stinging cells?	19. Which group of animals are segmented and have an endoskeleton of cartilage or bone?
20. Which group of animals have scaly legs and a skin with feathers?	21. Which group of animals are segmented, have bristles, a mouth and anus?	22. Which group of animals have no special shape and are simply collections of cells lacking tissue organisation?
23. Which group of animals have a dry scaly skin and use lungs?	24. Which group of animals have simple lungs, external fertilisation and an aquatic juvenile stage?	25. Which group of animals have skin with hair, internal fertilisation and young that develop internally?

Clades, cladistics and cladograms

Clade
➢ All of the organisms, both living and fossil, descended from a common ancestor.

Cladistics
➢ A method of classifying living organisms based on the construction and analysis of cladograms.

Cladogram
➢ An evolutionary tree showing points at which clades diverged from a common ancestral form.
➢ Evidence comes from biochemical data:
  • number of differences in the DNA base sequence of a gene, or
  • number of differences in the amino acid sequence of a protein.
➢ Sequence differences accumulate gradually.
➢ Thus there is a positive correlation between the number of differences between two species and the time difference since they diverged from a common ancestor.

Cladogram terms

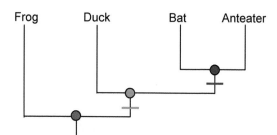

➢ The coloured circles where the tree branches are called **nodes**.
➢ Groups of organisms that share a common ancestor form a **clade**.
➢ This is easily seen with the 'snip rule'.
➢ The bat and anteater form a clade if you snip at the blue line.
➢ The duck, bat and anteater form a clade if you snip at the orange line.
➢ The duck and bat do not form a clade because snipping at the orange line means the anteater falls off as well and must therefore be included.

Cladogram structure
➢ The pattern of branching in a cladogram aims to match the evolutionary origins of each species.
➢ The sequence of splits at nodes indicates when species diverged.
➢ Clades connected to a single node are more closely related than clades connected via two or more nodes.
➢ The length of the branches in morphological cladograms is arbitrary and does not show evolutionary distances.
➢ The length of the branches in biochemical cladograms sometimes shows evolutionary distances based on the number of changes.

IBHL Biology 2016 © Ashby Merson-Davies

Constructing a cladogram using biochemical data
Example 1
The table shows the number of amino acid differences between the human haemoglobin beta chain and a number of other animals.

Human	horse	grey kangaroo	cow	gorilla	rhesus monkey
0	25	38	25	1	8

Rearrange the data into descending order.

grey kangaroo	horse	cow	rhesus monkey	gorilla	human
38	25	25	8	1	0

Assuming that the rate of change is constant a cladogram can be drawn to scale.

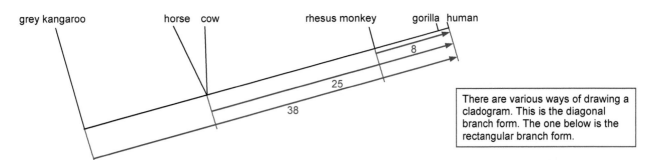

> There are various ways of drawing a cladogram. This is the diagonal branch form. The one below is the rectangular branch form.

Example 2

Number of nucleotide substitutions	chimpanzee	gorilla	orangutan	gibbon	Japanese macaque	rhesus monkey
human	0.094	0.110	0.179	0.205	0.268	0.271
chimpanzee		0.113	0.192	0.214	0.285	0.298
gorilla			0.189	0.215	0.274	0.271
orangutan				0.211	0.289	0.292
gibbon					0.293	0.280
Japanese macaque						0.037

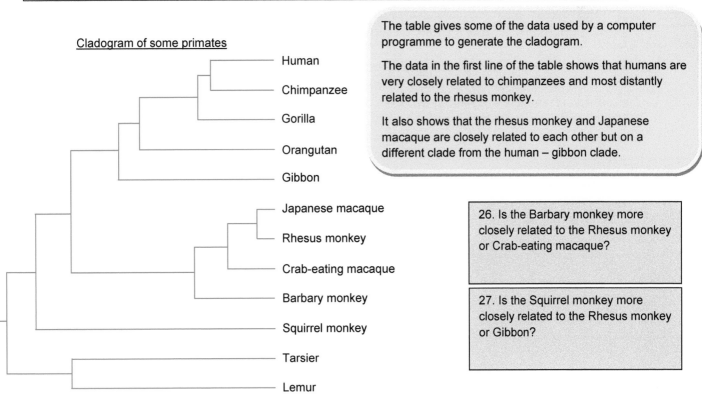

Cladogram of some primates

> The table gives some of the data used by a computer programme to generate the cladogram.
>
> The data in the first line of the table shows that humans are very closely related to chimpanzees and most distantly related to the rhesus monkey.
>
> It also shows that the rhesus monkey and Japanese macaque are closely related to each other but on a different clade from the human – gibbon clade.

26. Is the Barbary monkey more closely related to the Rhesus monkey or Crab-eating macaque?

27. Is the Squirrel monkey more closely related to the Rhesus monkey or Gibbon?

Example 3

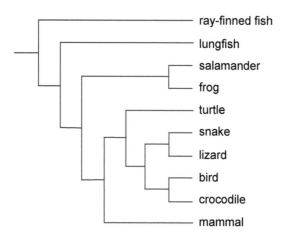

Cladogram of some vertebrate groups.

| 28. Do the snake and lizard form a clade? |
| 29. Do the lizard and bird form a clade? |
| 30. Do the ray-finned fish and lungfish form a clade? |
| 31. Do the snake, lizard, bird and crocodile form a clade? |

Homologous and analogous characteristics

Homologous characteristics
Ones that share a common evolutionary origin but do not necessarily have the same function now.
Examples:
- bird wing and bat wing,
- human arm and horse front leg,
- whale flipper and chimpanzee arm.

Analogous characteristics
Ones which now have a similar function but different evolutionary origins.
Examples:
- bird wing and butterfly wing,
- wasp eye and octopus eye,
- beetle leg and cat leg.

Reclassifying organisms using cladistics
- Up until towards the end of the 20th Century classification was based primarily on morphological characteristics.
- A natural classification should be based on homologous characteristics.
- Analogous characteristics can cause confusion and muddle the true classification.
- Analysis of DNA base and amino acid sequences allowed biochemical cladograms to be drawn.
- This resulted in the reclassification of several groups, some being merged, others divided, and sometimes species moving from one group to another.

Example – the Figwort family, *Scrophulariaceae*
This family has a worldwide distribution but no clearly defined traits that could be used for classification, so more and more plants were added resulting in a rather mixed collection of some 5000 species in over 270 genera.
Analysis of three chloroplast genes indicated several clades had been wrongly included in the family.

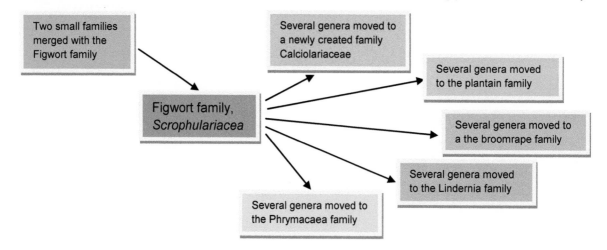

IBHL Biology 2016 © Ashby Merson-Davies

Glossary

BILATERAL SYMMETRY	Left and right sides of an organism when divided down the back are mirror images.
ENDOTHERMIC	Regulating body temperature using heat generated internally.
ECTOTHERMIC	Regulating body temperature using heat from the sun.
METAMORPHOSIS	Changing body form through juvenile stages to an adult.
PLOIDY	The number of sets of chromosomes in a nucleus. Haploid = 1 set, diploid = 2 sets, polyploidy = 3 or more sets.
RADIAL SYMMETRY	The two halves of a body are mirror images regardless of the angle of the cut through the centre.

Answers to Grey Box Questions

1a. Mutation.

1b. Crossing-over; random assortment / alignment; random fertilisation.

2. Older rocks contain older fossils.

3a. Structures that have the same evolutionary origin but may not have the same function.

3b. Pentadactyl limb.   4. (Industrial) melanism.

5a. Speciation.   5b. Isolating barrier.

6. Stabilising; directional; disruptive.   7. Eubacteria; Archaea; Eukarya.

8. Kingdom; phylum; class; order; family; genus; species.   9. Genus + species.

10. The system is international.

Names are agreed at congresses.

All biologists use the same names.

Misunderstandings through language differences are prevented.

The first name is the genus name and shows which other species are closely related.

11. Filicinophyta.   12. Angiospermophyta.   13. Coniferophyta.

14. Platyhelminthes.   15. Mollusca.   16. Fish.

17. Arthropoda.   18. Cnidaria.   19. Chordata.

20. Birds.   21. Annelida.   22. Porifera.

23. Reptiles.   24. Amphibia.   25. Mammals.

26. Crab-eating macaque.   27. Gibbon.

28. Yes.   29. No.   30. Yes.   31. No

Self-test Quiz

1. Use the key to identify the leaf.

1 leaf margin even..................................... 2
  leaf margin wavy.......................................oak
2 veins branch off central vein in pairs..............5
  veins branch off alternately left and right........ 3
3 tip of leaf blade rounded........................... lilac
  tip of leaf blade pointed............................ 4
4 leaf margin smooth..................................beech
  leaf margin toothed..................................rose

© Ashby Merson-Davies

oak	lilac	beech	rose
a.	b.	c.	d.

2. Which of the following is a correct sequence for the hierarchy of taxa?
   a. Phylum, class, genus, family,
   b. Phylum, family, order, genus,
   c. Class, order, genus, species,
   d. Class, phylum, genus, species.

3. Which of the following is the correct definition of evolution?
   a. A change in the heritable characteristics of a population.
   b. An increase in the mutation rate of a population.
   c. A high level of selection pressure on a population.
   d. The selection of a specific desirable characteristic in an individual.

4. The greenhouse effect is due to:
   a. the accumulation of dust in the atmosphere,
   b. an increase in the heat output of the sun,
   c. an increase in heat output due to the rise in human population,
   d. a decrease in the proportion of solar energy radiated back into space from the earth's atmosphere.

5. Which of the following factors is **least** likely to bring about a reduction in global warming:
   a. using natural gas rather than oil as a source of energy,
   b. consuming only food grown in the country of origin,
   c. increased use of renewable energy sources,
   d. recycling organic waste materials as a manure.

6. Which of the following are greenhouse gases?
   a. water, methane, carbon dioxide, hydrogen,
   b. nitrogen oxide, carbon dioxide, oxygen,
   c. methane, carbon dioxide, nitrogen oxide,
   d. nitrogen oxide, water, methane, oxygen.

7. In the binomial system of classification:
   a. all organisms are divided into two groups,
   b. all organisms have two names representing the genus and the species,
   c. all organisms have two names representing the family and the species,
   d. organisms are always arranged in pairs.

8. Darwin and Wallace made the following observations in support of their theory of natural selection.
   'Populations tend to produce more offspring than the environment can support'.
   'Populations tend to remain constant.'
   What was their deduction from these observations?
   a. The populations would produce fewer offspring.
   b. The populations would migrate to regions with more resources.
   c. Resources within the ecosystem would increase to support the larger populations.
   d. Individuals within the populations would find it difficult to survive.

9. Multiple antibiotic resistance in bacteria arises due to:
   a. repeated exposure of the bacteria to a range of antibiotics,
   b. repeated exposure of the bacteria to a specific antibiotic,
   c. patients spending too long in hospitals where antibiotics are used,
   d. use of antibiotics after their 'use by' date.

10. Darwin's finches on the Galapagos Islands show a range of beak shapes and sizes. Which of the following reasons would **not** be an explanation for this?
    a. There was competition for food resources.
    b. Selection pressure eliminated unsuitable beak shapes.
    c. There was a range of food sources available on the islands.
    d. There was completion for nesting sites.

11. Homologous structures are best described as:
    a. structures which have the same function but different origins,
    b. structures which have the same origin and the same functions,
    c. structures which have the same origin but different functions,
    d. structures which all look the same.

12. Which of the following statements about speciation is correct?
    a. Development of new species as a result of populations becoming isolated from each other.
    b. Development of new species due to mutations arising in the original population.
    c. Development of new species as a result of two isolated populations merging together.
    d. Development of new species due to a population moving to a different habitat.

13. Which one of the following graphs indicates that directional selection pressure has occurred, assuming the original population had a normal distribution of the characteristic?

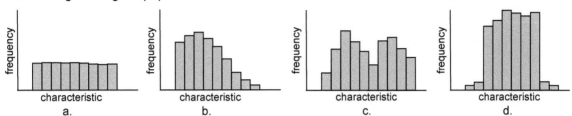

a.   b.   c.   d.

14. Which of the following groups do jellyfish belong to?
    a. fish,
    b. mollusca,
    c. porifera,
    d. cnidaria.

15. Which of the following groups do ferns belong to?
    a. coniferophyta,
    b. bryophyte,
    c. angiospermophyta,
    d. filicinophyta.

16. Which of the following groups do snails and squids belong to?
    a. arthropoda,
    b. mollusca,
    c. annelida,
    d. chordata.

17. Which of the following groups do crabs and insects belong to?
    a. arthropoda,
    b. cnidarian,
    c. porifera,
    d. platyhelminthes.

18. Which of the following groups shows radial symmetry?
    a. annelida,
    b. arthropoda,
    c. mollusca,
    d. cnidaria.

19. Which of the following groups does not have a vascular system?
    a. filicinophyta,
    b. bryophyte,
    c. angiospermophyta,
    d. coniferophyta.

20. Which of the following groups have a dry scaly skin and lay eggs with a leathery coat?
    a. reptiles,
    b. amphibians,
    c. birds,
    d. chordates.

Appendix 1

Answers to Self-test Quizzes

Chapter 1

1. d
2. a. 7500x.   b. 7000x.   c. 5000x.
3. a. 11mm.   b. 200mm.   c. 62μm.
4. Mean = 1.72m.   Median = 1.65m.   Mode = 1.6m
5. $\underline{23} \times 100 = 49\%$ increase.
    47
6. $\underline{85} = 1$ $\underline{376} = 4.4$ Ratio = 1 : 4.4
    85   85
7. Mean 13mm. Standard deviation 1.6mm.

Don't forget the units

8. Negative.

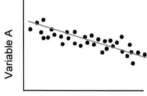

Variable A

Variable B

9. She was right to say the standard deviation was small but not very small. 33% of 47 is 15.5 and 13 is very close to this , so it is actually close to being a large standard deviation.
10. a
11. c
12. The null hypothesis states that there is no difference in the height of the bean plants grown under the two different temperatures.

Mean height of bean plant, mm	Observed O	Expected E	O – E	$(O - E)^2$	$\dfrac{(O - E)^2}{E}$
10⁰C	17	24	-7	49	2.04
20⁰C	31	24	+7	49	2.04
Totals	48	48	0		$\Sigma = 4.08$

Null hypothesis – there is no difference between the means of the heights of the plants grown at different temperatures.

Conclusion – There is a significant difference so the null hypothesis has been disproved. Reasoning – the 5% critical value for 1 degree of freedom is 3.84 and the calculated value is greater than this.

13. Conclusion – there is a significant difference between the observed ratio of 3.7 : 4.7 : 1 and expected ratio.
    Reasoning – the 5% critical value for two degrees of freedom is 5.99 and the calculated value of 9.14 is greater than this, being very close to the 1% value.

14a.

Number of quadrats	Number of quadrats		Row totals
	Moss present	Moss absent	
Liverwort present	120	29	149
Liverwort absent	46	5	51
Column totals	166	34	Grand total 200

14b.

Number of quadrats	Number of quadrats		Row totals
	Moss present	Moss absent	
Liverwort present	123.7	25.3	149
Liverwort absent	42.3	8.7	51
Column totals	166	34	Grand total 200

14c. One.

14d. Chi-squared = 2.51. The critical value for 5% is 2.84. The calculated value is less than this and so the null hypothesis is accepted – there is no association between the moss and liverwort.

15.

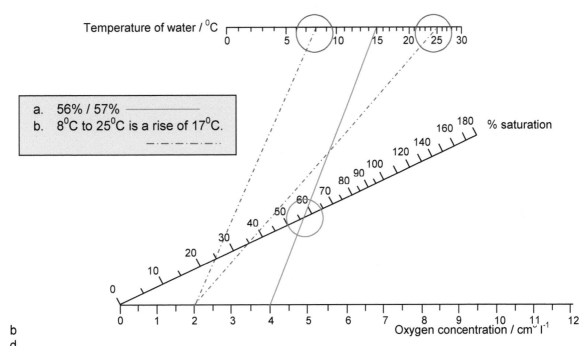

a. 56% / 57%
b. $8^{0}C$ to $25^{0}C$ is a rise of $17^{0}C$.

16. b
17. d
18. d
19. c
20. a

	Chapter							
	2 Part 1	2 Part 2	3	4	6	7	8	9
1	a	c	d	b	b	b	a	c
2	b	a	d	d	d	d	c	c
3	b	b	b	b	c	c	a	a
4	d	d	a	b	c	d	c	d
5	c	c	c	a	a	b	d	a
6	c	c	a	d	a	a	d	c
7	b	a	c	b	c	a	c	b
8	c	a	b	c	d	c	b	d
9	b	c	a	c	c	d	c	a
10	a	b	a	a	a	b	b	d
11	b	d	d	d	b	c	a	c
12	d	a	d	d	a	a	d	a
13	a	c	a	b	d	d	d	b
14	a	b	c	c	d	b	c	d
15	d	a	d	b	c	a	a	d
16	c	d	d	b		c	b	b
17	a	b	a	a		d	b	a
18	c	a	d	c		b	c	d
19	b	c	c	d		a	a	b
20	c	d	a	b		b	c	a
21		d	c	c			d	
22		d	d	c			b	
23		a	c	a			c	
24		b	c	b			d	
25		b	a	a			b	
26		d	a	c				
27		a	d	b				
28		d	b	a				
29		b	d	b				
30		d	c	d				
31		b	b					
32		a	a					
33		d	a					
34		d						
35		c						
36		b						
37		b						
38		b						
39		d						
40		c						
41		a						
42		c						
43		d						

	Digestion
1	c
2	a
3	a
4	b
5	d
6	d
7	a
8	b
9	b

	Gas exchange
1	a
2	c
3	d
4	c
5	a
6	d
7	b
8	d

	Blood system
1	d
2	c
3	d
4	a
5	b
6	c
7	c
8	a
9	b
10	d
11	a
12	a
13	d
14	b
15	a

	Defence
1	d
2	c
3	a
4	d
5	c
6	c
7	b
8	b
9	c
10	a
11	b
12	c

	Nervous system
1	b
2	d
3	c
4	a
5	a
6	b
7	d
8	b

	Endocrine system
1	a
2	c
3	d
4	b
5	a
6	c
7	c

	Osmoregulation
1	b
2	d
3	a
4	b
5	d
6	b
7	a
8	a
9	c
10	b
11	b
12	d
13	a
14	c
15	d
16	c
17	a
18	d
19	c
20	b
21	b
22	d

	Movement
1	c
2	a
3	b
4	d
5	b
6	a
7	c
8	c
9	a
10	d

	Reproduction
1	b
2	c
3	a
4	c
5	d
6	a
7	a
8	c
9	b
10	d
11	a
12	c
13	b
14	a
15	b
16	b
17	c

Appendix 2

Answers to Chapter 8 (Genetics) Test Problems

1. The majority of all the young mice is black so that tells us that black is dominant. The grey male mouse must be homozygous recessive. Since about half the offspring of the first black female are grey she must have the grey allele in her genotype. Thus she is heterozygous. The second female only produces black offspring and so, given the numbers, it is likely that she is homozygous black.

   Key: B = black; b = grey.

		black female A	×	grey male	×	black female B
P		Bb		bb		BB
G_1		Ⓑ ⓑ		ⓑ		Ⓑ

   F_1

	B	b
b	Bb	bb
	black	grey

	B
b	Bb
	black

2. The F_1 Bandycoot babies were all yellow but orange ones appeared in the F_2. This tells us that yellow must be dominant and orange recessive. The test for heterozygosity is a test cross, that is with the homozygous recessive. A homozygous dominant genotype will not give any orange offspring whereas about half the offspring will be orange with a heterozygous genotype.

   Key: Y = yellow; y = orange.

		heterozygous Bandycoot	×	orange Bandycoot	×	homozygous Bandycoot
P		Yy		yy		YY
G_1		Ⓨ ⓨ		ⓨ		Ⓨ

   F_1

	Y	y
y	Yy	yy
	50% yellow	50% orange

	Y
y	Yy
	All yellow

3. We are told that green is dominant.
   Key: G = green; g = blue.
   The blue-eyed beetle must therefore have the genotype gg. Its parents were both green-eyed and either had the genotype GG or Gg. However since the beetle must inherit one allele from each parent both parents must be Gg.
   The female beetle is green eyed but the first baby Boring beetle is blue eyed. Hence her genotype must be Gg.
   If they have another baby beetle it could be green-eyed with the genotype Gg.

	green-eyed parent	green-eyed parent		blue-eyed beetle	green-eyed beetle
P	Gg	Gg	P	gg	Gg
G_1	Ⓖ ⓖ	Ⓖ ⓖ	G_1	ⓖ	Ⓖ ⓖ

   F_1

	G	g
G		
g		gg blue-eyed beetle

   F_1

	g
G	Gg green eyes
g	gg blue eyes

> Note how the Punnett grids are big enough to include the phenotypes. This is a quicker and more accurate / efficient way of linking genotype and phenotype.

IBHL Biology 2016 © Ashby Merson-Davies

4. Since all the first generation Quolls had luminous eyes, luminous must be dominant. Furthermore since the first generation did not contain any blue-eyed Quolls we can assume that the luminous-eyed parent was homozygous.

Key: L = luminous and l = blue.

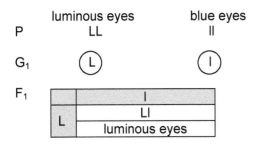

```
        luminous eyes        blue eyes
P           LL                  ll

G₁          (L)                 (l)

F₁
```

	l
L	Ll
	luminous eyes

These offspring all met luminous-eyed Quolls and since their offspring were also all luminous-eyed we can again assume they were homozygous, LL.

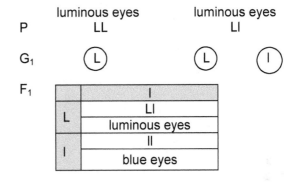

```
        luminous eyes            luminous eyes
P           LL                       Ll

G₁          (L)                  (L)    (l)

F₁
```

	l
L	Ll
	luminous eyes
l	ll
	blue eyes

Lonely Quoll though met a blue-eyed Quoll, and since blue eyes must have the genotype ll this would produce 50% blue-eyed offspring.

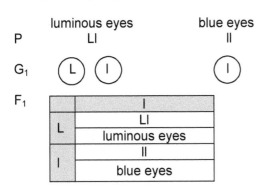

```
        luminous eyes        blue eyes
P           Ll                  ll

G₁       (L)  (l)               (l)

F₁
```

	l
L	Ll
	luminous eyes
l	ll
	blue eyes

5.

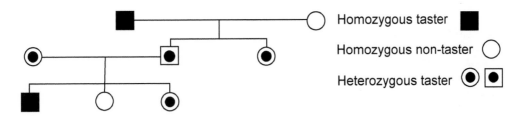

```
Homozygous taster       ■
Homozygous non-taster   ○
Heterozygous taster     ◉ |●|
```

The genotypes of the three children could be swapped around.

6. If Grandpa was blood group O then his genotype had to be ii. His son Horace married a person who was also group O and therefore genotype ii. Their two daughters were group B and this I^B allele therefore had to have come from their father Horace. This meant that his genotype was I^B?, but since his father could only have given him an i allele we can deduce his genotype was $I^B i$. This means that the I^B allele must have come from his mother, making her genotype I^B?. Grandpa's second child was group A, and using a similar argument we can deduce that the I^A allele must have come from Grandma. Finally therefore we can deduce that Grandma's genotype was $I^A I^B$ and hence her blood group AB.
    This therefore makes it impossible for Grandpa and Grandma to have a group O child – all their children have to be either group A or group B.

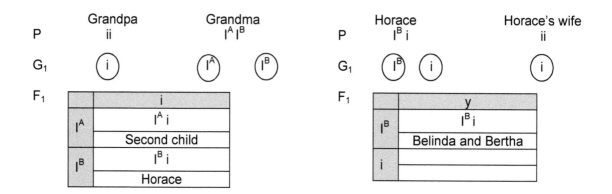

7. We are told the characteristic is sex linked. Female Dingbats are XX and the males XY. The baby Dingbat is a female and therefore inherited one of her X chromosomes from the father. This chromosome carried the web allele, and her other X chromosome from her mother carried the normal allele. Since baby has normal feet we can deduce that normal is dominant. Males always inherit their X chromosome from their mother, and since both her X chromosomes carry the normal allele he too will have normal feet.

Key: N = normal feet, n = webbed feet.

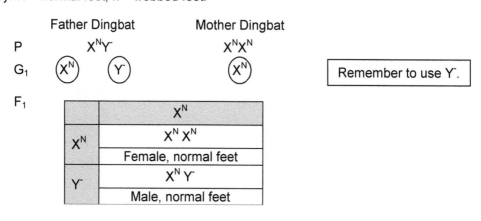

Remember to use Y⁻.

8. There are only four possible phenotypes and the offspring include each type. Hence both parents must possess recessive alleles for each gene. The Punnett grid must have four F_1 boxes and this can be obtained either with a 4 x 1 grid, meaning one parent gives 4 types of gamete and the other one type, or a 2 x 2 grid meaning that both parents give 2 types of gamete.

4 x 1 grid.

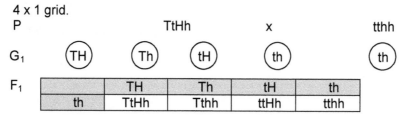

Tthh and ttHh both give two types of gamete. We could not have Tthh x Tthh as this gives a 3:1 phenotype ratio (there is no H). Similarly ttHh x ttHh gives a 3:1 phenotype ratio (there is no T). However Tthh x ttHh does give the required ratio.

2 × 2 grid.

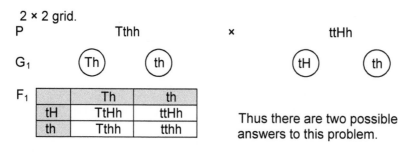

Thus there are two possible answers to this problem.

9. The genotype of the green bumpy plant is yyB?, (see key below) and that of the yellow smooth plant is Y?bb. We have to put in the question marks as we do not yet know whether these are homozygous or heterozygous. We can though deduce that they must be heterozygous in order for the recessive characteristic to show in the offspring, eg. if yyB? was yyBB then there would be no smooth offspring, and similarly if Y?bb was YYbb there would be no green offspring.

Key : Y = yellow, y = green; B = bumpy, b = smooth.

	green, bumpy		yellow, smooth	
P	yyBb	×	Yybb	

G₁ (yB) (yb)   (Yb) (yb)

F₁

	yB	yb
Yb	YyBb	Yybb
	yellow, bumpy	yellow, smooth
yb	yyBb	yybb
	green, bumpy	green, smooth

In the ratio 1:1:1:1

10. We are not told which characteristics are dominant but we can easily deduce this because black wing cases and short antennae form the largest number of offspring.
The ratio is closest to 9:3:3:1, which gives a total of 16. Only a 4 x 4 grid gives 16 and so we know that each parent must form four different types of gamete. The only genotype that does this is the double heterozygous.

Key : B = black , b = white; H = short, h = long. (Remember that S is a bad letter to choose).
Genotype of both parents is BbHh.

F₁

	BH	Bh	bH	bh
BH	BBHH	BBHh	BbHH	BbHh
	black, short antennae	black, short antennae	black, short antennae	black, short antennae
Bh	BBHh	BBhh	BbHh	Bbhh
	black, short antennae	black, long antennae	black, short antennae	black, long antennae
bH	BbHH	BbHh	bbHH	bbHh
	black, short antennae	black, short antennae	white, short antennae	white, short antennae
bh	BbHh	Bbhh	bbHh	bbhh
	black, short antennae	black, long antennae	white, short antennae	white, long antennae

9 B_H_ black, short antennae
3 bbH_ white, short antennae,

3 B_hh black, long antennae,
1 bbhh white, long antennae.

Look back at the coloured Punnett grid on page 262.

11. The genotype of the plant with large white flowers has to be homozygous recessive. This produces one type of gamete. Since all the offspring had green flowers we can deduce that the small green parent could not have a white allele since otherwise there would be white offspring. However it had to have a large allele as there are large offspring.

Key : A = small, a = large; G = green, g = white.

Genotypes – large white parent aagg; small green parent is AaGG.

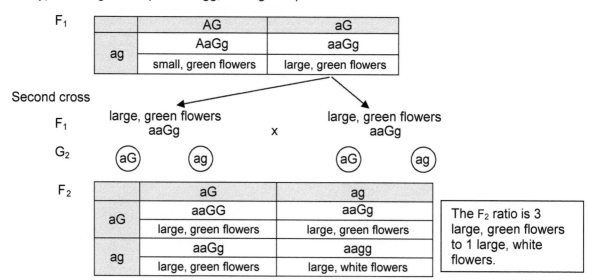

F₁

	AG	aG
ag	AaGg	aaGg
	small, green flowers	large, green flowers

Second cross

F₁   large, green flowers   large, green flowers
         aaGg   x   aaGg

G₂   (aG)   (ag)   (aG)   (ag)

F₂

	aG	ag
aG	aaGG	aaGg
	large, green flowers	large, green flowers
ag	aaGg	aagg
	large, green flowers	large, white flowers

The F₂ ratio is 3 large, green flowers to 1 large, white flowers.

12. Since the offspring were all pink this tells us that the Pogwort flower colour genes are codominant. The red and white flowered parents therefore had to be homozygous.

Key: C^R = red, C^W = white

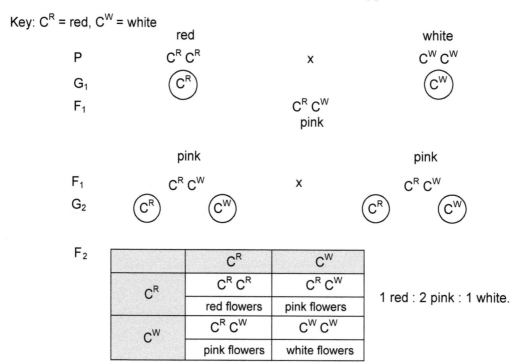

	red		white
P	C^R C^R	x	C^W C^W
G₁	(C^R)		(C^W)
F₁		C^R C^W	
		pink	

	pink		pink
F₁	C^R C^W	x	C^R C^W
G₂	(C^R) (C^W)		(C^R) (C^W)

F₂

	C^R	C^W
C^R	C^R C^R	C^R C^W
	red flowers	pink flowers
C^W	C^R C^W	C^W C^W
	pink flowers	white flowers

1 red : 2 pink : 1 white.

13. The numbers of offspring – one large pair and one small pair - clearly tells us that there is linkage and crossing over. We are not told which characteristics are dominant but we can easily deduce it. We are told that the black straight haired rat was true breeding and therefore must be homozygous. If it was homozygous dominant all the offspring would have black straight hair. Hence black and straight must be recessive.
This means the other rat had to have red curly hair and also had to be heterozygous for both genes.

Key: R = red, r = black; Y = curly, y = straight.

The red curly parent could be R Y or   R y.
                                              r y   r Y
Looking at the offspring, the large numbers are always the parental combinations, i.e. black is linked to straight and red is linked to curly, so the genotype is the first one.

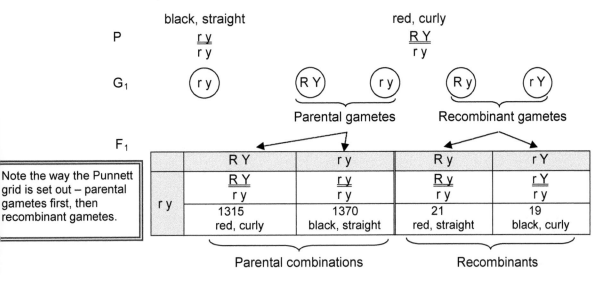

Note the way the Punnett grid is set out – parental gametes first, then recombinant gametes.

	R Y	r y	R y	r Y
r y	$\underline{R\ Y}$ r y	$\underline{r\ y}$ r y	$\underline{R\ y}$ r y	$\underline{r\ Y}$ r y
	1315 red, curly	1370 black, straight	21 red, straight	19 black, curly

Parental combinations   Recombinants

14. Once again the data clearly shows linkage and crossing over. Again the numbers tells us the linkage pattern. Yellow is linked to large and white to small.

Key: Y = yellow, y = white; L = large, l = small.

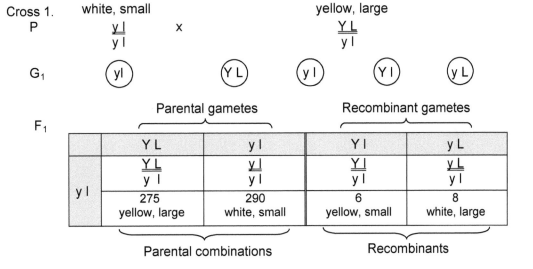

	Y L	y l	Y l	y L
y l	$\underline{Y\ L}$ y l	$\underline{y\ l}$ y l	$\underline{Y\ l}$ y l	$\underline{y\ L}$ y l
	275 yellow, large	290 white, small	6 yellow, small	8 white, large

Parental combinations   Recombinants

15. Since Zom Bees are the same as the fruit fly the female is XX and male XY. We are told red is dominant. The female bee has red legs but we are not told if she is homozygous or heterozygous. However we can deduce this because we are told that all the F_1 males have red legs. If she was heterozygous then there would be some males with blue legs since they inherit their X chromosome from the female parent.

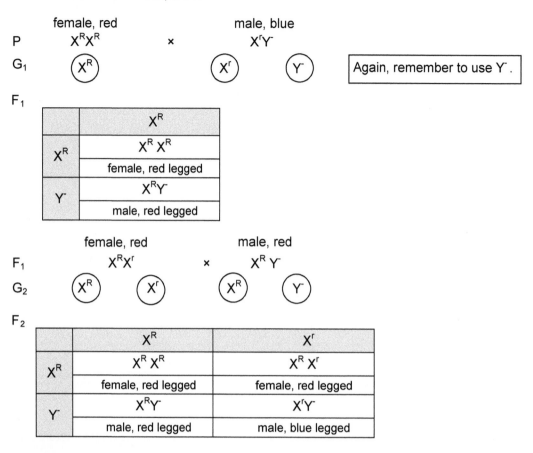

Thus in the F_2 we have a ratio of:
2 female, red legged,
1 male, red legged,
1 male, blue legged.

16. The offspring numbers tell us that the genes are linked and crossing over has occurred. The tall white flowered plant is homozygous recessive, but the short blue flowered plant must be heterozygous for both genes in order for the F_1 to show recessive phenotypes. However, look carefully at the numbers. This time they tell us that short, a dominant allele, is linked to white, a recessive allele, and similarly with tall linked to blue.

Key: B = blue, b = white; H = short, h = tall.

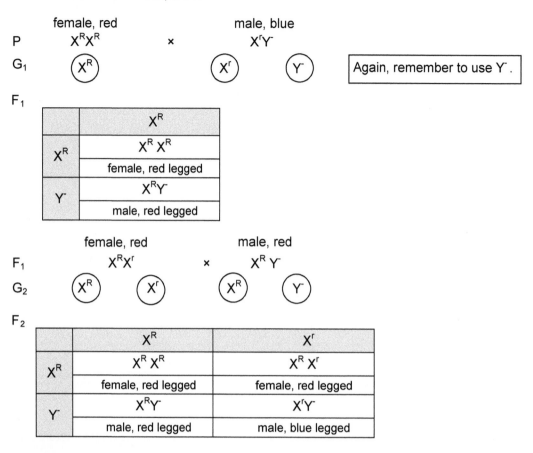

IBHL Biology 2016 © Ashby Merson-Davies

17a. Purplepear, (long fruit and simple flower), will have the genotype rrL? and Grapecluster (round fruit and complex flower), will have the genotype R?ll. Since the F₁ all had simple flowers and produced round fruits that means that the parents had to be homozygous for these alleles. The numbers again tell us there is linkage with crossing over.

Key: R = round, r = long; L = simple, l = complex.

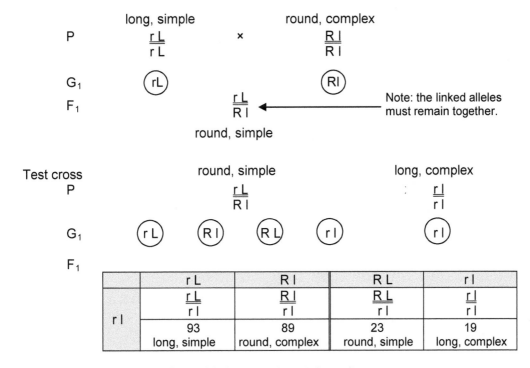

	r L	R l	R L	r l
	rL	Rl	RL	rl
	rl	rl	rl	rl
r l				
	93	89	23	19
	long, simple	round, complex	round, simple	long, complex

These theoretical results fit in with the experimental results.

17b. If the genes were not linked we would get a 1:1:1:1 ratio because it is double heterozygous x homozygous recessive – RrLl x rrlll.
1 round fruit, simple flowers: 1 round fruit, complex flowers: 1 long fruit, simple flowers: 1 long fruit, complex flowers.
The reason for this is that, being unlinked, the alleles can assort independently and hence obey Mendel's second law.
Total number = 93 + 89 + 23 + 19 = 224. Each phenotype would be ¼ of this which is 56.

18. Key: H = white, h = yellow; B = black, b = pink
The white mole with black feet is homozygous and so must have the genotype HHBB. It can only produce HB gametes. The yellow mole with pink feet must have the genotype hhbb and can only produce the gametes hb. This means all the offspring must have the genotype HhBb. If the genes are unlinked these F₁ will produce the gametes HB, Hb, hB and hb in equal numbers and the usual 4 x 4 Punnett grid will result in the ratio 9 white fur, black feet : 3 white fur, pink feet : 3 yellow fur, black feet : 1 yellow fur, pink feet. The actual ratio produced is approximately 16 white, black : 5 yellow, pink : 1 white, pink : 1 yellow, black. This is clearly nothing like the expected ratio and this would indicate that the genes are linked. If this is the case then the genotype of the F₁ is HB. This means there would be large numbers of the HB and hb gametes, and small numbers
hb of the Hb and hB gametes.
This would produce a higher than expected number of yellow moles with pink feet and a smaller number of the white/pink and yellow/black combinations, which is in fact what was produced.
The total number of offspring is 113 + 32 + 7 + 8 = 160 so with unlinked genes the expected numbers would be –
9/16 of 160 white fur black feet = 90,
3/16 of 160 white fur pink feet =30,
3/16 of 160 yellow fur black feet = 30,
1/16 of 160 yellow fur pink feet =10.

Appendix 3

Component	Overall weighting %	Duration hours	Format and syllabus coverage
Paper 1	20	1	40 multiple choice questions.
Paper 2	36	2¼	**Section A** One data-based question and several short-answer questions (all compulsory). **Section B** <u>**Two**</u> extended response questions from a choice of three.
Paper 3	24	1¼	**Section A** Two or three short answer questions based on experimental skills and techniques, analysis and evaluation using unseen data linked to the core material. **Section B** Short answer and extended response questions from <u>**one Option**</u>.

Appendix 4

Objective 1

Define	Give precise meaning of a word, phrase, concept or physical quantity.
Draw	Represent by means of a labelled, accurate diagram or graph, using a pencil. A ruler (straight edge) should be used for straight lines. Diagrams should be drawn to scale. Graphs should have points correctly plotted (if appropriate) and joined in a straight line or smooth curve.
Label	Add labels to a diagram.
List	Give a sequence of brief answers with no explanation.
Measure	Obtain a value for a quantity.
State	Give a specific name, value or other brief answer without explanation or calculation.

Objective 2

Annotate	Add brief notes to a diagram or graph.
Calculate	Obtain a numerical answer showing the relevant stages in the working (unless instructed not to do so).
Describe	Give a detailed account.
Distinguish	Make clear the differences between two or more concepts or items.
Estimate	Obtain an approximate value.
Identify	Provide an answer from a number of possibilities.
Outline	Give a brief account or summary.

Objective 3

Analyse	Break down in order to bring out the essential elements or structure.
Comment	Give a judgement based on a given statement or result of a calculation.
Compare	Give an account of similarities between two (or more) items, referring to both (all) of them throughout.
Compare and Contrast	Give an account of similarities and differences between two (or more) items, referring to both (all) of them throughout.
Construct	Display information in a diagrammatic or logical form.
Deduce	Reach a conclusion from the information given.
Design	Produce a plan, simulation or model.
Determine	Obtain the only possible answer.
Discuss	Offer a considered and balanced review that includes a range of arguments, factors or hypotheses. Opinions or conclusions should be presented clearly and supported by the appropriate evidence.
Evaluate	Make an appraisal by weighing up the strengths and limitations.
Explain	Give a detailed account including reasons or causes.
Predict	Give an expected result.
Sketch	Represent by means of a diagram or graph (labelled as appropriate). The sketch should give a general idea of the required shape or relationship, and should include relevant features.
Suggest	Propose a solution, hypothesis or other possible answer.

Appendix 5

Here are ten extended response titles typical of those in Paper 2. I have picked four of the Command Terms – Outline, Describe, Discuss and Explain.

Notice how in some of them I have broken each answer up into paragraphs, each paragraph dealing with a different component of the question. This helps to produce a clear and well-structured answer, and also, which is VERY important, helps the examiner to mark it.

I have not included drawings in these answers. However answers can be greatly enhanced by drawings and they also help you to structure your answer. The page number for the topic is given.

Outline the use of restriction enzymes (endonucleases) and DNA ligase in gene technology. [6]
Page 249

Endonucleases are a particular group of enzymes that cut DNA at specific places. These cuts are asymmetric and result in sticky ends.

sticky end of unpaired bases

DNA ligase is an enzyme that can join pieces of DNA that have corresponding sticky ends.
An example of gene technology is the production of human insulin by modified *E. coli* bacteria. These bacteria contain small circular pieces of DNA called plasmids. Plasmids are removed and cut with a specific endonuclease. The insulin gene is obtained from insulin mRNA and corresponding sticky ends added. DNA ligase is then used to add the insulin gene to the cut plasmid before the recombinant plasmid is inserted into *E. coli* bacteria. These bacteria are cloned in a suitable medium in order to produce insulin.

Outline the process of fertilisation in humans [5] *Page 193.*

The sperms are attracted to the oocyte by chemicals released from the oocyte. This is called chemotaxis. When the sperm head contacts the zona pellucida it binds to specific glycoproteins. The acrosome fuses with the plasma membrane and releases its contents via exocytosis. This is the acrosome reaction. Enzymes from the acrosome now allow the sperm head to penetrate the zona pellucida and bind to receptors on the plasma membrane of the oocyte.

As soon as this happens the cortical granules, which are tiny vesicles close to the oocyte plasma membrane, fuse with the plasma membrane and release their contents into the fluid filled space between the plasma membrane and the zona pellucida. This is the cortical reaction. Enzymes from the cortical granules have two effects. Firstly they remove the sperm binding receptors on the plasma membrane, and secondly cause changes in proteins in the zona pellucida which result in the formation of the fertilisation membrane. Both of these changes prevent polyspermy.

Meanwhile penetration of the oocyte plasma membrane by the sperm head triggers the completion of meiosis in the oocyte. The sperm and ovum nuclei fuse to form a diploid nucleus completing the process of fertilisation.

Describe the features of alveoli that make them well adapted for gas exchange. [5] *Page 147.*

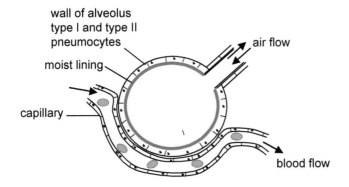

wall of alveolus
type I and type II
pneumocytes

moist lining

capillary

air flow

blood flow

Remember that you can use both blue and black, and using both colours in diagrams and graphs can be helpful.

For the black part of diagrams **always** use an HB pencil.

It is better to label in pencil as well, and use a **ruler** for the label lines.

Drawings and diagrams should always be **large, clear** and **neat**.

Alveoli are the air sacs where gas exchange takes place. Their tiny size gives them a very large surface area to volume ratio and they are covered in a dense network of capillaries. The wall is only one cell thick and the cells are called pneumocytes. There are two types. Type I is the most common and they are especially thin which makes it much more efficient for gas exchange between the blood and alveolar air. Type II secretes a watery solution. This provides a moist surface lining the alveoli which helps gas exchange, and it also contains a surfactant which prevents the walls of the alveoli from sticking together which would reduce the surface area.

Discuss the role played by phagocytic leucocytes (phagocytes) in protecting the body from pathogens. [5] *Page 158.*

Phagocytes are a type of white blood cell forming a non-specific defence mechanism in the blood. They attack pathogens in the blood stream but they are also able to leave capillaries and attack pathogens in tissues where they concentrate at sites of infection. They recognize pathogens by detecting foreign protein molecules on the pathogen surface and this is made easier if antibodies have become attached to the pathogen. The phagocyte engulfs the pathogen by phagocytosis to form a vesicle in the cytoplasm. Lysosomes release digestive enzymes into the vesicle to destroy the pathogen.

Explain the processes of active and passive transport that move materials across a membrane. [8] *Pages 86/8.*

Active transport is a process which moves substances across a membrane against a concentration gradient and consequently this requires energy from ATP. In addition an integral membrane protein is required which has a specific binding site for the substance to be transported. Some transport proteins transfer more than one specific substance. These substances may be transported in the same direction or, as with the Na^+/K^+ pump in neurons, in opposite directions.

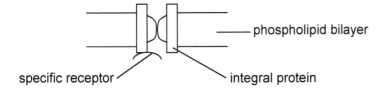

phospholipid bilayer

specific receptor

integral protein

Phagocytosis (transporting particles) and pinocytosis (transporting solution) are ways in which substances can be brought into a cell - endocytosis. Both require energy.

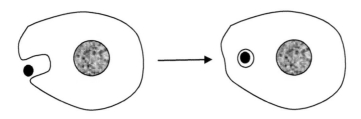

On the other hand passive transport only moves substances across a membrane down the concentration gradient and does not use energy. This is because particles move in a random way and will spread from a region where there is a high concentration to a region where the concentration is lower due to their molecular kinetic energy. Simple diffusion is when substances such as oxygen pass through the phospholipid bilayer. Facilitated diffusion is when an integral protein channel allows a substance to pass across the membrane easily. These channels are specific such as the sodium and potassium ion channels in neurons. Flow through these channels can be controlled if the channel is gated.

Osmosis is the passive movement of water across a membrane. Most water crosses a membrane through specific integral protein channels but some can move by simple diffusion even though the core of membranes is hydrophobic. This is possible because water is sufficiently small.

Explain why enzymes are substrate specific and why their activity is affected by substrate concentration. [8] *Pages110–1.*

Enzymes are large proteins folded into a 3D shape which allows for the formation of an active site where the substrate binds. This active site has a specific shape which corresponds to the shape of the substrate in the same way that a key fits a lock. Furthermore the chemical properties of the active site correspond to the chemical properties of the substrate allowing the two to lock together. The combination of these two points means that an enzyme can only react with a specific substrate.

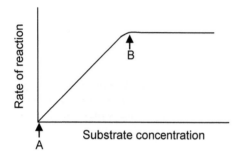

The graph assumes the concentration of the enzyme is fixed. The substrate and enzyme molecules move around randomly and at some point will collide in such a way that the substrate binds to the active site. Between A and B as more substrate is added there is a proportional increase in reaction rate because more collisions are taking place. At point B at any moment in time all the active sites are occupied and so further addition of substrate will have no effect and there can be no further increase in reaction rate.

Explain the control of blood glucose levels in humans. [9] *Page169.*

Blood glucose needs to be kept at a near constant level called the norm. Deviations from this norm are corrected using a negative feedback control mechanism. Blood glucose is monitored by cells in the islets of Langerhans in the pancreas.

If the level of blood glucose rises above the norm as a result of eating sugary or starch foods then beta cells in the islets release the hormone insulin. This circulates in the blood and causes a number of tissues to respond to reduce the blood glucose level. Liver and muscle cells increase their uptake of glucose and convert it into glycogen which can be stored. Adipose tissue cells absorb glucose and convert it into fat. Liver cells can also increase their rate of respiration simply to burn up the excess glucose.

If the level of blood glucose falls then alpha cells in the islets release the hormone glucagon. This stimulates liver cells to break down stored glycogen to release glucose into the blood. Muscle tissue cannot do this. If necessary the adipose tissue can break down fat which can be converted to glucose, and in extreme situations amino acids from the breakdown of protein can be used to make glucose. This is called gluconeogenesis.

Explain the principles of synaptic transmission. [8] *Page 167.*

When an impulse arrives at the synaptic terminal it causes depolarisation of the presynaptic membrane. This allows calcium ions to diffuse from the synaptic gap into the presynaptic terminal. This influx of calcium ions causes vesicles of neurotransmitter to move towards and fuse with the presynaptic membrane. Neurotransmitter is released by exocytosis and diffuses across the synaptic gap where it binds to specific receptors on the postsynaptic membrane. This causes channels to open allowing sodium ions to diffuse from the synaptic gap into the postsynaptic terminal depolarising the neuron membrane. This stimulates a postsynaptic action potential.

The neurotransmitter now has to be removed from the synaptic gap. In the case of the neurotransmitter acetyl choline it is broken down by the enzyme acetyl cholinesterase and the end products, acetate and choline, are taken back into the presynaptic terminal to be recycled into new vesicles.
The calcium ions are pumped back into the synaptic gap by active transport.

Explain the reactions that occur in the matrix of the mitochondrion that are part of aerobic respiration. [8] *Page 129.*

Pyruvate, a 3 carbon molecule, is the end product of the anaerobic pathway that occurs in the cytoplasm.

The pyruvate moves into the mitochondrial matrix by facilitated diffusion and the link reaction starts. Carbon dioxide is removed by decarboxylation and coenzyme A is added resulting in a 2 carbon molecule acetyl CoA. In addition an oxidation reaction occurs which removes hydrogen onto the carrier NAD^+ forming reduced NAD or $NADH + H^+$.

The acetyl CoA now enters Krebs cycle by joining with a 4 carbon molecule to form a 6 carbon molecule. The CoA is released to be recycled in another link reaction. The 6 carbon molecule undergoes two decarboxylation and oxidation reactions resulting in the formation of a a 4 carbon molecule, two molecules of carbon dioxide, and two molecules of reduced NAD.
The 4 carbon molecule undergoes several stages to convert it into the starting 4 carbon molecule. These stages include two further oxidation reactions resulting in the formation of another reduced NAD and also another hydrogen carrier, reduced FAD or $FADH_2$. In addition one molecule of ATP is formed.

Thus the 3 carbon pyruvate entering the matrix is broken up to release the 3 carbons as three carbon dioxide molecules and the hydrogen is transferred onto hydrogen carriers – 4 x reduced NAD + 1 x reduced FAD. One molecule of ATP is also produced.

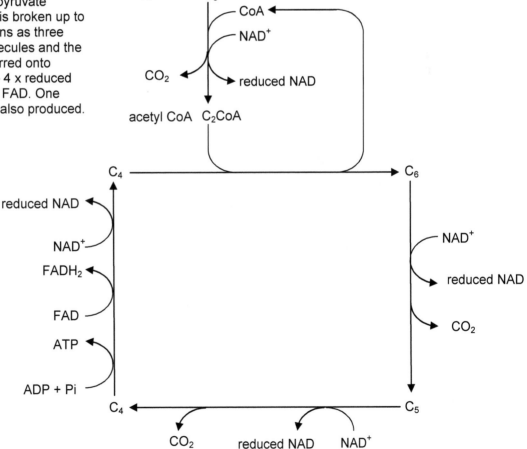

Explain how the nerve impulse passes along a neuron. [9] *Pages 165/6.*

The neuron contains a number of components for transmission of an impulse. These are voltage gated sodium and potassium ion channels (VGNa and VGK channels), open potassium channels, and linked sodium/potassium active pumps.

During the resting potential the pump transports sodium ions out of the axoplasm and potassium ions in. Potassium ions diffuse out of the axoplasm through the open channels. Along with negative ions retained in the axoplasm this produces a resting potential of -70mV across the neuron membrane. When the neuron is stimulated VGNa channels open allowing sodium ions to diffuse in making the axoplasm less negative. If the threshold potential is reached depolarisation continues and the axoplasm reaches a potential of +30mV. This is the first phase of the action potential.

The second phase of the action potential, repolarisation, then occurs. Potassium ions continue to diffuse out of the open channels but the flow is increased due to VGK channels opening. This makes the axoplasm less positive. Finally the active pump removes the sodium ions that diffused in.
In order to propagate a nerve impulse the action potential must occur in the adjacent region of the neuron. Local currents set up in the axoplasm during depolarisation stimulate adjacent VGNa channels to open and this is repeated along the length of the neuron. In a myelinated neuron the action potential only occurs at nodes of Ranvier and so the action potential jumps from node to node. This is called saltatory conduction and transmission is faster than in a non-myelinated neuron.

Appendix 6

Exam Equipment and Mobile Phones

Having invigilated many exams it never ceases to surprise me what vital items students forget to bring in. If you never use an item then fine, but if you need it and haven't got it then it creates, at minimum, stress, and at worst an inability to complete your answer.

If English is not your first language then for some exams you are allowed to take in a basic language dictionary. Check with your IB co-ordinator first though.

I would suggest taking the following into **every** exam, i.e. **all** subjects, in a large **transparent** pencil case –

- ❑ 2 or 3 black pens and blue pens – you can use both in your answers,
- ❑ several spare cartridges if you use liquid ink,
- ❑ highlighters (for highlighting key words and points in questions),
- ❑ 15cm transparent ruler with a good clean edge – for labelling drawings,
- ❑ 30cm transparent ruler with a good clean edge – for graphs,
- ❑ 2 HB propelling pencils,
- ❑ clean pencil eraser,
- ❑ compass with a sharp pencil ready fitted,
- ❑ pencil sharpener,
- ❑ set square and protractor,
- ❑ calculator – put new batteries in.

Further calculator points

Check with your Maths teacher that you have a permitted calculator. Certain models are not permitted and could be confiscated. Other models are permitted but have to be set up in a specific exam mode, for example the TI Nspire. Certain programmes and applications are permitted and others are not.

If you are found to have an illegal programme / application on your calculator in an exam you may be reported to the Exam Board.

For Paper 1 Multiple Choice papers you are not allowed a calculator but for Paper 2 you are. These papers run consecutively so your exam supervisor will make the arrangements for you to have your calculator for Paper 2.

Mobile phones, iPods and other electronic communication devices

NEVER TAKE THESE INTO THE EXAM ROOM

This is a serious breach of exam regulations and you may have that exam paper removed from your record.

This could mean failing your Diploma.

Good luck!

Acknowledgements

Links to third party websites are provided in good faith and for information only. The publisher disclaims any responsibility for the contents of any third party website referenced in this work.

Chapter 2

© Shutterstock, chapter image, 2.1; 2.2; 2.3; 2.4; 2.5; 2.9; 2.11; 2.12; Image courtesy of André Brown and John Weisel, MRC Laboratory of Molecular Biology, 2.6; © Ashby Merson-Davies, 2.7; 2.8 ; Reproduced with the kind permission of Medicom Health Interactive, 2.10; David Perez (Own work) [GFDL (http://www.gnu.org/copyleft/fdl.html) or CC-BY-3.0 (http://creativecommons.org/licenses/by/3.0)], via Wikimedia Commons, 2.13; Image courtesy of Dr Paul Verkade in the Bristol Bio Imaging Centre of Bristol University, 2.14.

Chapter 3

© Ashby Merson-Davies, 3.1; 3.25a & b; With kind permission of Larry Phelps, University of Wisconsin, 3.35; © Shutterstock, chapter image, 3.2; 3.4; 3.5; 3.6; 3.7; 3.8a & b; 3.9; 3.10; 3.11; 3.12; 3.15b; 3.23; 3.32; 3.34; Flyingdream at en.wikipedia [Public domain or Public domain], from Wikimedia Commons, 3.3; Images courtesy of Dr Paul Verkade in the Bristol Bio Imaging Centre of Bristol University, 3.13; 3.16; 3.21; Images courtesy of John Pacy, King's College Electron Microscopy Unit, 3.14; 3.15a; 3.18; 3.19a & b; 3.27; © Don W. Fawcett/SCIENCE PHOTO LIBRARY, 3.17, 3.20; Image courtesy of Professor Anton Page, Biomedical Imaging Unit, University of Southampton, 3.22; Boghog2 (Boghog2 work) [Public domain], via Wikimedia Commons, 3.24; 3.24 Acknowledgement needs changing – Images courtesy of Professor Rikard Blunck, Department of Physiology, Université de Montréal, Montreal, QC, Canada. 3.26; © American Society of Plant Biologists. Reprinted with permission, 3.28; and3k and caper437 (Own work by uploaders) [CC-BY-SA-3.0 (http://creativecommons.org/licenses/by-sa/3.0) or GFDL (http://www.gnu.org/copyleft/fdl.html)], via Wikimedia Commons, 3.29a; © Don W. Fawcett/SCIENCE PHOTO LIBRARY, 3.29b; By Afunguy at en.wikipedia [Public domain], via Wikimedia Commons, 3.30; staticd (Own work) [CC-BY-SA-3.0 (http://creativecommons.org/licenses/by-sa/3.0)], via Wikimedia Commons, 3.31; Image courtesy of Brian Leatherbarrow *FRCS FRCOphth*, 3.33.

Chapter 4

Donald Nicholson ©2002 International Union of Biochemistry and Molecular Biology, chapter image. © Shutterstock, 4.1; Images courtesy of John Pacy, King's College Electron Microscopy Unit. Laboratory, Ml August, *...the path of carbon in photosynthesis.* Berkeley, Ca.: [Lawrence] Radiation http://babel.hathitrust.org/cgi/pt?id=mdp.39015086549345;view=1up;seq=1, 4.2; Photo courtesy of Lawrence Berkeley National Laboratory, 4.4; http://www.flickr.com/people/fanny/ (http://www.flickr.com/photos/fanny/555925/) [CC-BY-SA-2.0 (http://creativecommons.org/licenses/by-sa/2.0)], via Wikimedia Commons, 4.5; © BIOPHOTO ASSOCIATES/SCIENCE PHOTO LIBRARY, 4.6; Reprinted with kind permission of Professor Terry Frey. T.G. Frey (SDSU) and G. Perkins (UCSD), 4.7a - c.

Chapter 5

© Ashby Merson-Davies, 5.1; 5.2a; 5.3a & b; 5.8; 5.10a & b; 5.11a & b; 5.13; 5.17a & b; 5.19; 5.22; 5.24; 5.25; 5.30a & b; 5.33; 5.34; © Shutterstock, chapter image, 5.2b; 5.4a & b; 5.5; 5.6; 5.9a & b; 5.12; 5.15a;5.15b; 5.16; 5.18; 5.21; 5.23; 5.28; 5.29; 5.31; 5.32; 5.36; 5.37; 5.38; Ed Uthman [CC BY 2.0 (http://creativecommons.org/licenses/by/2.0)], via Wikimedia Commons, 5.7; Image courtesy of André Brown and John Weisel, MRC Laboratory of Molecular Biology, 5.14; © D.G Mackean www.biology-resources.com Reprinted by kind permission of Ian Mackean, 5.20; 5.26; Image courtesy of Paul A Gibb FRCS, FRCS (Orth) Consultant Orthopaedic Surgeon, 5.27; Pixabay, 5.35; 5.39; 5.40b; Photo courtesy of Carli Hækkerup, 5.40a.